S0-ARL-302

Eugene S. Schwartz Memorial Library

OCEAN ENVIRONMENTAL MANAGEMENT

A Primer on the Role of the Oceans and How to Maintain Their Contributions to Life on Earth

Ernst G. Frankel

Massachusetts Institute of Technology

Prentice Hall P T R, Englewood Cliffs, New Jersey 07632

Library of Congress Cataloging-in-Publication Data

Frankel, Ernst G.
Ocean environmental management : a primer on the role of the oceans and how to maintain their contributions to life on earth / Ernst G. Frankel.
p. cm.
Includes bibliographical references and index.
ISBN 0-13-184557-8
1. Marine Pollution. I. Title.
GC1085.F75 1995
333.91′6415—dc20 94-33448
CIP

Editorial production: bookworks
Acquisitions editor: Bernard Goodwin
Cover designer: Sue Behnke
Manufacturing manager: Alexis R. Heydt

Prentice-Hall, Inc.
A Simon & Schuster Company
Englewood Cliffs, New Jersey 07632

The publisher offers discounts on this book when ordered in bulk quantities. For more information, contact:

Corporate Sales Department
Prentice Hall P T R
113 Sylvan Avenue
Englewood Cliffs, New Jersey 07632

Phone: (800) 382-3419 or (201) 592-2498
FAX: (201) 592-2249
E-mail: dan_ rush@prenhall.com

Printed in the United States of America

10 9 8 7 6 5 4 3 2 1

ISBN 0-13-184557-8

Prentice-Hall International (UK) Limited, *London*
Prentice-Hall of Australia Pty. Limited, *Sydney*
Prentice-Hall Canada Inc., *Toronto*
Prentice-Hall Hispanoamericana, S.A., *Mexico*
Prentice-Hall of India Private Limited, *New Delhi*
Prentice-Hall of Japan, Inc., *Tokyo*
Simon & Schuster Asia Pte. Ltd., *Singapore*
Editora Prentice-Hall do Brasil, Ltda., *Rio de Janeiro*

Contents

PREFACE IX

INTRODUCTION XI

CHAPTER 1 ENVIRONMENTAL AND ECONOMIC ROLE OF THE OCEANS 1

1.1 The Function of the Ocean Environment 3
- 1.1.1 Coastal Ecology 6
- 1.1.2 Deep-Ocean Ecology 8

1.2 Ocean Resources and Uses of the Ocean 12
- 1.2.1 Ocean Oil and Gas Production 14
- 1.2.2 Fishery Production 16
- 1.2.3 Ocean Mineral Production 31
- 1.2.4 Energy Production in the Oceans 35
- 1.2.5 Industrial Use of Ocean Resources 36

1.3 Ocean Transportation Use 38
- 1.3.1 Ocean Recreation Use 39

1.4 Ocean Environmental Management Issues 40

CHAPTER 2 SOURCES AND MAGNITUDE OF OCEAN ENVIRONMENTAL DEGRADATION 44

2.1 Marine Pollution by Ocean Users, Voluntary and Accidental 48
2.1.1 Oil Slick Spreading 63
2.2 Runoff and Drainage from Rivers, Flood Plains, Wastewater, and Similar Pollution Sources. 64
2.2.1 Wastewater Pollution and Liquid Waste Disposal 66
2.2.2 Effect on Fisheries and Aquaculture 67
2.3 Solid Wastes and Hazardous Materials Pollution 68
2.4 Port and Industrial Pollution 74
2.4.1 Port Pollution 75
2.4.2 Industrial Pollution 91
2.5 Air Pollution 92
2.5.1 Ship Air Emissions 93
2.6 Other Ocean Environmental Problems 93
2.6.1 Transfer of Biological Poison 94
2.6.2 Radioactive Wastes and the Oceans 94
2.6.3 Ocean Pollution by Poisonous Algae 96

CHAPTER 3 IMPACT OF OCEAN ENVIRONMENTAL DEGRADATION 97

3.1 Degradation of Recreational Uses 100
3.2 Degradation of Ocean Resource Exploitation 106
3.2.1 Effect on Fisheries and Aquaculture 106
3.2.2 Environmental Degradation by Port Activities 110
3.2.3 Environmental Degradation by Ocean Mining 115
3.2.4 Effects of Port and Coastal Pollution on Mangroves and Beaches 117
3.3 The Costs of Ocean Pollution 118

CHAPTER 4 PHYSICAL AND OPERATIONAL OCEAN POLLUTION PREVENTION, CONTAINMENT AND CLEANUP 119

4.1 Physical Ocean Pollution Prevention 119
4.1.1 Prevention and Mitigation of Pollution by Port and Harbor Activities 120
4.1.2 Safe Tanker Design and Operations 125
4.1.3 Safe Navigational Channels 128

4.1.4 River and Runoff Pollution Prevention 135
4.1.5 Offshore Resource Exploitation Pollution Prevention 136

4.2 Spill Containment and Recovery 136
4.2.1 Oil Pollution Containment and Recovery 137
4.2.2 Chemical and Radioactive Pollution Containment and Recovery 145

4.3 Pollution Cleanup Methods 145

4.4 Operational Ocean Pollution Prevention 146
4.4.1 Operational Tanker Pollution Prevention 146
4.4.2 Oil Spill Response Plans 147

4.5 Outfall and Dredging-Induced Pollution Prevention 148
4.5.1 Sewage and Cooling Water Disposal by Outfalls 149
4.5.2 Safe Disposal of Dredge Spoils 149

4.6 Nuclear and Toxic Waste Pollution Containment and Prevention 152
4.6.1 Nuclear Submarine and Disarmament Waste in the Oceans 153
4.6.2 Use of the Abyssal Ocean for Waste Disposal 154
4.6.3 Ocean Island Geological Nuclear and Toxic Waste Repositories 155

4.7 Environmental Geotechnical Engineering 156

CHAPTER 5 OCEAN ENVIRONMENTAL REGULATION 157

5.1 International Ocean Environmental Regulations 160
5.1.1 International Ocean Sewage Disposal Regulations 161
5.1.2 Port State Control 164
5.1.3 IMO Regulations for the Prevention of Marine Pollution by Tankers 165

5.2 American Ocean Environmental Regulation 167
5.2.1 Early Developments in U.S. Ocean Environmental Regulation 171
5.2.2 Recent Developments in U.S. Ocean Environmental Regulation 180
5.2.3 Local Authority and State Controls 187
5.2.4 Sewage Disposal Regulations 188
5.2.5 Dredging and Dredge Spoil Disposal Regulations 188
5.2.6 Air Pollution Regulation in the Oceans 189
5.2.7 Solid Waste Disposal 190

5.3 Enforcement of Ocean Environmental Regulations 190

5.4 Operational Issues and Policies 191

5.4.1 The Role of Human Error in Ship Accidents 191
5.4.2 Environmental Response Planning and Prevention Training 193
5.5 Environmental Awareness, Political Will, and Economic Costs 194

CHAPTER 6 ECONOMICS OF OCEAN ENVIRONMENTAL MANAGEMENT 196

6.1 Ocean Environmental Accounting 197
6.1.1 Environmental Auditing 200
6.1.2 Ocean Environmental Economic Charges 201
6.1.3 Ocean Environmental Market Accounting 204
6.1.4 Methods of Environmental Accounting 205
6.1.5 Port Environmental Audits 208
6.1.6 Debt for Nature Swaps in the Oceans 210
6.2 Costs and Benefits of Ocean Environmental Management 210
6.2.1 Cost of Oil Spills in the Ocean 211
6.2.2 Costs and Benefits of Oil Pollution Prevention by Tankers 215
6.3 Economic Impact of Ocean Pollution 225
6.3.1 Costs of Pollution 227
6.3.2 The Economic Effectiveness of Environmental Regulation 231
6.4 Contingent Value and Worth of the Ocean 235

CHAPTER 7 OCEAN ENVIRONMENTAL MANAGEMENT 237

7.1 Environmental Management Functions 241
7.2 Monitoring Ocean Environmental Effects 242
7.3 Cultural Factors in Ocean Environmental Management 243
7.4 Performance of Ocean Environmental Management 244
7.4.1 Planning Environmental Management 245
7.4.2 The Ocean Environmental Management Process 246
7.4.3 Economic Factors in Ocean Environmental Management 250
7.4.4 Ocean Environmental Management 251
7.5 Role of International Agencies, National Governments, and Local Authorities 254
7.5.1 International Maritime Organization (IMO) 255
7.5.2 The Environmental Protection Agency (EPA), U.S. Army Corps of Engineers, and U.S. Coast Guard (USCG)

7.5.3 Oil Pollution Liability and Compensation 258
7.5.4 The Global Environment Facility (GEF) 260
7.6 Managing Ocean Pollution by Ships 261
7.6.1 The Solid Waste Service Industry 263
7.6.2 Trade and Environment 264
7.6.3 Spill Contractors and Response Management 264
7.7 Environmental Impact Assessment of Ocean Development Projects 265
7.7.1 Environmental Risk Assessment 269
7.7.2 Economic Impact of Ocean Pollution 270
7.7.3 Uncertainty in Environmental Evaluation 270
7.7.4 Ocean Environmental Impact Assessment Methodologies 271
7.8 Managed Fishing 277
7.9 Strategies for Ocean Environmental Management 278
7.9.1 Source and Cause of Environmental Management Strategy 281
7.9.2 Ocean Environmental Management Financing 285
7.9.3 Application of Source-Oriented Ocean Environmental Management 286
7.9.4 Company Involvement in Ocean Environmental Management 293
7.9.5 Financing Ocean Environmental Management 294
7.9.6 Priority Financing of Ocean Environmental Management 295

EPILOGUE 296

APPENDIX A OCEAN ENVIRONMENTAL REGULATION IN THE UNITED STATES 299

A.1 National Environmental Policy Act 300
A.2 Port Environmental Regulation 302
A.2.1 Construction in Wetlands 309
A.2.2 Deep-Water Port Construction 310
A.3 Water Pollution Regulation 311
A.3.1 Nonoily Water Pollution 311
A.3.2 Oily Water Pollution 314
A.3.3 Marine Sanitation Devices 324
A.4 Ports and Waterway Safety 328
A.5 Federal Air Pollution Law 329
A.6 State Air Pollution Regulation 333

APPENDIX B OCEAN ENVIRONMENTAL CONVENTIONS AND AGREEMENTS 327

B.1 International Agreements 327
B.2 Regional Agreements 342
B.3 EEC Directives 343
B.4 Subregional Agreements and Bilateral Treaties 343
B.5 Institutional Arrangements for Regional Marine Pollution Control 344

APPENDIX C LONDON DUMPING CONVENTION 346

APPENDIX D OCEAN MINING TECHNOLOGY 360

APPENDIX E ABBREVIATIONS 365

REFERENCES 367

INDEX 377

Preface

Ocean environmental management is becoming an important issue especially because of continued ocean pollution, notwithstanding some notable successes in reducing it. The oceans are the most important part of the earth's life support system, and their environmental management is necessary if serious problems are to be prevented. Although every one agrees that the pollution problem is serious and that it requires urgent measures, few countries—even those vocal in defense of action—are willing to take the necessary drastic preventative steps. Worldwide demand for action and the goals expressed at the World Environmental Conference in Rio de Janeiro are far removed from the proposed implementation and enforcement mechanisms adopted. Sovereignty and national interests often interfere or conflict with environmental rulings even when proposed or adopted by the country concerned. As a result, many ocean environmental regulations and agreements have become platitudes that express, but do not satisfy, an urgent need.

Effective ocean environmental management can be profitable as well as responsible. Similarly, maintaining the ocean environment does not have to cost money but, if well managed, can actually save money and enhance the economic potentials of the oceans.

Just as quality in manufacturing does not necessarily add to product costs but results in better and often less expensive products, effective environmental management of the oceans enhances ocean resource abundance and reduces the cost of ocean resource use.

The purpose of *Ocean Environmental Management* is to explain the causes of and problems introduced by ocean pollution, to present some of the preventative and mitigating methods available, to evaluate regulations and agreements promulgated to control ocean environmental impacts, and to suggest approaches for the more effective management of the ocean environment.

This book is targeted to those curious about environmental developments in the oceans, to undergraduate students of environmental engineering and science, and to others concerned with the maintenance of this most important resource, the world's oceans. This is not a scientific treatise or technical text, but a volume in which the important functions of the oceans are discussed and the effects of pollution on the ocean ecology are evaluated in physical, biological, and economic terms.

Although designed to be used as a reference or a study aid, it is not a textbook in the traditional sense but it could be used in introductory senior undergraduate or graduate courses.

ACKNOWLEDGMENTS

I would like to express my gratitude to all who helped in or supported the development of *Ocean Environmental Management*. In particular, T. Francis Ogilvie, head of the Department of Ocean Engineering, encouraged me to take up this challenge and assisted by providing MIT financial resources for this effort. Various people—too many to mention—commented on portions of this volume, and to them all, I express my sincere thanks. Most important, the competent help of Sheila McNary in compiling and drafting this book is gratefully acknowledged.

Obviously, any errors or omissions are solely my responsibility.

Ernst G. Frankel

Introduction

Growing population, urban, economic, industrial, and agricultural activities have an increasingly devastating effect on the world's environment. Resource exploitation and use often take precedence over long-term environmental effects to advance short-term economic growth. At the same time, the link between sustainable economic development or growth and effective environmental management has become increasingly evident, and the maintenance of the environment is now recognized as an essential factor in long-term human advance.

If sustainable economic development is to last beyond short-term economic gains, the support of an effectively managed environment is required. Growth derived from ecological depletion is not economically sustainable beyond a very short time horizon.

The problem of environmental depletion for economic growth is particularly difficult to solve because environmental impacts stemming from resource depletion and other economic activities usually cross national boundaries and are often global in scope. This is particularly true with energy, industrial, and agricultural activities that generate wastes that ultimately end up in the oceans.

Although most of the damage to the environment, and particularly the oceans, has been done, and continues, by the industrial countries, there is evidence that environmental impacts on the oceans are increasingly introduced by activities in developing countries. For example, relocating environmentally objectionable activities to these countries and the lack of environmental standards by developing countries, that often feel the right to "use up their share of pollution" for economic gain, can result in uncontrolled pollution.

Actually, environmental management may be more important for developing countries that cannot afford the high cost of environmental cleanup. A typical example is ocean pollution affecting fisheries, a major food source for many developing countries. It is therefore necessary to encourage an environmental consciousness that makes it more profitable to manage than to destroy the environment. Developing countries depend more on national resource exports, fisheries, and agriculture in their economies than do developed countries, which makes it imperative that they manage their environment effectively so as to permit sustainable use of these essential assets for their economic development.

Increased production of carbon dioxide (CO_2) and other trace gases in the atmosphere as a result of energy conversion and industrial activities is expected to cause greenhouse effects and resulting global warming. This will affect the oceans in various ways. Carbon dioxide concentrations in the atmosphere have increased by 25% since the late 1700s and are expected to increase by another 40% by 2050 if the present trend in fossil fuel use continues.

Global warming will cause higher sea levels, which affect coastal area use habitation, river estuaries, and flood plains. About 66% of the CO_2 release by human activities results from combustion of fossil fuels. Nearly 50% of that is produced by the 7 major industrial nations, (United States, England, France, Germany, Canada, Italy, Japan) with Eastern Europe contributing another 25%.

Similarly, the global average level of stratospheric ozone fell by 5% between 1979 and 1986 and is estimated to have fallen another 4% by 1991. Ozone acts as a filter for the sun's ultraviolet radiation, which has detrimental effects on marine life.

Another atmospheric pollutant is acid rain, the result of acid precipitation through chemical transformation of sulfur dioxide and several nitrogen oxides. Sources from humans account for about 50%

of acid rain worldwide, although in the United States they account for more than 90% of the total. Such emissions grew from 7 million tons per year in 1860 to over 155 million tons per year in 1985, worldwide.

An increasing number of countries have inadequate natural freshwater supplies and rely increasingly on filtered, processed, or distilled water. The pollution of river and coastal waters makes treating water for human consumption expensive and sometimes impossible. Marine environmental protection is of great concern now because humans have become increasingly dependent on the oceans for food, resources, and recreation. At the same time, the oceans have become the principal dumping ground for liquid and often solid wastes. Although much of that waste is treated, significant amounts are discharged untreated.

Ocean pollution is also caused by atmospheric drainage or runoff, industrial and human liquid waste outflow, solid waste disposal, oil discharge, and a variety of natural pollution sources such as subsea vents. The quality of the ocean environment has declined steadily over many years, but the rate of pollution has now escalated to dangerous levels at a time when humans are becoming more dependent on the oceans for various resources and food.

The sources of ocean pollution and the methods of mediating, reducing, or eliminating them are indemnified in this book, and the techniques for pollution containment, reduction, and cleanup are discussed.

Methods for evaluating the economic impact of ocean pollution, and the expected effect on economic growth and sustainable development, are also presented. For too long, the oceans have been considered a huge dumping ground for human waste. Because the oceans are sparsely inhabited and used, environmental impacts have often not been immediately recognized, objections to ocean environmental degradation have been slow, and enforcement of even general standards has been lax. This presents a dangerous precedent and an issue humans will have to deal with, if life on Earth as it is known and the future of humans on this planet are to be assured.

As oceans become an increasingly important resource for the sustenance of life on Earth and are assumed to offer an unlimited dumping ground for waste produced by human activities, the management of the ocean environment has become an urgent task. The world's oceans are vast and occupy not only large surface areas of the earth, but because they extend to great depths, large volumes also. At the same time, oceans are extremely sensitive, and radical changes in their chemical, thermal, and physical balance can produce great damage not only to biological, chemical, and physical activities in the oceans but also to the earth's atmosphere and inner crust that are greatly affected by the oceans.

The world's oceans have an area of 361,740,000 square kilometers and therefore occupy 72.93% of the earth's surface. The Pacific Ocean alone occupies 32.0% of the earth's surface, or 45.12% of all the ocean surfaces. The volume of water in the oceans is 1,205,600,000 km3, or 308,408,000 mi^3. The average depth of the world's oceans is over 4,000 m, compared with an average height of the earth's land mass of less than 600 m.

The oceans provide primary means of communications and transport; food resources in terms of fish, seafood, and various aquaculture vegetation; ocean and ocean-bottom minerals; subocean oil, coal, and mineral resources; and potentials for major renewable energy generation from thermal underwater vents, waves, currents, tides, and thermal columns. The oceans abound with resources, but many of these are not yet effectively known nor is their exploration and exploitation effectively developed.

As humans grope toward a better understanding of the last frontier for human support development and effective use of a near infinite source of resources for biological sustenance on Earth, conflicts between the effective use of ocean resources and the pollution of the oceans that would negate such use in the long run become increasingly evident. The effective management of the ocean environment may ultimately affect the ability of the globe to support life as it is known and thereby the future of humanity.

The field of ocean environmental management deals with the analysis of the traces or chains of actions or reactions that lead from the various sources of ocean pollution, or from their initial causes, to the resulting ecological effects or impacts. Such analysis ultimately leads to attempts at eliminating sources of pollution and ameliorating the detrimental effects. Ocean environmental management therefore involves reduction of the effects of ocean pollution or degradation at all levels of the cause-and-effect chain.

Similarly, issues involved in ocean environmental management include identifying the sources, sizes, and reasons of ocean and coastal pollution. In other words, it is important to find the causes of ocean pollution. Because much of the pollution is caused by uses and users of the oceans and coastal zones, the study of cause is essential.

After identifying the causes, the physical, chemical, and biological effects of ocean pollution are addressed, and the ecological impact of ocean pollution on uses, users, and the interface effects of the oceans and coastal zones is discussed.

Once the environmental causes and effects of ocean pollution are determined, prevention and reduction of ocean pollution from land, ships, ocean resource developments, aquaculture, fishing, recreation, and special coastal development are covered, including monitoring ocean pollution and measuring its impacts. Ocean pollution from natural causes such as thermal vents, atmospheric, biological, and physical interfaces are addressed; these causes contribute significantly to the ocean environment.

In dealing with ocean pollution, several problems are confronted. After-the-fact management of pollution effects by abatement, containment, and cleanup of ocean pollution through operational, physical, chemical, and biological means, and prevention of ocean pollution at the source by deviation of the potential solution present many challenges. Ocean pollution can also be reduced or prevented by changes in operations, technology, and use of the oceans.

The management of ocean pollution can be assisted by the use of effective models that predict the spread, containment, response time, and impact of various pollution intrusions. These topics are also discussed.

In recent years, local, national, and international regulations and conventions relative to ocean environmental management have been introduced and are in force in different parts of the world. After evaluating these arguments, their effectiveness and enforceability are reviewed. Also discussed is how meaningful some of these regulations are. Finally, the economic impacts of ocean environmental management are estimated in terms of short- and long-term costs and benefits and are compared with the economic costs and benefits of ocean environmental management that involves active and passive pollution prevention, pollution impact reduction, and governmental actions, such as regulations.

For some time now, the management of the environment has become a political as well as social and economic issue. Most people agree that the environment should be protected from degradation and particularly from irreversible impacts, but the methods and approaches suggested to do so have often been subjected to opposition or downright ridicule. Because so much of the oceans are in international waters outside national jurisdictions and are open for the use of all, all and none are responsible for the maintenance of the ocean's environment. Thus ocean environmental management—even more so than other issues—is subject to differences in opinion, judgment, and interpretation.

In discussing the conditions of the oceans, their increasing use, and the regulations introduced for the protection of the ocean's environment, by necessity their value, enforceability, and the effectiveness of the national and international safeguards introduced are also evaluated.

This book covers ocean environmental management in terms of the state of environmental impacts or pollution, their sources, methods for the prevention and ameliorization of pollution, effective management of ocean use and ocean resources, containment and cleanup of pollution, and planning the long-term effective management of ocean use in an environmentally safe manner.

Material was obtained from a variety of sources. As in environmental management in general, ocean environmental management is subject to diverse interpretations, policies, and goals. An effort is made to present the whole range of opinions and consideration without bias so as to allow the reader to use his or her own interpretations of fact and opinion. Ocean environmental management, like other human activities, is subject to social, economic, and political and strategic considerations that although often hidden, are nonetheless real and that affect policy and decision making in ocean environmental issues. Again an effort is made to identify, and where possible to quantify, the economic and social costs and benefits.

The objective here is to provide an introduction to ocean environmental management that will not only educate future professionals in the problems faced in maintaining the world's oceans healthy and productive but will also provide them with the scientific, engineering, and economic skills to analyze effectively environmental problems faced by the oceans. In addition, to develop implementable solutions for the prevention, amelioration, and cleanup of environmental problems so as to ensure that this most important resource is able to sustain life on Earth indefinitely is a main goal of *Ocean Environmental Management*.

1

Environmental and Economic Role of the Oceans

The oceans are not only an essential part of the world biosphere; they also provide the most essential physical, chemical, and biological interactions for maintaining an effective global environmental balance. Oceans cover nearly 72.93% of the world's surface, yet they contain over 90% of the world's water. They not only play an essential role but are largely the dominant factor influencing or controlling the processes of the earth. As a result, their well-being is essential for the effective workings of these processes that make life as we know it possible on this planet.

A huge capacity for the production of biological, plant, and mineral resources is provided by the oceans. Plants produced in the oceans of the world are about equal in total volume to those grown on land. The oceans thereby provide an important contribution to the cyclical exchange of nitrogen, oxygen, hydrogen, and various hydrocarbons. Most importantly, the oceans absorb carbon dioxide and thereby help to maintain the earth's temperature.

By offering resources such as fish, plants, facilitation of transport, ocean energy generation, below–ocean-bottom fuel resources, recreational opportunities, waste disposal facilities, chemical extraction, and harvesting of minerals and construction materials, the oceans play a major role in providing resources and opportunities to satisfy human needs. Although the ocean's resources are abundant, various ocean uses are in potential conflict, and many introduce significant environmental risks. Therefore, although the oceans offer large, essentially untapped sources of resources for use by humans, their increased use heralds environmental hazards that are now often difficult to manage or contain. Among these hazards are the detrimental impacts of:

1. waste inputs into the oceans through runoffs, sewage, ship waste, solid waste disposal, and offshore incineration waste;
2. oil pollution from ship operations, ship casualties, offshore oil exploration or production, and oily outflows from sewage systems and runoffs;
3. uncontrolled nutrient inflows from fertilizers, detergents, and other agricultural chemical runoff;
4. excessive phytoplankton growth resulting from particular sewage wastes and agricultural runoffs;
5. toxic material inflows such as synthetic organic compounds and DDT;
6. metal intrusion, particularly of trace metals from industrial wastes;
7. radioactive materials, particularly artificially produced radionuclides disposed accidentally or voluntarily; and
8. the large amounts of debris, structural materials, and manufactured waste disposed in the oceans.

As human activities in the oceans proliferate, the environmental conditions of the oceans have deteriorated very rapidly since the early 1970s. The results can now be seen in virtually all the world's oceans. Although pollution initially affected mainly narrow strips of coastal waters or stagnant bays and estuaries, the impact has grown to where it now affects large bodies of oceans, waters, or seas, such as the North, Baltic, Black, Caspian, Aral, South China, and Mediterranean Seas and the Gulf of Mexico. As a consequence, major efforts are now under way to contain the environmental damage that has greatly affected the effective functions and uses of these waters.

1.1 THE FUNCTION OF THE OCEAN ENVIRONMENT

The oceans are the most important element in the regulation of the earth's atmosphere and thermal conditions. The primary productivity of plants in the oceans is about equal to that growing on land. Therefore, the oceans provide an important contribution to the atmospheric gas cycles of nitrogen, oxygen, and carbon. The interaction of the atmosphere above land and ocean generates the varying patterns of weather and provides a continuously regulating pressure on global weather.

Yet this primary function of the oceans, particularly in stabilizing atmospheric conditions and plants, as well as in other biological productivity, is increasingly exposed to adverse environmental impacts caused by pollution. The pressures exerted on the marine environment are summarized in Table 1–1. The magnitude of these pressures and environmental impacts has doubled nearly every ten years since 1960. In other words, waste inputs, nuclide disposal in the oceans, debris inflows, and until recently, oil pollution have increased in volume by nearly 100% every ten years. Although this is due in part to the more intensive exploitation of ocean resources, much is due to population pressure, changing lifestyles, and lack of effective consideration for, and control of, adverse environmental actions.

The effects of pollution on the ocean chemistry and marine life are increasingly hazardous and persistent. Pollution destroys or infects marine life and seriously endangers potential human uses of the oceans and ocean resources. The environmental pressures increasingly cause a change in the ocean chemistry. Mutations of natural ocean life occur more frequently than previously and often have long-term effects. Disease and infection of marine life now often run rampant through the waters, and abnormalities and reproductive defects in marine life are common. These are just some of the effects of pollution. The worst part is that some of the dangers of other forms of pollution are not even known yet. By contaminating the oceans with pollutants, the most beautiful and plentiful asset that exists on this earth is being degraded, and the long-term future of life on earth may be affected. Although the biological damages caused by ocean pollution are usually the most readily evident effects, ocean pollution causes many, and often long-term, chemical and physical effects as well.

TABLE 1–1 Pressures on the Marine Environment

PRESSURE	SUBSTANCE OR ACTIVITY INVOLVED	MAJOR ANTHROPOGENIC SOURCES	POTENTIAL EFFECTS
	Nutrients	Sewage; agriculture; aquaculture; industry	Eutrophisation
Waste inputs to the oceans	Pathogens	Sewage; agriculture	Disease and infection; shell-fish contamination
	Oil	Industry; sewage; shipping; auto-mobiles; urban runoff	Oiling of birds and animals; seafood tainting; beach contamination
	Synthetic organic compounds forestry	Industry; sewage; agriculture	Metabolic dysfunction
	Radioactive wastes	Nuclear weapon tests, nuclear fuel reprocessing; ocean dumping nuclear generating station acci-dents	Metabolic dysfunction
	Trace metals	Industry; sewage; ocean dumping; automobiles	Metabolic dys-function

	Plastics and debris	Litter; shipping wastes; lost fishing gear	Entanglement of wildlife; digestive interference
	Solid waste (organic and inorganic)	Sewage; ocean dumping; industry	Reduced oxygen; habitat smothering
Environmental restructuring	Coastal development	Dredging; industrial, residential, and tourism development	Aesthetic and habitat loss; coastal erosion
Resource exploitation	Fish and shellfish harvesting	Harvesting activities	Stock depletion; ecosystem changes
	Petroleum development	Drilling; accidents	Oil and chemical contamination
	Mineral development	Dredging; tailings disposal; extraction	Decreased water quality, coastal erosion
Atmospheric change impacts	Carbon dioxide; CFCs and other "greenhouse" gases	Energy production; transportation; agriculture; industry	Sea-level rise; coastal flooding; wetland loss; damage to infrastructure; habitat alteration; decreased oceanic productivity

SOURCE: " Economic Implications & Pollution Control: A General Assessment," (Paris: OECD, 1974).

1.1.1 Coastal Ecology

Coastal land has always had a major fascination for people and has become a very desirable and increasingly scarce resource. This has resulted in a high concentration of shore development that in turn has caused reductions in coastal vegetation, such as mangroves and other forests, a reduction of dunes and elimination of dune plants and life, and a high concentration of coastal runoffs and drainage flows. Runoffs often contain high levels of new nutrients, such as nitrates and phosphates from sewage, lawn fertilizer, and various other waste flows, that either drain directly into the coastal waters or are passed by the watershed into the groundwater and then through the sediment interface into the coastal waters.

These changes in the chemical composition, nutrients, and sediment loading of coastal waters have a profound effect on coastal chemical, physical, and biological processes. Chain reactions, such as the effects on algae growth and composition that in turn influence marine life growth and survival, often result.

Coastal waters with well-balanced nutrient loadings will encourage growth of macroalgae and seagrasses in shallow coastal waters. If algae are overnourished, other marine life may suffer, because increases in algae reduce the oxygen in the water, which then lowers the survival rate of fish and shellfish in such waters. Although algae produce oxygen through photosynthesis, they often consume much more oxygen during respiration periods.

The algae problem in coastal waters has become a worldwide problem. The lagoon of Venice, the coastal waters of the Sinai Peninsula, and many more areas are now choking with seaweeds. This is usually the result of eutrophication or unnatural nutrient enrichment. This process is slow and therefore difficult to perceive, yet the damage caused is usually long term or permanent. Little is done to reduce this often catastrophic impact on the coastal ecology that in the long run will negate the attraction for coastal development by transforming coastal waters into lifeless and often smelly, stagnant ponds. Although oil spills receive great publicity, they usually cause only temporary and local damage. The coastal ecology in many parts of the world is not only under attack, but is increasingly out of balance and moving towards irreversible changes in its physical, chemical, and biological state.

Waters in the coastal zone, usually defined by the continental shelf or the area lying between the back shore zone and the outer edge of the continental shelf, are affected by the processes related both to land and ocean. It is the interaction of the coastal water processes, the loose sediments generated by the land, the runoff, and coastal boundary effects with the sea that give the coastal zone its special significance.

Structurally, the coastal shelves are part of the continental land masses, but once ocean waters invaded the zone, the environment was affected and complex processes were introduced. Although large portions of the shelf and coast are formed of solid rock, elsewhere is a thick layer of loose sediment that contributes to the formation of beaches, dunes, or marshland along the coast. The dynamic coastal processes depend on the depth of water, coastal formation, coastal topology, sediment loading, and exposure to tidal, littoral, and other currents as well as to open ocean waves.

Waves and currents play a major role in shaping beaches and coastal formations, while winds are effective in dune formation, particularly where sand is available. Coastal features, such as sand banks, barriers, and forelands, are often developed by long swells that form the dominant waves, particularly on sandy coasts.

Major coastal construction, such as reclamations, piers, or changes in the coastal profile, can strongly influence wave and current refraction and therefore the direction of long swells and dominant current direction and speed. In turn, this often affects deposition of sediment in the highly sediment-loaded coastal waters and may cause siltation of channels, water intakes, and water outflows as well as undesirable or unpredicted shoreline erosion or accretion.

Tidal currents often form offshore banks where rectilinear and sandy sediment is present. This also occurs in deeper coastal waters, such as at the entrance to the English Channel and the southern part of the North Sea. The greater the density of sediment loading, the greater the risk of formation of turbidity currents that may cause severe submarine erosion.

The material in suspension in coastal waters is considerably greater than in oceans and rivers. Other discharges introduce large quantities of chemicals, nutrients, and freshwater, combined with larger variations of precipitation and evaporation than exist in the open seas. As a result, the temperature and salinity in coastal waters are often quite different and vary more rapidly than in the deep oceans. For example, the Baltic Sea is much fresher than the adjacent North Sea, while the Mediterranean and Red Seas are more saline and warmer than other seas, owing to excessive evaporation and the high atmospheric temperature that also warms coastal soils. Most coastal waters contain considerably more nutrients than the open seas. Historically, this has resulted in greater biological activity, particularly breeding, which usually benefits from warmer, shallower, and nutrient-rich waters.

In other words, marine biological life is closely linked with ocean water characteristics, and coastal waters usually support intensive benthic, demersal, and other forms of marine life. As a result, the shallow continental shelf seas provide a large proportion of the food extracted from the oceans. The wide shelves of northwest Europe, North America, and South America have always provided some of the richest fishing grounds in the world.

Coastal waters also sustain a greater variety of flora and fauna because of a greater abundance of nutrients and sunlight and greater carbon densities. Another factor is the effect of tidal and littoral currents in coastal waters that often prevent thermoclines from being formed, thus allowing plant production during long periods of time. Benthic plants are therefore most prevalent in shallow waters.

For tens of thousands of years, coastal waters have provided the basis or cradle of most marine life and have similarly accumulated many of the minerals and organic materials of importance to humans. In other words, to assure that the oceans remain the great resource of food, minerals, fuels, and energy that humans need, it is essential to maintain the ecological balance of the coastal zone. If this balance is upset, resources degrade or diminish rapidly.

Since World War II, most of the world's coastal zones have been severely polluted, physically, chemically, and often even biologically. The quantities of pollutants discharged into these waters can no longer be neutralized or absorbed. As a result, major bodies of coastal waters in the Baltic Sea and seas such as the Aral in the former Soviet Union have become essentially inert and unable to support marine life. If the oceans are to continue to perform their functions, it is essential that humans clean up and prevent serious future pollution of coastal waters.

1.1.2 Deep-Ocean Ecology

The world's oceans store heat and water, which greatly affect weather and climate. They contain substantial amounts of nutrients and biological material, minerals, and metals, as well as huge amounts of marine life and organisms. The water of the oceans is formed by moisture released by the hardening of molten rocks, such as lava; the moisture is retained in the air and returned to the earth's surface, and ultimately to the oceans, by the earth's gravity. This is facilitated by the pressure and temperature conditions on the earth that assure that most of the globe's moisture remains in liquid form.

The oceans occupy nearly 73% of the earth's surface and, as shown in Table 1–2, have a mean depth of over 4,000 m or 13,000 ft.

Most deep basins are covered by thick layers of pelagic clay. Red pelagic clay is mainly inorganic and consists of ferric oxide and various other oxides as well as manganese dioxide and other elements. The pelagic clays deposit at a rate of about 1 cm per 1,000 years; therefore, samples drawn from great depths in the bottom clay layers may contain materials deposited a million years ago or more.

Oceans have abundant surpluses of major plant nutrients such as nitrate, potassium, phosphorus, magnesium, calcium, and silicon. Although only low concentrations of phosphorus, nitrate, and silicon are found in surface waters with significant sunlight and therefore photosynthesis, these nutrients are found in much larger concentrations at greater depths. In addition to dissolved salts, oceans contain large concentrations of dissolved gases such as helium, nitrogen, oxygen, carbon dioxide (CO_2), neon, and argon. Dissolved nitrogen and oxygen are the most abundant gases in the oceans.

Marine organisms abound in the oceans and feed on other organisms such as plankton and the abundant nutrients available in the seas. Huge arrays of life forms, from very primitive single-cell organisms to complex ocean-inhabiting mammals, exist in the oceans. Similarly, plant life in the oceans is very diverse because plants there grow with few of the constraints imposed on plant growth on land, such as gravity, winds, storms, animals, and hu-

TABLE 1–2 Major Oceans

	AREA (MI^2)	MEAN DEPTH (FT)	MEAN DEPTH (M)
Arctic	5,427,000	5,010	1,514
North Atlantic	17,646,000	10,780	3,257
South Atlantic	14,098,000	13,420	4,054
North Pacific	31,639,000	14,050	4,245
South Pacific	32,361,000	12,660	3,820
Indian	28,400,000	13,002	3,928
Southern	12,451,000	12,240	3,698

mans. Plant life in the oceans, however, is governed by the sinking rate of phytoplankton and the movements of nutrients, among other factors.

Deep-ocean ecology is quite diverse, and the various oceans experience many different environmental factors. The ecology of the Atlantic Ocean differs from that of the Pacific Ocean. The greatest ecological differences though exist between the Arctic and Antarctic Oceans.

Some oceans, such as the Arctic Ocean, are covered by a perennial cover of packed ice and are nearly surrounded on all sides by land. The Arctic Ocean relies heavily on inflows through the Bering Strait and Norwegian Sea and outflows through the Barents Sea, Greenland Sea, and Canadian Archipelago; there is very little inflow from land-based runoff or precipitation or outflow by evaporation.

Other oceans experience a very different balance. For example, the East Greenland current accounts for nearly two-thirds of the water outflow, with other outflows around the periphery of the Arctic Ocean small indeed. In the Antarctic Ocean, which is wide open to the main deep oceans (Atlantic, Pacific, and Southern), this is quite different. Similarly, the thermal conditions of the Arctic Ocean are not largely affected, as in other oceans, by atmospheric evaporation but more by conduction to the ice cover and glacial discharges as well as by geothermal conduction and insolation. The flora and fauna in the Arctic Ocean are sparse indeed. The lack of effective solar penetration reduces plankton growth to very low levels, and even deep-sea marine organisms are not abundant.

By comparison, the Atlantic Ocean is the warmest ocean, with salt content in excess of that of the Pacific and Southern Oceans. The Atlantic probably receives the largest percentage of runoff and river water of all oceans. In fact, it receives about four times as much freshwater inflow per unit volume of seawater than the other major oceans. At the same time, a larger percentage of the Atlantic Ocean is near the equator than other oceans, and the amount of evaporation generated per unit of water volume also far exceeds that of other major oceans.

Although the average surface temperature is primarily a function of latitude, it is greatly affected by currents, such as the Gulf of Mexico and Labrador currents. Because these currents as well as seasonal factors change, temperature variations of surface waters in the Atlantic can be as high as 15%, particularly along the northeastern shores of North America.

The Atlantic experiences its greatest outflow or water loss by evaporation. This also accounts for the largest heat loss: latent heat to evaporation. The Atlantic has among the largest accumulations of marine deposits or sediments of all oceans. Pelagic deposits (with some clay and volcanic matter) mainly in deep water, calcareous oozes calcium carbonate $CaCO_3$ ($CaCO_3 > 30\%$), hemiphelagic and terrigenous deposits that occur from the continental shelves to the abyssal plains, and both organic (calcareous and siliceous) and inorganic mud that occurs in suspension or on the coastal slopes are some of the deposits found in the Atlantic. The distribution of living species of pelagic foraminifera is dependent on temperature, salinity, and currents.

The amount of nutrients introduced into the northern Atlantic by turbulence, convection currents, and rivers is smaller than that introduced from the Antarctic region in the south, yet it is sufficient to encourage extensive fish production in the North Atlantic. This production is largely concentrated in the major inflows around Greenland and Iceland and in shallow ocean water, such as the Great Banks. In the southern Atlantic, tremendous plankton and fish populations grow around the Falkland Islands and the major inflow from Antarctica.

The Pacific is the largest and deepest ocean. It is connected to the Indian and Southern Oceans, which stretch from East Africa and southern Asia to Australia and Antarctica. The land area draining into the Pacific Ocean is only about one quarter of that draining into the Atlantic Ocean. The Pacific experiences a thick sediment layer over a large proportion of its bottom. The components of the sediments have diverse origins, and compositions and sediment beds are often several hundred meters thick. In deep parts of the ocean, > 4,500 m, pelagic clays dominate. In other places, carbonate oozes and terrigenous sediments abound. Ferromanganese nodules are present in most locations and are particularly common in pelagic clay sediments. The Pacific Ocean also encourages the growth of many major coral reefs, particularly in the South Pacific. The dense cover of pelagic sediment on the bottom on the Pacific Ocean is largely deposited from sediments in the overlaying waters, although volcanic activity and topographic sliding contribute significant sediment buildup as well.

The Pacific Ocean interacts greatly with the Indian and Southern/Antarctic Oceans. Biotic factors are largely determined by the behavioral, reproduction, and food-supply cycles. Extensive migratory patterns of animals feeding on phytoplanktons (free-floating and drifting single-cell forms of plants), zooplanktons that include fine herbivorous crustacean copepods and carnivorous chaetognaths, and nektons make the Pacific a rich and varied fishing ground. The phytoplanktons are the primary producers of organic matter in the Pacific and other oceans. Although phytoplankton are concentrated in the upper 100 m of the water column, nekton and zooplankton are found at all depths and in all regions, even in waters not ever penetrated by sunlight.

The Indian Ocean is the smallest of the major oceans, and like the Southern Ocean it is largely in the Southern Hemisphere. It has narrow continental shelves. Unlike the Atlantic, the Indian Ocean contains many microcontinents such as Madagascar and Seychelles. Sediments are widely distributed, but in addition to the pelagic sediments prevalent in the Atlantic and Pacific Oceans, the Indian Ocean contains terrigenous sediments, coral reefs, and biothermal facies or reefs associated with midoceanic plateaus. The Indian and adjacent Southern Oceans provide rich organic (plankton) feeding and fishing grounds.

1.2 OCEAN RESOURCES AND USES OF THE OCEAN

In addition to the essential functions oceans perform in maintaining the physical and chemical environment of the earth, the oceans offer enormous opportunities for exploitation of resources and various uses by humans. The amounts of products harvested from or on the oceans and the uses of the oceans for various human activities have escalated to an extent that their impact on the well-being of the oceans has assumed serious proportions.

Ocean resource exploitation and use are largely uncontrolled and lack effective management. Attempts have been made to introduce some national and international regulation of the use of ocean resources, such as the Law of the Sea Treaties sponsored by the United Nations. These have resulted in establishing the International Seabed Authority, a U.N. agency responsible for regulating ocean mining in international waters, and other regulations and agreements (discussed in Chapter 5 and summarized in Appendix A). Most ocean resource exploitation occurs unimpeded, however, because of lack of enforcement or regulation.

The growth of the world's population—combined with rapidly

increasing consumption of food and energy to sustain demand for higher standards of living, often interpreted in terms of consumption levels—has forced a rapid depletion of traditional land-based sources of fuel, food, minerals, and chemicals. In turn, this has pushed humans more and more towards exploitation of ocean resources to replace depleted or inadequate land-based sources.

The primary production of organic matter in the oceans through growth of photoplankton is estimated to be 8.6×10^{10} tons per year (dry weight), which is equivalent to an annual production of 2.6×10^7 tons of biogenic hydrocarbon.

Organic material in the oceans is produced by photosynthesis in the enphotic zone (the depth to which light penetrates) where CO_2 and water are used to synthesize organic material. In addition, chemosynthesis occurs at all ocean depths. Heterotrophic bacteria uses organic matter to synthesize bacterial protoplasm.

Decomposition of living organisms and organic material occurs at all depths. These residues removed from the cyclic processes in the sea are considered the precursors of petroleum and are estimated to form at a rate of about 1.4×10^9 tons per year, even now.

Although petroleum is thought to originate from marine biosynthesis, changes brought about over geological time scales have resulted in petroleum having a wider range of chemical structures and homologues in each class than could be expected to arise from pure marine biosynthesis. This makes it less absorbable by ocean processes.

Sharing and protecting ocean resources go hand in hand with the efficient use of ocean resources and environmentally sound technologies in ocean resource exploitation. The oceans are the earth's largest reservoir of resources required to sustain and advance human life. These resources are largely untapped, and technology for ocean resource exploitation is basically in a state of infancy. In fact, it is curious to note that the cumulative investment made in space technology is about 100 times that devoted to ocean technology development during the twentieth century alone.

Most of the technology used in ocean resource exploitation—such as aquaculture, ocean mining, fishing, offshore oil production, and ocean energy conversion—is comparatively simple, and recent developments are more in ocean resource exploration than in exploitation or production technology. This may be well conceived, at this time, because the extent of recoverable ocean resources is largely unknown and their volume and locations must be identified. There is an urgent need, however, to improve exploitation and recovery or harvesting technology that, with the exception of oil and gas production in the ocean, is still rather primitive.

1.2.1 Ocean Oil and Gas Production

World production of many important commodities increasingly comes from the oceans. Over 26.8% of oil production, for example, is now from offshore wells. This is expected to reach 29% by the year 2000 (Table 1–3). Natural gas production from offshore wells, on the other hand, has hovered roughly between 15% and 19% of world production since the late 1960s, mostly because of large land site production surpluses in the Soviet Union, North America, Indonesia, and North Africa. Table 1–4 details world production of natural gas. Gas production from offshore wells is expected to grow in the future as cleaner fuels are more in demand. Furthermore, this, and offshore oil production, will be facilitated by newer, more efficient technol-

TABLE 1–3 Crude Oil Production (in billions of barrels)

	WORLD PRODUCTION	OFFSHORE PRODUCTION	PERCENTAGE OFFSHORE
1972	49,968	8,859	17.8
1973	55,212	10,067	18.2
1974	56,772	9,268	16.3
1975	53,850	8,278	15.4
1976	57,210	9,432	16.5
1977	56,567	11,437	20.2
1978	60,337	11,481	19.0
1979	62,678	12,492	19.9
1980	59,812	13,587	22.7
1981	55,886	13,665	24.5
1982	53,191	13,521	25.4
1983	53,259	13,791	26.7
1984	54,090	15,311	28.3
1985	53,391	15,128	28.0
1986	55,864	13,923	24.9
1987	56,070	14,741	26.3
1988	58,009	14,402	24.8
1989	59,661	14,833	24.9

Note: 1 metric ton = 6.998 barrels

SOURCE: *Offshore Journal* (Tulsa: Penwell Publishing Co., Jan. 1990).

TABLE 1–4 World Production of Natural Gas (Excluding Socialist Countries) (in billion ft^3)

	WORLD PRODUCTION	OFFSHORE PRODUCTION	PERCENTAGE OFFSHORE
1976	50,407	10,847	21.5
1977	53,883	6,663	12.4
1978	53,859	9,509	17.8
1979	57,194	9,369	16.4
1980	58,636	10,161	17.3
1981	57,816	10,085	17.4
1982	55,894	10,357	18.5
1983	55,665	10,360	18.6
1984	59,932	12,197	20.4
1985	62,721	12,451	19.9
1986	63,683	11,643	18.3
1987	68,168	11,299	16.6
1988	70,979	10,948	15.4
1989	74,225	10,869	14.6

SOURCE: *Offshore Journal* (Tulsa: Penwell Publishing Co., Jan. 1990).

ogy and the capability to explore and exploit reserves in deeper and more hostile ocean environments effectively.

Of particular interest will be the development of submerged production platforms operated completely by remote control. Offshore oil and gas production has an increasing impact on the oceans, not only because of the potential for environmental impacts from oil spills but also because the proliferation of thousands of offshore oil and gas rigs introduces major impediments to navigation. In addition, some say that these rigs have detrimental effects on marine life. This has been questioned, however, because there is evidence that fish and other marine life prefer to breed and habituate in waters sheltered by structures, such as offshore rigs.

Offshore platforms and rigs can be floating, floatable, erected, or placed on the ocean bottom or on a legged platform (rigid or jackup). The type chosen usually depends on

1. water depths,
2. environmental conditions,
3. ocean-bottom conditions,
4. depth of well,

5. magnitude of expected well production, and
6. distance from land and tank farms.

As oil and gas production in deeper, more remote waters becomes common, new technologies will probably be developed.

World oil production declined from a high of 62.7 million barrels per day in 1979 to 59.7 million barrels per day in 1989. Production has since grown to over 60.2 million barrels per day in 1991, a volume that is expected to be exceeded in 1992 and 1993. Although fossil fuel energy conversion efficiency has improved and has increased from about $11,900 gross world product (GWP) per ton of oil equivalent of world primary energy use[1] to over $2,340 GWP per ton between 1980 and 1990, it now appears to have leveled off, particularly in the United States and in developing countries. At the same time, nuclear power production is at a standstill and may even decline. As a result, world oil production is expected to continue its growth, with a large proportion of new or expanded production developed offshore.

1.2.2 Fishery Production

Fishery resource exploitation is the second most valuable use of the ocean. World production of fish and shellfish has tripled since the 1960s and is increasing at about twice the rate of the world's population growth (Figure 1–1). This indicates an increasing shift in protein consumption. The major locations of fishery resources are in the North Pacific and North Atlantic, and most fish and shellfish are caught in the 200-mile zone that usually comprises the continental shelf and margin (Figures 1–2 and 1–3). Similar nominal fish catches are shown in Figure 1–4. These indicate the rapid growth of production in both the South and North Pacific, which together grew from just over 13 million tons per year in 1970 to over 37.3 million tons per year in 1990 and are expected to exceed 38.6 million tons in 1992.

The world's nominal marine catch by continent (Table 1–5A) and by major fishing area (Table 1–5B) shows the rapid change in production in various areas. World fish catch has grown rapidly from 22 million tons (9 kg per capita) in 1950 to 100 million tons (19 kg per capita) in 1989?[2] It has since fallen to 97 million tons in 1990

[1]World Bank, 1992. Development Report.

[2]Food and Agriculture Organization (FAO), *Production Yearbook* (Rome: FAO, 1992).

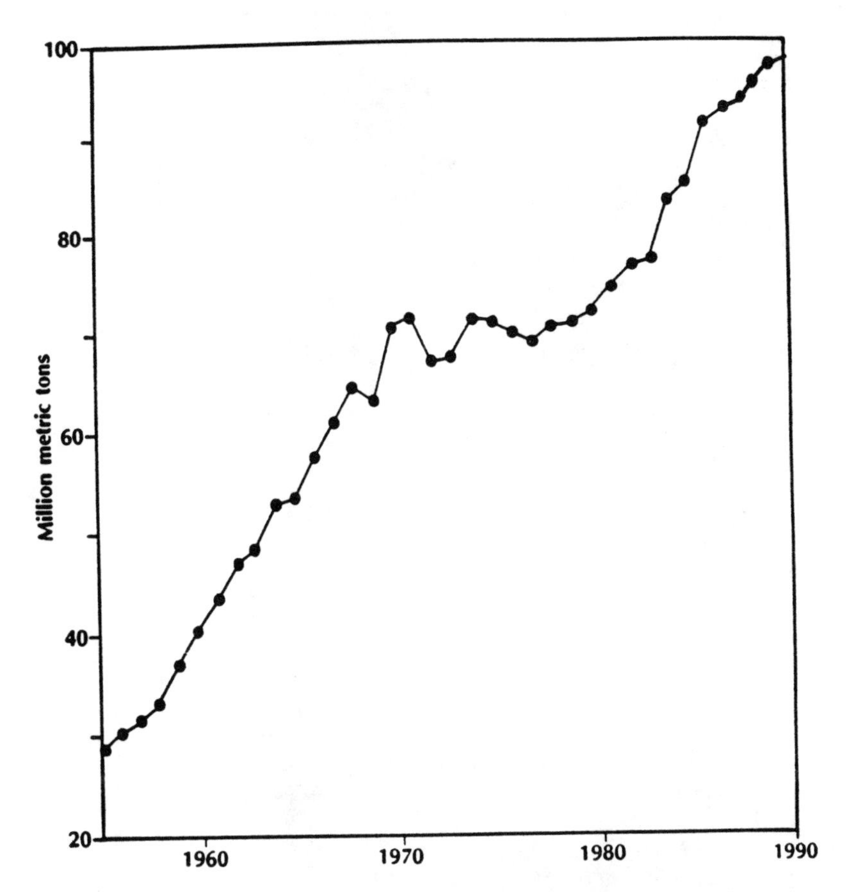

Figure 1–1 Global Catch. From Food and Agriculture Organization (FAO), *Production Yearbook 1987, 1989* and *1991* (Rome: FAO, 1987, 1989, and 1991).

and 95 million tons in 1991. Fish account for 16% of animal protein intake worldwide, but for 40% or more in Japan, Norway, and some developing countries. Aquaculture produced nearly 15 million tons of fish in 1988 and is expected to grow to an output of 20 million tons or 25% of world fish production by the year 2000.

North Atlantic fisheries, for example, have experienced a gradual decline, while all Pacific areas are experiencing continuous growth. This trend is detailed in Table 1–5C, which shows marine catch by country and provides a good measure of per capita fish consumption. One reason for the decline may be overfishing. In addition, a comparatively small amount of catch is produced by fish farming in the North and South Atlantic and adjacent seas. In fact,

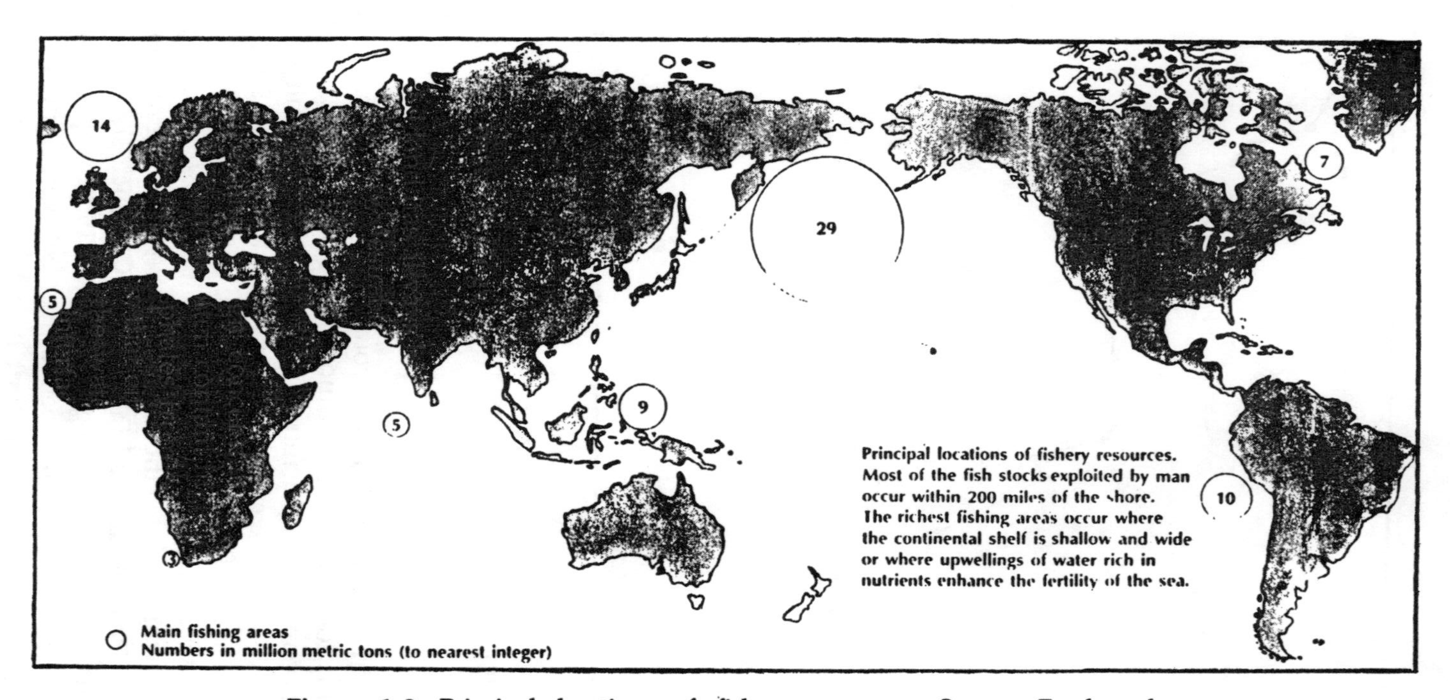

Figure 1–2 Principal locations of fishery resources. Source: Food and Agriculture Organization (FAO), *Production Yearbook 1987, 1989,* and *1991* (Rome: FAO, 1987, 1989, and 1991).

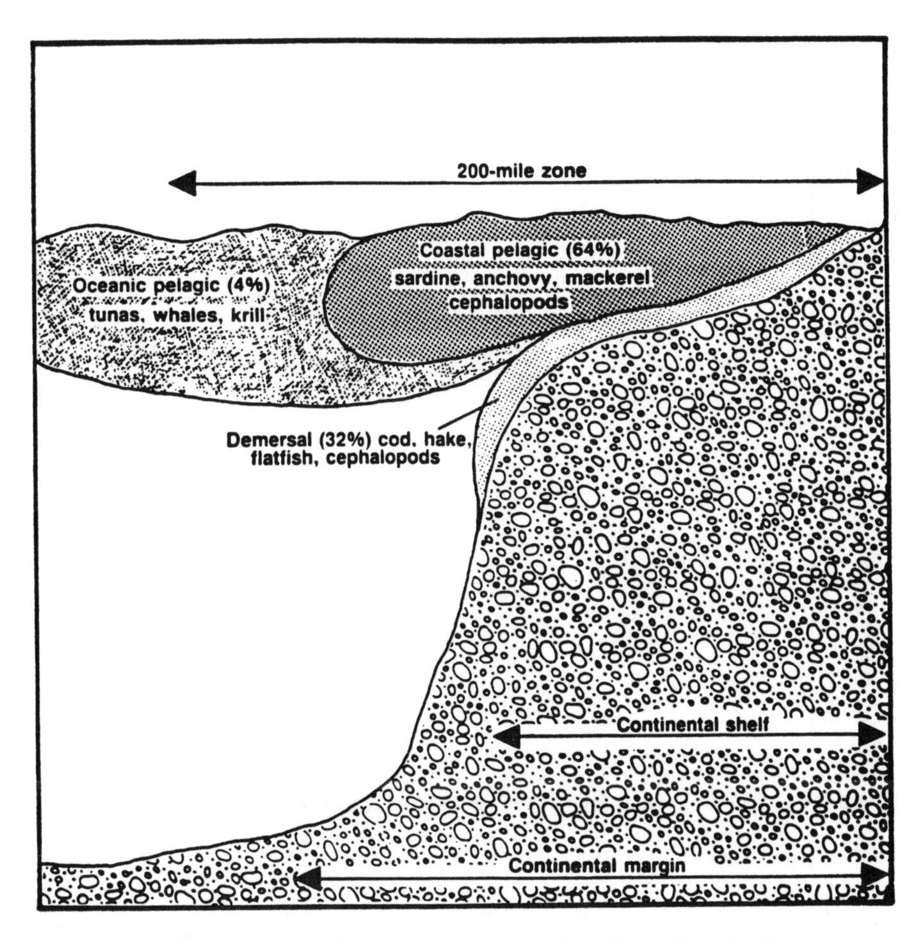

Figure 1–3 Basic distribution of marine catches, by regions in the sea. Source: Food and Agriculture Organization (FAO), *Production Yearbook 1987, 1989,* and *1991* (Rome: FAO, 1987, 1989, and 1991).

most European and American fish is produced by traditional fishing methods.

On the other hand, aquaculture provides an increasing percentage of fish and shellfish and can be expanded without limitation. This may be necessary to ensure more effective management of fish and shellfish populations and the effective biological balance of the oceans, and particularly the coastal zones.

Although aquaculture provided only 10% of the fish and shellfish catch worldwide in 1968, its contribution has grown both in absolute and relative terms (Table 1–6A and B). Aquaculture provides

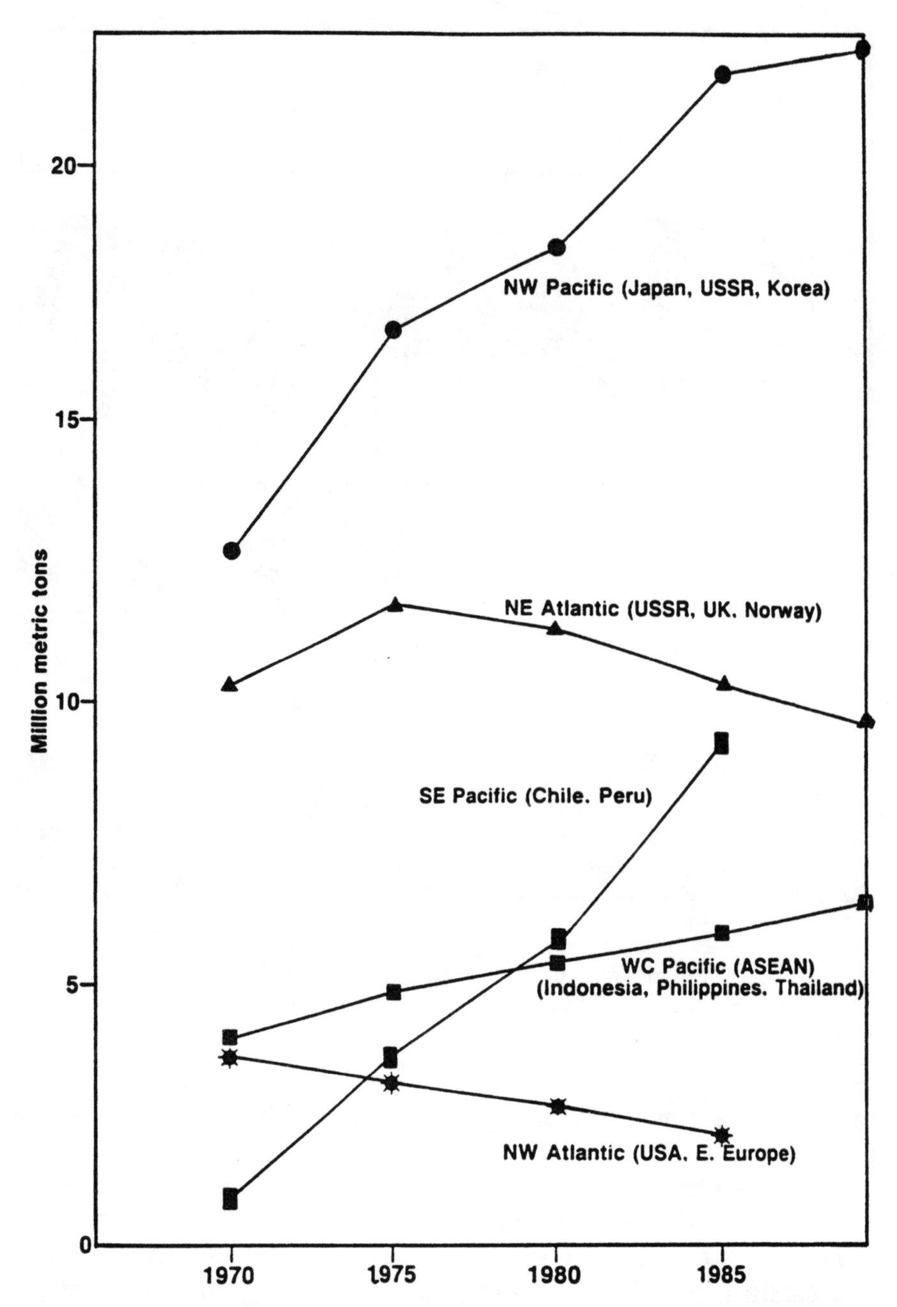

Figure 1–4 Nominal fish catches by countries or areas. Includes fish, mollusks, and crustaceans. Source: Food and Agriculture Organization (FAO), *Production Yearbook 1987, 1989,* and *1991* (Rome; FAO, 1987, 1989, and 1991).

TABLE 1–5A World Nominal Marine Catch (in 1,000 metric tons)

	1970	1980	1985	1986	1987	1986–1987 (% Change)
Africa	3,131	2,725.0	2,704.1	2,929.4	3,514.7	+20.0
North America	4,750	6,698.1	7,883.3	8,109.5	8,925.7	+10.1
South America	14,629	7,438.2	11,478.5	13,691.4	11,655.8	–14.9
Asia	19,453	26,258.0	30,606.0	32,984.3	33,320.5	+1.0
Europe	11,815	12,169.4	12,519.0	12,244.4	12,130.7	–0.9
Oceania	194	448.3	595.2	669.1	782.5	+16.9
USSR	6,399	8,722.6	9,617.2	10,333.0	10,171.2	–1.6
World Totals	61,432[a]	64,459.6	75,403.3	80,961.1	80,501.1	–0.6

[a]Exceeds the sum of the figures by continent due to the inclusion of catches not elsewhere included.

SOURCE: Food and Agriculture Organization (FAO), *Production Yearbook 1985, 1987,* and *1989* (Rome: FAO, 1985, 1987, 1989).

an increasing percentage of fish and shellfish: 10% in 1968, 15% in 1980, and 18.2% in 1990. It provides not only for efficient gathering but also for improved conversion of the marine food chain and land waste transformation. But it may cause serious pollution by waste fish food, fish feces, and steroids and antibiotics if used in the diets of fish that may remain active on discharge.

Marine pollution can have a significant impact on aquaculture. Poor water quality and toxic phytoplankton blooms, such as the toxic algae bloom that occurred in the North Sea off Norway in the spring of 1988, can preclude, disrupt, or destroy aquaculture operations.

Another related issue is competition for coastal land use. Aquaculture sites usually located in coastal waters may block or restrict public access to important recreational areas, may inhibit residential development, or may impact on wildlife habitat.

The continued expansion of the aquaculture industry depends on the cost of production, the availability of suitable locations, technology, resources, and the influence and effectiveness of government regulations. Aquaculture's dependence on cheap, abundantly available fishmeal could become a limiting factor of this industry's development, although current research indicates that alternative food materials could be used in the future.

Aquaculture has become a safe environmental method for seafood production without the hazards of traditional fishing that

TABLE 1–5B World Nominal Marine Catch by Major Fishing Area (in million metric tons)

	1970	1980	1986	1987	1986–1987 (% Change)
Atlantic, NW	4.23	2.87	2.94	3.01	+2.38
Atlantic, NE	10.70	11.81	10.57	10.39	–1.70
Atlantic, N.	14.93	14.68	13.51	13.40	–0.81
Atlantic, WC	1.42	1.80	2.08	2.17	+4.33
Atlantic, EC	2.77	3.43	3.05	3.25	+6.56
Mediterranean and Black	1.15	1.64	2.01	1.91	–4.98
Atlantic, C	5.34	6.87	7.14	7.33	+2.66
Atlantic, SW	1.10	1.27	1.74	2.23	+28.16
Atlantic, SE	2.52	2.17	2.12	2.69	+26.89
Atlantic, S	3.62	3.90	4.32	5.36	+24.07
Atlantic	23.53	25.45	24.97	26.09	+4.49
Indian, W	1.72	2.09	2.61	2.59	–0.77
Indian, E	0.81	1.46	2.32	2.38	+2.59
Indian[a]	2.53	3.55	4.93	4.97	+0.81
Pacific, NW	13.01	18.76	25.87	25.91	+0.15
Pacific, NE	2.65	1.97	3.21	3.38	+5.30
Pacific, N	15.60	20.73	29.08	29.29	+0.72
Pacific, WC	4.22	5.49	6.57	6.50	–1.07
Pacific, EC	0.91	2.42	2.63	2.43	–7.60
Pacific, C	5.12	7.91	9.20	8.93	–2.93
Pacific, SW	0.17	0.38	0.75	0.90	+20.00
Pacific, SE	13.76	6.23	11.98	10.27	–14.27
Pacific, S	13.93	6.62	12.73	49.39	–12.25
Pacific	34.71	35.26	51.01	49.39	–3.18
World total	61.43	64.39	80.96	80.50	–0.57
Northern regions	30.59	35.41	42.59	42.69	+0.23
Central regions	13.00	18.33	21.27	21.23	–0.19
Southern regions	17.54	10.65	17.09	16.57	–3.04

[a]Temperature and tropical.

Note: Totals and subtotals may differ from the sum of included figures due to rounding and the inclusion of catches not elsewhere included.

SOURCE: Food and Agriculture Organization (FAO), *Production Yearbook 1989* (Rome: FAO, 1989).

TABLE 1–5C World Nominal Marine Catch by Country (in 1,000 metric tons)

	1970	1980	1986	1987	1986–1987 (% Change)
Anglo-America:					
Canada	1,290.1	1,292.7	1,463.7	1,410.5	–3.6
Greenland	39.8	103.6	101.0	101.0[a]	0.0
United States	2,729.3	3,565.0	4,871.2	5,661.3	+2.5
Total	4,060.1	4,981.7	6,444.2	7,181.3	+11.4
Latin America					
Argentina	186.1	376.9	411.8	551.6	+33.9
Brazil	432.7	548.5	617.5[a]	578.1[a]	–6.4
Chile	1,200.3	2,816.7	5,570.6	4,813.4	–13.6
Colombia	21.3	29.3	27.4	23.4	–14.6
Costa Rica	7.0	19.7	20.6	19.7	–4.4
Cuba	105.3	180.1	227.0	197.6	–13.0
Dominican Republic	5.0	8.2	16.3	18.5	+13.5
Ecuador	91.4	639.0	1,002.5	678.1	–32.4
Guyana	17.4	30.8	39.4	40.8	+3.6
Mexico	344.1	1,212.6	1,184.9	1,245.8	+5.1
Panama	52.2	216.4	129.4	167.9	+29.8
Peru	12,532.9	2,696.1	5,581.4	4,547.1	–18.5
Uruguay	13.2	120.1	140.1	136.9	–2.3
Venezuela	122.6	169.4	294.0	276.0	–6.1
Other	64.2	84.3	92.3	105.2	+13.9
Total	15,215.5	9,148.1	15,355.2	13,400.1	–12.7
Northern Europe:					
Belgium	53.0	45.6	38.9	39.8	+2.3
Denmark	1,217.1	2,010.5	1,671.9	–8.5	
Faeroe Is.	207.8	274.7	352.9	355.4	+0.7
Finland	62.6	111.0	121.8	126.8	+4.1
France	764.4	761.4	835.3[a]	803.8[a]	–3.8
Germany, F.R.	597.9	288.7	178.2	177.8	–0.2
Greece	91.5[a]	95.9	113.7	124.8	+9.8
Iceland	733.3	1,514.4	1,656.4	1,632.5	–1.4
Ireland	78.9	149.4	228.9	247.3	+8.0
Italy	379.3	467.3	509.7	499.3	–2.0
The Netherlands	298.8	338.4	450.5	430.0	–4.6
Norway	2,906.2	2,408.6	1,898.0	1,928.9	+1.6
Portugal	464.4	270.4	400.4	392.8	–1.9
Spain	1,517.0	1,281.8	1,407.2[a]	1,364.7[a]	–3.0
Sweden	284.2	230.7	211.9	210.7	–0.6
U.K.	1,091.3	844.2	844.9	947.8[a]	+12.2
Other	1.4	2.6	2.6	2.5	–4.1
Total	10,749.1	11,095.5	11,078.6	10,956.8	–1.1

TABLE 1–5C Continued

	1970	1980	1986	1987	1986–1987 (% Change)
Socialist Eastern Europe:					
Bulgaria	86.8	114.0	95.2	97.7	+2.6
German D.R.	308.2	223.1	189.3	173.5	–8.3
Poland	451.3	621.9	615.8	640.2	+4.0
Romania	24.8	120.9	205.3	197.5	–3.8
USSR	6,386.5	8,722.6	10,333.0	10,171.2	–1.6
Yugoslavia	26.7	34.9	51.4	56.2	+9.3
Other	4.0	7.0	8.8	9.3	+5.7
Total	7,288.3	9,844.4	11,498.8	11,345.6	–1.3
Far East:					
Algeria	25.7	48.0[a]	70.0[a]	70.0[a]	0/0
Egypt	27.2	32.2	39.0	48.3[a]	+23.8
Iran	18.0[a]	40.0	121.8	120.0[a]	–1.5
Morocco	246.8	329.6	597.2	489.7[a]	–18.0
Oman	180.0[a]	79.0[a]	96.4[a]	115.0	+19.3
Saudi Arabia	21.1	26.4	45.5	45.5[a]	0.0
Tunisia	24.0	60.1	92.6	99.2	+7.1
Turkey	165.3	394.6	539.6	580.9	+7.7
U.A. Emirates	40.0	64.4	79.5	85.4	+7.4
Yemen A.R.	7.6[a]	17.0	22.2	22.3	+0.5
Yemen, Dem.	120.0	58.3	47.7	48.5	+1.7
Other	35.7	77.2	44.4	52.7	+18.8
Total	911.4	1,226.8	1,795.9	1,777.5	–1.0
Sub-Saharan Africa:					
Angola	368.2	77.6	50.5	73.3	+45.1
Cameroon	19.2	73.0[a]	64.0	62.5	–2.3
Cape Verde	5.1	8.8	6.5	6.9	+6.2
Congo	15.2	21.0	18.0	17.5	–2.8
Gabon	4.5[a]	18.0[a]	18.8	19.0[a]	+1.1
Ghana	141.5	191.9	267.7	317.8	+18.7
Guinea	5.6[a]	18.9[a]	28.0[a]	28.0[a]	0.0
Ivory Coast	66.5[a]	67.9	76.2	74.3	–2.5
Madagascar	13.1	12.2	17.6	17.6[a]	–0.1
Mauritania	47.6	15.6[a]	92.1[a]	93.3[a]	+1.3
Mozambique	7.6	30.4	31.2	35.9	+15.1
Namibia	711.2	252.6	201.2	519.4	+158.2
Nigeria	105.9	292.4	161.5	145.8	–9.7
Senegal	169.2	217.8	271.9	284.0[a]	+4.5
Sierra Leone	29.6	34.2	37.0[a]	37.0[a]	0.0

TABLE 1–5C Continued

	1970	1980	1986	1987	1986–1987 (% Change)
Sub-Saharan Africa:					
Somalia	30.0[a]	14.3	16.5	17.0	+3.0
South Africa	511.1	601.9	627.9	901.3	+43.5
Tanzania	18.3	38.0	44.1	47.8	+8.4
Togo	6.4	8.4	14.1	14.5	+2.8
Other	53.5	53.8	74.1	85.2	+14.9
Total	2,314.5	2,048.6	2,118.9	2,798.0	+32.1
South Asia:					
Bangladesh	90.0[a]	122.0	207.5	232.9	+12.2
India	1,085.6	1,554.7	1,716.9	1,681.5	–2.1
Maldives	34.5	34.6	45.8	46.9	+2.4
Pakistan	149.3	232.9	331.7	336.1	+1.1
Sri Lanka	89.8	165.2	142.9	153.5	+7.4
Total	1,449.2	2,109.4	2,444.8	2,450.9	+0.2
East Asia:					
China	2,192.5	2,995.4	4,636.6	5,408.4	+16.6
Hong Kong	133.3	187.5	207.8	221.6	+6.6
Japan	8,658.4	10,213.3	11,777.6	11,615.1	–1.4
Korea, D.P.R.	447.0	1,330.0[a]	1,600.0[a]	1,600.0[a]	0.0
Korea, Rep.	725.5	2,052.0	3,046.5	2,819.3	–7.5
Taiwan	540.4	761.3	828.5	930.7	+12.3
Other	9.6	6.9	8.0	3.5	–56.3
Total	12,706.7	17,546.4	22,105.0	22,598.6	+2.2
Southeast Asia:					
Burma	311.4	428.8	535.2	540.9	+1.1
Indonesia	804.0	1,387.0	1,850.0	1,967.9	+6.4
Malaysia	338.5	733.2	607.0	598.6	–1.4
Philippines	844.1	1,134.3	1,377.8	1,426.0	+3.5
Singapore	17.3	15.5	20.3	15.1	–25.6
Thailand	1,343.5	1,653.0	2,348.3	2,000.4	–14.8
Vietnam	668.3	398.7	582.1	620.4	+6.6
Other	21.7	45.2	19.6	19.6	0.0
Total	4,348.7	5,795.7	7,340.3	7,188.9	–2.1
Australasia:					
Australia	100.7	130.3	176.5[a]	197.5[a]	+11.4
Fiji	3.9	23.6	23.9	30.5	+27.6
Kiribati	9.7	18.9	33.6	43.9	+30.7
New Zealand	59.2	190.9	345.0	430.5	+24.8
Solomon Is.	1.0	34.8	55.4	44.5	–19.7

TABLE 1–5C Continued

	1970	1980	1986	1987	1986–1987 (% Change)
Australasia:					
Other	20.7	15.9	23.3	24.0	+2.9
Total	195.2	414.4	657.7	770.9	+17.2
Other NEI[b]	240.6	327.9	119.1	34.1	–71.4
World Total	59,495.0	64,539.5	80,961.1	80,501.2	–0.6

[a]FAO estimate.

[b]Not elsewhere included. These values differ from those found in the source due to the exclusion of Taiwan's catch from the FAO sum, the inclusion of the catches for the French Southern and Antarctic Territories in the FAO sum, and small discrepancies due to rounding.

Note: Nominal marine catch. Countries that reported marine catches of less than 10,000 metric tons in 1986 are included under "Other" for all years.

SOURCE: FAO, unless otherwise noted.

sometimes cause the destruction of sea-bottom habitats and corals, overfishing, and the unnecessary killing of undesirable species, including undersized creatures. Fishing is a crude, self-destructive harvesting method that is not only expensive but that also reduces the maintenance of a healthy stock and replenishment of the species.

Most fishing relies on crude mechanical gathering methods, such as nets, with a limiting net gauge that may allow very small, undersized catches to escape but that has no escape mechanism for

TABLE 1–6A Total Aquaculture Production (in 1980 metric tons)

REGION	TOTAL	FINFISH	MOLLUSKS	CRUSTACEANS	SEAWEED
Africa	4,532	4,061	471	—	—
Asia and Oceania	7,351,821	2,561,203	2,568,925	60,260	2,206,434
Europe	135,792	630,196	505,516	30	50
Latin America and Caribbean	75,244	25,480	44,404	5,360	
North America	139,974	57,386	76,993	5,596	
TOTAL	8,707,363	3,233,326	3,196,308	71,245	2,206,484

SOURCE: T.V.R. Pillay, Opening Address, Proceedings of the World Aquaculture Conference, Venice, 1981.

TABLE 1–6B Aquaculture

	AQUACULTURE PRODUCTION				
	FISH (metric tons)	MOLLUSKS (metric tons)	VALUE (millions of U.S. dollars)	FISHERIES PRODUCTION TOTAL (millions of U.S. dollars)[a]	AQUACULTURE VERSUS FISHERIES (%)
Canada	3,100	8,600	23	930	2
United States	224,100	57,700	496	2,760	18
Japan	291,600	892,600	3,620	17,220	21
Australia	1,200	8,400	—	400	
New Zealand	500	15,000	13	—	—
Denmark	27,400	—	15	440	17
Finland	10,100	—	45	40	116
France	38,500	173,300	404	980	41
Germany[b]	20,200	21,000	55	120	45
Greece	4,600	2,300	19	360	5
Ireland	1,800	11,000	11	80	13
Italy	33,000	87,900	128	1,300	10
Netherlands	700	102,000	51	360	14
Norway	50,000	200	233	670	35
Portugal	2,800	8,200	—	320	—
Spain	16,900	250,400	60	1,550	3
Sweden	4,000	300	13	100	14
United Kingdom	21,200	4,100	92	530	17

Note: Aquaculture refers to farming of fish, crustaceans, and algae both in inland and in marine waters.

[a]Includes fish for reduction, but excludes aquaculture. Production of fisheries, however, includes aquaculture for France and Japan.

[b]Includes western Germany only.

SOURCE: OECD.

undesirable or unwanted larger creatures. It also severely interferes with the balanced maintenance of a healthy food chain by upsetting the ratios of species in the chain. This may result in overpopulation of sea life at the top of the chain and a further depletion of lower chain food species. The lower food chain species, like shrimp, crabs, and bottom fish, constitute the major seafood consumption of both humans and higher-order ocean creatures, such as sharks, whales, dolphins, and various other types of sea mammals.

Modern aquaculture permits controlled revitalization of food stocks in the ocean while encouraging redevelopment of a healthy food chain balance. In other words, humans' quest for food from the seas can be compared to hunting versus controlled meat growing. The world's population of cattle, sheep, pigs, poultry, and so forth would have long been completely depleted if human meat consumption had continued to rely on hunting and trapping, but that is exactly what people are still doing in the world's oceans.

Managing land food animals and birds has not only allowed humanity to meet its ever growing food needs in an increasingly economic manner, but meat production has become more humane, and the world population and health of the land food animal stock has continued to grow in line with increasing demand.

In contrast, ocean food growing and harvesting from biological and vegetational sources lags behind that of food animals. Aquaculture—as a method of food production from the seas—is really in its infancy, notwithstanding the growing demand for food from the sea that is generally found to be more healthy for human consumption than more traditional sources of protein.

The oceans not only occupy nearly 73% of the earth's surface; they also harbor the bulk of the earth's nutrients. The food chain in the oceans is largely intact and provides an orderly progression from plankton to the largest mammals in existence. The oceans—more than vegetation on land—affect the production of essential greenhouse gases for the sustenance of life. Therefore, it is important to learn how to manage ocean food production resources. Oceans reach depths of over 7,575 meters and, in terms of foods' chain reactions and various chemical as well as physical interactions, are productive at all depths.

The total volume of water in the earth's oceans is equivalent to a volume with a height of 27,200 ft above all the land surface of the earth. In other words, the oceans have a productive volume that comprises a volume equal to all the earth's land areas to a height of an average airplane flight. Compared with the earth or soil and atmospheric volume used by humans and nature to produce vegetation and other food on land, the oceans offer a productive volume that is at least 300 times greater.

Together with the abundance of nutrients, stabilizing physical, chemical, and thermal interaction, and the large amount of subsea energy and chemical emission from the inner crust of the earth, the oceans provide a unique, mostly untapped source of food and energy for humans and other inhabitants of the earth. World consumption of seafood now exceeds 90 million metric tons per year. This replaces about 200 million steers or 750 million pigs.

Today, most parts of the world are overfished. Fish production is too large. With modern electronics and fishing gear, productivity of fishing has grown manifold in the United States, the Far East, and many ports of Europe. Even though fishing regulations exist in many areas, modern technology and the rapid growth of fishing fleets continue to exacerbate the problem of overfishing.

Not only has the world catch grown rapidly since the 1960s, but an increasing amount of fishery commodities are traded now. The value of world international trade in fishery commodities, which was only $3.275 billion in 1970, had grown to $30.509 billion by 1987 and exceeded $35 billion in 1990 (Table 1–7), or more than a tenfold increase in just 20 years. The disposition of fish production (Table 1–8) shows that an increasing percentage is used for human consumption (67.1%) and of this, nearly 28% is now marketed fresh.

Although fishing has traditionally been the most important ocean resource exploited by humans, there is increasing evidence that the very resources people aim to exploit are being destroyed by polluting the coastal zone; poisoning breeding grounds; overfishing; capturing and destructing young fish, marine life, and organisms without commercial value that are caught and destroyed by thoughtless or primitive fishing methods; and physical destruction of habitats. Similarly, over 1.5 million dolphins and small whales are killed each year by tuna fishers, by ocean pollution, or in target hunts. Larger whales are also hunted, and their number continues to decline.

Although uncontrolled harvesting of world fisheries has been reduced somewhat, disagreements persist among fishing nations regarding sustainable harvesting levels. Overfishing remains a problem for some species and in some regions, particularly in the North Atlantic.

At the same time, with increasing demand for fish, declining fish populations, and growing concern with ocean pollution, demand for farmed fish will increase. Farmed seafood is safer and as a result healthier than caught fish. Aquaculture farms usually have well-controlled environments and feeding, which assure healthier seafood and nutritional quality. Farmed seafood can be grown to contain certain nutritional ingredients and therefore assure greater nutritional value. Fish and seafood farming, which has grown

TABLE 1–7 Trade of Fisheries Commodities by Major Importing and Exporting Countries (in millions of U.S. dollars)

	1970	1980	1986	1987	1986–1987 (% Change)
Imports:					
Japan	291.9	3,158.7	6,593.4	8,308.1	+26.0
United States	835.8	2,633.2	4,748.9	5,662.3	+19.2
France	203.9	1,131.2	1,510.0	2,022.5	+33.9
Italy	159.6	831.7	1,264.5	1,738.2	+37.5
United Kingdom	294.0	1,033.7	1,216.6	1,386.8	+14.0
Spain	46.6	544.0	721.2	1,321.8	+83.3
Germany, F.R.	264.8	1,023.9	1,113.3	1,270.5	+14.1
Denmark	47.1	330.7	596.6	842.5	+41.2
Hong Kong	56.0	361.4	624.5	794.3	+27.2
Belgium	86.3	408.3	425.6	529.9	+24.5
Canada	51.0	301.6	433.3	511.9	+18.1
The Netherlands	93.2	389.4	387.8	509.4	+31.4
Portugal	32.6	100.0	256.6	424.7	+65.5
Sweden	98.8	325.2	333.4	404.9	+21.4
Switzerland	47.5	211.8	264.5	332.8	+25.8
Singapore	28.9	142.1	257.8	313.0	+21.4
Australia	41.6	178.5	226.7	299.6	+32.2
Thailand	3.9	23.4	283.4	267.1	–5.7
Republic of Korea	5.0	35.7	117.7	212.5	+80.5
Nigeria	4.1	422.0	90.0	168.0	+86.6
Subtotal	2,692.6	13,587.2	21,465.7	27,320.9	+27.3
Other	582.4	2,370.2	2,728.7	3,188.1	+16.0
World total	3,275.0	15,957.4	24,194.5	30,509.0	+26.1

SOURCE: Food and Agriculture Organization (FAO) *Annual Report 1990* (Rome: FAO, 1990).

rapidly in the Orient, is now catching on in the West. This can be expected to become a real growth industry as people learn that managing seafood by proper farming is not only economically but also nutritionally more attractive than catching fish. Hunting fish is like hunting land animals; it is archaic and in most cases counterproductive because it does not permit proper nutritional and population control.

TABLE 1–8 World Nominal Fish Catch, Disposition (in million metric tons)

	1970	1980	1985	1986	1987	1986–1987 (% Change)
Human consumption	44.6 (100.0)	53.3 (100.0)	60.7 (100.0)	65.5 (100.0)	67.1 (100.0)	+2.4
Marketing fresh	18.6 (41.7)	14.9 (27.9)	16.1 (26.5)	19.2 (29.4)	20.2 (30.1)	+5.2
Freezing	9.8 (22.0)	16.3 (30.6)	20.4 (33.6)	21.8 (33.3)	22.1 (32.9)	+1.4
Curing	8.1 (18.1)	11.3 (21.3)	12.7 (21.1)	13.0 (19.9)	13.2 (19.7)	+1.5
Canning	8.1 (18.2)	10.8 (20.2)	11.5 (18.9)	11.5 (17.4)	11.6 (17.3)	+0.9
Other purposes	26.0 (100.0)	18.9 (100.0)	25.3 (100.0)	26.8 (100.0)	25.6 (100.0)	–4.5
Reduction	25.0 (96.2)	18.1 (96.0)	24.3 (96.0)	25.8 (96.3)	24.6 (96.1)	–4.7
Miscellaneous	1.0 (3.8)	0.8 (4.0)	1.0 (4.0)	1.0 (3.7)	1.0 (3.9)	0.0
World total	70.6	72.2	86.0	92.3	92.7	+0.4

Notes: Percentages of subtotals shown in parentheses.

The figures for disposition are based on "live weight" and include freshwater catches.

SOURCE: Food and Agriculture Organization (FAO) *Annual Report 1990* (Rome: FAO, 1990).

1.2.3 Ocean Mineral Production

Subsurface production of oil and gas in the oceans has become a major economic activity and may equal liquid and gaseous fossil fuel production on land in the early twenty-first century. But with the exception of production of construction materials such as sand and gravel, which are traditionally gathered from the bottom of the seas or from the shores of oceans, ocean mineral production is still in its infancy. Superficial deposit extraction of manganese, barite, and phosphorous is only experimental at this stage. This is largely because it usually requires deep-sea mining, which is subject to permitting by the International Seabed Authority, and large investments, which are difficult to justify when these materials are abundantly available at reasonable costs on land.

Lime shells is one mineral produced in commercial quantities. Others are tin and titanium sands, both of which are mined in shallow coastal, often estuarial, waters (Table 1–9).

Subsurface bedrock ocean coal and iron ore mining are still economically significant in some parts of the world, although as a percentage of world coal and iron ore production they only amount to

TABLE 1–9 Minerals from the Oceans (in millions of U.S. dollars)

	PRODUCTION VALUE, 1972	PERCENTAGE FROM OCEAN
Subsurface		
Petroleum	10,300	18
Gas	4,200	33
Sulfur	25	—
Salt	—	—
Potash	—	—
Geothermal energy	—	—
Freshwater springs	35	—
Surface Deposits		
Sand and gravel	100	1
Lime shells	35	80
Gold	—	—
Platinum	—	—
Tin	53	7
Titanium sands, etc.	76	20
Iron sands	10	1
Barite	1	3
Manganese	—	—
Phosphoric	—	—
Subsurface Bedrock		
Coal	335	2
Iron ore	17	1
Extraction from Seawater		
Salt	173	29
Magnesium and compounds	116	51
Bromine	19	30
Freshwater	51	—
Heavy water	27	20

SOURCE: G. J. S. Govett and M. J. Govett, *World Mineral Supplies,* (Amsterdam, Elsevier, 1976).

2% and 1%, respectively. The most significant ocean mineral production is by extraction from seawater. Twenty-nine percent of the world's salt is produced this way, as is 51% of the world's output of magnesium and its compounds and 30% of bromine. Similarly, 20% of heavy water for nuclear reactor use is produced from seawater.

Mineral exploration at sea today is essentially at the "prospecting" stage. Although the approximate amount of mineral deposits on the ocean floor and the amount of minerals in solution or suspension in seawater are known, the accurate distribution or concentration of these ocean minerals is not known.

It is estimated that the quantities of minerals in the ocean are immense. There are essentially four classes of mineral concentration in the ocean:

1. soluble salts,
2. placer minerals (current and wave action),
3. authigenic minerals (precipitation), and
4. continental shelf minerals.

In all these, mineral exploration or extraction is still highly speculative. For example, while manganese nodules in the Pacific Ocean alone are estimated to contain minerals in billions of tons or in thousands of equivalent years of world consumption, practically no exploitation of these resources is currently under way.

It is generally agreed that the development of ocean mineral resources has a long-term economic potential and that ocean mining can be conducted within acceptable limits of environmental risk. Offshore storage, transfer, and transport of minerals is within reach of existing technology. Similarly, limited technology now exists for outer continental shelf mining of unconsolidated hard minerals by dredging in depths of up to 300 ft. Furthermore, fluid extraction of minerals is a tested, although not very economical, method.

On the other hand, technology for mining ferromanganese nodules from the deep-ocean bottom is still in a highly experimental stage and must be improved to meet the demands of full-scale deep-ocean mining. Although some mining equipment components for this purpose have been developed and tested, complete deep-ocean mining systems are not available now even in experimental or prototype form. The development of deeply submerged bottom production platforms for petroleum exploitation may eventually trigger new and more efficient approaches to this problem.

1.2.3.1 Mineral reserves in the oceans. The basic availability of minerals on the ocean floor is probably in excess of that potentially available in accessible places on land. The extraction of minerals from seawater has been practiced on a small scale for many years, but it is generally found not to be economically attractive (except for the case of special situations such as "Dead Sea" mineral recovery using sunlight alone).

Among other ocean floor minerals of significance are phosphorite deposits on coastal shelves such as Peru, Chile, Mexico, U.S. East Coast, U.S. West Coast, Argentina, South Africa, Japan, and the Indian Ocean islands, and off California (1×10^9 tons, of which only 100 million tons is economical to mine at this time). High-grade deposits in the Red Sea consisting of high percentages of iron, manganese, copper, zinc, and silver nodules have been discovered and are in minable concentrations, but exist largely at great depths.

Only some coastal areas, and to a very limited extent deep-ocean areas, have been surveyed for mineral deposits. In fact, less than 2% of the continental shelf of North America and less than 1% of the world's continental shelf areas have been effectively surveyed. Surveys on the continental slopes and the deep ocean are even scarcer. The classification of ocean mineral resources into dissolved, unconsolidated, and consolidated deposits was made, and using existing data, an estimate of mineral deposits in the Pacific (placer, authigenic, and shelf) was made. The results shown in Table 1–10 indi-

TABLE 1–10 Estimated Mineral Deposits in the Pacific Ocean

Mg	25.0 billion tons	600,000 equivalent years
Al	43.0 billion tons	20,000 equivalent years
Ti	9.9 billion tons	2,000,000 equivalent years
V	0.8 billion tons	400,000 equivalent years
Mn	358.0 billion tons	400,000 equivalent years
Fe	207.0 billion tons	2,000 equivalent years
Co	5.2 billion tons	200,000 equivalent years
Ni	14.7 billion tons	150,000 equivalent years
Cu	7.9 billion tons	6,000 equivalent years
Zn	0.7 billion tons	1,000 equivalent years

SOURCE: G. J. S. Govett and M. J. Govett, *World Mineral Supplies* (Amsterdam, Elsevier, 1976).

cate that quantities of most minerals greatly exceed estimated deposits on dry land.

The potential and cost of exploitation of these mineral deposits cannot be estimated with any degree of reliability. With more advanced exploitation methods, the total estimated amount of minerals in seawater may be even greater. Table 1–11 indicates the amount, concentration per liter, value per average ton of seawater, and world reserve at the present consumption rate. Current costs of extraction by nonsolar means are excessive, and even extraction by solar evaporation is only economically feasible if mineral concentrations are higher, such as in Dead Sea water, and if solar heat is very intense.

1.2.4 Energy Production in the Oceans

Ocean energy generation has been a long-term objective. Humans have attempted to harness wave, current, and tidal energy for a long time. Major efforts have been made to convert these large, renewable energy sources into mechanical energy that could be converted to electrical energy and then distributed.

There are various other methods for generating ocean energy. Thermal columns resulting from large ocean-temperature gradients are generating small experimental amounts of energy in Hawaii and elsewhere, and hydroelectric power is generated by combinations of ocean tidal and current energy. Terrestrial and subsea hot springs in Iceland and New Zealand are used for domestic heat and small-intensity electric power generation. Most of these energy conversion methods have proven to be economically unattractive and remain experimental.

TABLE 1–11 Status of Economic Mineral Extraction from Seawater

	CONCENTRATION (mg/liter)	TOTAL AMOUNT OF MATERIAL (seawater tons)	VALUE PER TON (seawater in U.S. dollars)	RESERVE AT PRESENT CONSUMPTION RATE (million years)
NaCl	29,500	45.6×10^{15}	0.31	+1,000
Magnesium	1,350	2.1×10^{15}	1.00	+1,000
Sulfur	885	1.4×10^{15}	0.03	200
KCl	760	1.2×10^{15}	0.024	300
Bromine	65	100×10^{12}	0.02	1,000

SOURCE: G. J. S. Govett and M. J. Govett, *World Mineral Supplies* (Amsterdam, Elsevier, 1976).

In the long run, though, the oceans provide tremendous opportunities for harnessing renewable energy, not just from waves, currents, and tides or thermal gradients, but from more concentrated energy sources, such as submarine thermal vents (or underwater volcanoes and so forth) that emit large volumes of often toxic (gaseous or mixed-flow) lava that then rises by convection like a flume to the surface.

The temperature at the bottom is often of the order of 500°C, and the kinetic energy of the convection column is often of the order of millions of megawatts. In fact, estimates of the kinetic energy of the submarine vents on the bottom of the Mediterranean between Sicily and Tunisia (representing a chain that continues from Mount Vesuvius to Mount Stromboli and Mount Aetna) are that 5% of that energy, if harnessed and converted into electric power, could satisfy all Europe's electric power needs.

These hot vents, which exist not only in the Mediterranean and in the China Sea but also along midocean ridges, also evolve exotic ecosystems made possible by complex interactions of thermal, chemical, and nuclear energy. The heat escaping from such vents is originally produced by radioactive decay in the earth's interior, which then reaches the earth's surface.

Such hydrothermal vents arise usually from the rift valleys on the ocean floor ridges. The emissions often contain high concentrations of hydrogen sulfide and some minerals that are usually leached from the rock of the earth's crust.

1.2.5 Industrial Use of Ocean Resources

Industry has only recently become aware of the many contributions oceans can make in facilitating or lowering the cost of industrial production or activities. The most common industrial uses of the oceans are as a source of cooling or process water and often, unfortunately, as a convenient depository for industrial waste. Yet, there are many other industrial uses for the oceans.

Ocean materials such as marine microalgae are used in emulsifying agents, dairy products and pharmaceuticals and in the manufacture of cosmetics. Similarly, kelb (macro cylis porifera) is harvested to produce alginic acid, which is modified to also produce emulsifiers for food, pharmaceutical, and cosmetic products. Carrageenan (algae *Chondras*), a gelatinous substance, is used in the manufacture of ice cream. Similarly, agar is made from microalgae.

The range of potential uses of the large number of different algae is not known yet, and research in this field is in its infancy.

Ocean microorganisms also have uses as biopolymer sources, and crustacean shells are used to produce chitin. There are many chemical, mineral, and biological materials available in the oceans with a large potential value to industry.

The most attractive near-term applications of ocean materials to industrial production may well be in the pharmaceutical industry. Among recent uses are chemicals obtained from marine life that can be used to provide data to speed the development of similar synthetic drugs that have the same effect. One example is manoalide, which is found in sponge on reefs around Koro, a Pacific Island in the West Carolina group. Manoalide acts to inhibit action of enzymes called phospholipase A_2, which causes swellings of arthritis, gout, and bee stings. Although manoalide cannot be marketed now, it can be used to lead to production of synthetic drugs with the same inhibiting effects. Another prospective medical use is carrageenan for gastric ulcers. Sulphated polysaccharides produced by some microalgae can increase connective tissue and collagen and can be applied to bone grafts to stimulate growth of connective tissue.

Seaweeds have now been recognized as a major resource for

1. food, industrial, and pharmaceutical purposes, and
2. agar, algin, and carrageenan extracted from seaweed and used as stabilizers and gels in food, medicine, and cosmetic manufacture as well as rubber, textile, paper, and ceramics production.

One-cell algae (very rapid growth) are now being used as a major protein source.

Another area of new industrial use of ocean resources is in energy extraction from aquatic biomass. Here hydrogen waste and methane are extracted from anaerobic fermentation; algae farms (little tanks) can produce all the hydrogen or methane required by a home or other facility. Although these plants today are mostly very small, large-scale plants are under consideration.

Biological aquatic systems are another area of great interest. Agriculture and aquaculture can sometimes be effectively integrated and made to complement each other. Also, almost any species of aquatic plant or animal can be cultivated, and their useful qualities can be enhanced by selective breeding and genetic engineering. So far, only four species of algae have been domesticated: *Porphyra* and *Eucheuma* (red algae) and *Laminaria* and *Undaria* (brown algae).

1.3 OCEAN TRANSPORTATION USE

The oceans have provided the principal opportunities for the transportation of goods and people for thousands of years. Water transport existed long before discovery of the wheel (and therefore before effective nonanimal or humanborne land transport). Even today, well over 80% of international trade transport and over 40% of goods transported by volume, and a somewhat larger percentage in ton miles, is transported by water, mostly over oceans. As a consequence, most major cities were originally located at coastal sites to provide effective access to the oceans by navigation.

Oceanborne trade in tons has remained virtually constant since the late 1970s, with oil trade hovering between a low of 1.212 billion tons in 1983 and a high of 1.702 billion tons in 1978. Current world oil trade (1991) was just under 1.6 billion tons, a volume that is expected to grow at 1% to 3% per year and reach 1.9 billion tons by the year 2000 if the world economies revive. Much will obviously depend on

1. world economic conditions,
2. the enforcement of air pollution regulations, and
3. the development of new energy conversion technology, particularly for road transport such as electric cars.

World seaborne dry cargo trade is growing gradually and is now just under 2.5 billion tons.

The major components of oceanborne dry cargo trade in 1991 were

Iron ore	342 million tons
Coal	360 million tons
Grain	180 million tons
Other	1,610 million tons
Total	2,492 million tons

Today, nearly 50% of the dry bulk cargo not referred to as iron, ore, coal, cement, and grain is carried in containers. Therefore, total world oceanborne cargo transport carries a volume of about 4.38 billion tons, which is expected to grow at just under 3% to about 4.93 billion tons by the year 2000.

This ocean trade had a value estimated at about $5.1 trillion or about 23.4% of the world gross product in 1991. The value of oceanborne trade as a percentage of WGP is growing at nearly twice the rate as the volume in tons. This is largely accounted for by the increase in the average value of traded goods.

This trade is transported by a world oceangoing fleet of 62,824 vessels of 1,000 deadweight tons (DWT) or larger with a combined carrying capacity of 613.84 million DWT. The average age of the world fleet is now nearly 14 years, with nearly one-quarter of the vessels more than 20 years old. Therefore, a large rebuilding program must be instituted if a safe, viable, and economically attractive fleet is to be maintained.

The total cost of running the world's oceangoing fleet was about $298 billion in 1991 (ship operating costs), excluding port and cargo transfer charges. Including these administrative charges, the cost of operating the world's oceangoing shipping was just over $500 billion, or about 10% of the value of world oceanborne trade. Total oceanborne trade transport costs are obviously higher if land and inland feeder, marketing, freight forwarding, and other costs, as well as profit margins or commissions, are added. Overall, it is estimated that the cost of integrated transport of oceanborne trade is nearly $900 billion.

The use of the oceans for transportation is therefore enormous and will continue to grow as nations become more and more economically interdependent. Ocean transportation is rapidly changing, not only in ship technology, where instead of using economies of scale that drove up ship sizes from 1955 to 1980, the economy of technological advance is increasingly used now. As a result, new ships are highly automated, have small yet highly skilled crews, navigate largely automatically, are propelled by efficient machinery, and have their cargo loading, stowage, and unloading planned and controlled by export systems. Similarly, ship terminals and ports are relocated in deep water outside traditional port cities and often on newly constructed or reclaimed special-purpose port islands.

1.3.1 Ocean Recreation Use

The oceans have been valued as a recreational asset mainly for the beaches and coves bordering many seas. In recent years, though, ocean recreation has expanded to include boating and sailing, recreational fishing, and cruising, which all have become major economic uses of the oceans in their own right.

Pleasure boating has become a $16.2 billion industry worldwide, with over 2 million pleasure boats in use, a number that is now growing at a rate of nearly 6% per year. Nearly 40% of these boats are in use in the United States and the Caribbean. Although most of these boats are privately operated, nearly 8% of the U. S. and Caribbean boats are owned by rental firms or clubs.

The world boating and sailing industry also contributes greatly to coastal developments. Marinas sprout up everywhere. Boatbuilding repair and services provide additional economic activity. Recreational fishing is still small in economic terms, but growing rapidly. Although recreational catches constitute less than 4% of total catches, they contribute significantly in catches of so-called game fish.

The most important recreational use of the oceans is now cruising, an industry that was nonexistent in the early 1960s. It has grown from fewer than 100,000 passenger trips per year in 1968 to over 6.2 million in 1991. Of these, in excess of four million trips were sold in the United States and the Caribbean. There are now well over 142 dedicated cruise (excluding ferry) vessels in service, with a combined capacity of 72,000 passenger berths, offering nearly 6,700 cruises of various duration per year. Total cruise passenger capacity is about 10.2 million per year. The cruise business has become a $24.8 billion worldwide business, now growing at a rate of about 4.2% per year.

1.4 OCEAN ENVIRONMENTAL MANAGEMENT ISSUES

Ocean environmental management is designed to address issues that help to maintain the oceans as a vital physical, chemical, and economic asset to humans and the planet. It is therefore concerned with the following.

1. **Ocean Environmental Economics**

   The oceans contribute significantly to the world economy. The value of all ocean resources exploited and the use of the oceans together add up to about $842 billion per year in 1991 or just over 4.2% of the world gross product. But the economic impact of the oceans is much greater, and the indirect economic benefits provided by the oceans are worth a multiple of that sum. The major economic costs of ocean environmental degradation are:

a. Economic impact on fishing
b. Costs of cleanup and restitution
    - Environmental degradation costs
    - Recreational economic costs
    - Economic costs of reduced potential of the oceans (fishing, aquaculture, mariculture, transport logistics, recreation, mining, subsea energy, oil, communications)

Ocean Environmental Management is concerned with maintenance of the ocean regime and the ocean environment and marine ecology.

2. The Ocean Regime

In terms of its

a. Content
b. Atmospheric effects
c. Behaviors
d. Ocean replenishment

3. The Ocean Environment and Marine Ecology

a. Physical
b. Chemical
c. Biological
d. Land and ocean interface
e. Air and ocean interface
f. Coastal and estuarial interface

4. Ocean Resources

Ocean resources as discussed fall into many different areas and offer opportunities for exploitation and use. Among these are:

a. Ocean resources
    - Physical and biological
b. Subocean resources
c. Hydrothermal vents
d. Metallogenesis (metal developments in the oceans)
e. Nonphotosynthetic marine life and deep-ocean marine life
f. Ocean habitats

- Artificial islands
- Subsea submerged habitats
- Coastal developments

g. Ocean energy developments
- Wave, current, tidal, and thermal vent resources

Ocean environmental management is primarily concerned with reducing or eliminating environmental impacts from
- Solid and liquid waste disposal
- Runoff from inland drainage areas
- Seabed introduced pollutants
- Air and water pollutant exchange
- Toxic and radioactive waste disposal

but as noted later, impacts may be caused by many different and often indirect factors.

With the world—and humanity—increasingly dependent on the oceans for physical and economic well-being, it is imperative to develop effective approaches for the management, and thereby the maintenance, of the ocean environment.

In the future, many more uses will be made of the oceans as humans' resource base is expanded and, in many cases, as lifestyles and ways of doing things are changed. For example, ocean food production, which played only a small role in the human diet early in the twentieth century, now supplies an increasingly significant percentage of human food consumption, particularly of proteins. Similarly, an increasing percentage of people's energy needs are met from ocean resources. If these are to provide opportunities for expansion and improved living standards in the future, ways to manage the ocean environment must be learned.

Humans have managed the oceans badly in the past. That the vastness of the oceans would permit major environmental transgressions at little or no costs was simply assumed, but this is not so. Unless this last and most important asset of our globe is maintained, the long-term future of life on this planet may be doomed.

Considering developments since World War II, especially worldwide population growth, particularly in developing countries, and the increased pressure for greater equity in the use of resources and economic development, there will be more and more pressure for the use of the oceans and ocean resources. The direct contribution of ocean resources to the world gross product grew from under 3% to over 4.2% between 1970 and 1991. This trend is expected to accelerate, and nearly 10% of the world gross product is expected to be generated from the use of the oceans and ocean resources by the year 2011. Looking at it differently, nearly 20% of the growth in world product in this period is expected to come from the oceans. This increasing dependence on ocean resources is natural and offers many new opportunities for humanity. These opportunities, however, will materialize only if people learn to manage the ocean environment more effectively then in the past.

2

Sources and Magnitude of Ocean Environmental Degradation

Ocean environmental degradation in chemical, physical, and biological terms is caused by pollution or intrusion, whether produced in nature or by humans, into the oceans, such as:

1. ocean uses, including ocean resource exploitation (mining, petroleum, and so forth), transportation, aquaculture, recreation, and industrial uses;
2. runoff and drainage into the oceans;
3. subsea vents and various other natural phenomena, including submarine eruptions, and earthquakes;
4. air pollution;
5. port and industrial operational pollution;
6. solid waste, hazardous material, and other waste discharged into the oceans; and
7. construction in the ocean or along the coast.

The magnitude of these sources of pollution, along with the amount of control humans have over their sources and their impact, varies.

Marine pollutants can generally be divided into the following major categories:

1. organic chemicals,
2. inorganic chemicals,
3. suspended soils,
4. nutrients,
5. halogenated hydrocarbons,
6. petroleum,
7. radioactive substances, and
8. thermal wastes.

Pollution in the oceans has a detrimental effect on most marine life forms. It affects breeding, growth, reproduction, and survival. In the reproductive chain, a polluted environment usually leads to fewer survivors and quicker or slower metabolism, changed patterns of reproduction, decreased photosynthesis, and often counterproductive reproduction patterns than found in a nonpolluted environment. In general, the marine life environment is detrimentally affected. The principal effects of particular pollutants are listed below.

1. **Organic Chemicals**

   Organic chemicals usually lead to severe oxygen depletion and the effects of oxygen depletion, such as an oxygen content often too low to sustain life and to sludge blanket or sludge layer formation at the bottom of the ocean. Because nearly all discharges occur near shore waters, where good and high biological activity abounds, closing nearby shellfish beds and recreational fishing areas due to unsightly floating matter or phytoplankton blooms is often practiced. Death of marine organisms is usually the result of large amounts or concentrations of organic chemicals in the waters. Although marine organisms carry some toxic metals, persistent organic compounds will severely affect the organisms' survival and growth.

2. **Sludge and Solid Wastes**

   Sludge and solid wastes in the ocean have the following effects on marine environments: reduced light penetration, reduced visibility, destroyed spawning areas, reduced food supplies, reduced plant cover, anaerobic conditions caused by trapped organic matter, flocculent planktonic algae, adsorption or absorption of organic molecules and ions, absorption of oil and toxic components, and impaired respiration caused by particles floating and blocking gills.

3. **Biodegradable Organics**

Biodegradable organics in the ocean usually cause the disappearance of shrimp, halibut, sturgeon, anchovies, flounder, and bass; the death of fish and a decline in fauna, particularly in rivers; and marked deoxygenation, little intertidal fauna, and no life near outfalls.

4. **Pathogens**

Pathogens in ocean waters, even in reasonable concentrations, interfere with public health; affect the quality and safety of seafood; infect bivalve mollusks (filter feeders) involved with pathogenic infection, such as oysters, clams, and mussels; and cause crustaceans (crabs and lobsters) to accumulate bacteria and viruses.

5. **Nutrients**

Nutrients that are usually discharged into the oceans by runoff or rivers may be helpful in the open sea and increase plankton growth and fish yield. But they have damaging effects on wetlands and shallow or restricted coastal zones because they can cause bursts of algae from sewage and other nutrients and can cause a loss of underwater plant life and water lilies.

6. **Heavy Metals**

Heavy metals, usually introduced into the oceans through industrial wastes, affect human consumption of seafood (plant and animal), particularly if a species is affected by toxic metals such as mercury, zinc, and copper, and cause damage to marine organisms and ecosystems. Such damage may be especially acute. For instance, mercury has a tendency to concentrate in aquatic animal tissue; it is stored in shellfish and fish tissue that is harmful to humans if consumed, causes methylmercury to travel up the food chain, has severe effects on commercial fishing, and is a pollution hazard. Similarly, cadmium-contaminated fish cause severe kidney damage when consumed by humans and may have lethal effects. Sublethal effects are caused by bioaccumulation, interference with neurological system (disruption of equilibrium), changes in speed of enzyme systems, changes in hormone activity, lesions, alterations in respiration, decreased production, and increased change of infection by parasites and diseases and cause detrimental effects in physiological systems.

7. Persistent Pollutants

Persistent pollutants, such as petroleum-based pesticides and phenol by-products, including DDT, cause birds consuming fish contaminated with such pollutants to suffer reproductive failures. Similarly, most pesticides are lethal to marine organisms. Bioaccumulation of pesticides in marine life causes a hazard to humans who consume seafood.

8. Chlorinated Hydrocarbon Pesticides (DDT, DDD, aldrin)

Chlorinated hydrocarbon pesticides accumulate in the fatty tissue of fish and cause hazards when consumed. They cause slow degradation of marine organisms or life. They further inhibit the growth of phytoplankton and cause higher death rates of marine life; they inhibit photosynthesis and inhibit growth of oysters, mollusks, and so forth; and by exposure, they cause death of crustaceans.

9. Oil Pollution

Oil pollution in the oceans introduces or causes hazards to humans through consumption of contaminated seafood and through damage to fisheries, seaweed, birds, marine mammals, and wildlife. Beaches and recreational areas can be destroyed or degraded by oil pollution. It further causes alterations to the ecosystem by affecting populations of marine life and its distributions and by modifying the ocean habitat. Sublethal effects include disruptions with normal functioning in cellular and physiological systems, changed characteristics of marine organisms, and altered ecological structure of the community. Chronic, persistent effects cause changes in population, slowly but permanently. The impact of petroleum toxicity causes marine organisms to be injured or killed by being covered with insoluble petroleum compounds; benthos to undergo harmful permutation; sublittoral organisms to be poisoned; beach flora and marsh to be destroyed by oil; and benzene, toluene, and naphthalene to bioaccumulate in marine flora, fauna, and marine life in general, causing danger to human consumption. Toxicity enhances death in larval species of marine organisms.

10. Radioactivity

Radioactivity in pollutants and wastes affects seawater, inorganic and organic particles, and marine organisms in the oceans. The accretion and concentration of radioactive material in marine life differs widely. Although some species are able to accumulate up to hundreds of thousands of times the amount of radionucleides existing in natural ocean waters, such accumulation is detrimental to the genetic makeup and composition of marine life. Ultimately, seafood infected by radioactivity becomes a hazard to human consumers. Although much is still unknown, it has been established that radioactivity—even in limited concentrations—will cause the death of fish eggs, alterations in the genetic code caused by radiation exposure, and mutations transmitted or death of species due to lack of gene function and will lead to less reproduction, fewer fish eggs, and more unhatched eggs than usual.

2.1 MARINE POLLUTION BY OCEAN USERS, VOLUNTARY AND ACCIDENTAL

All ocean users cause some marine pollution, but that caused by shipping, mainly tankers, is usually in the limelight. Although oil spills with a marine origin constitute only 53% of all ocean oil spills and accidental oil spills constitute only 11% of all oil pollution of the seas (Figure 2–1), there is still a large number of significant accidental spills. In recent years, however, the number of significant (usually accidental) oil spills in the seas (Figure 2–2) and the total volume of oil spilled have both declined quite significantly, as shown in Table 2–1. Since 1982, the casualty or loss rate of tankers (the total number of tankers sunk per year) has continued to decline.

Table 2–2 shows the causes of tanker accidents. Note that the

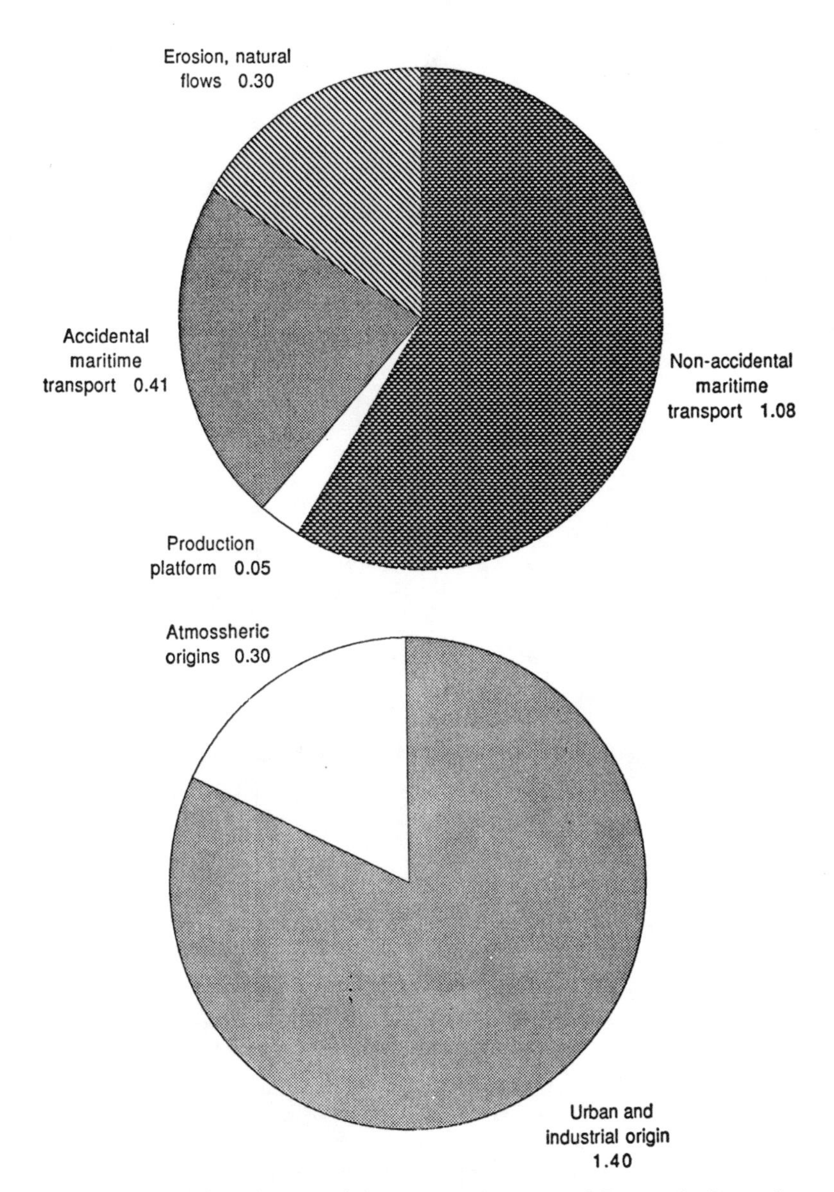

Figure 2–1 Oil pollution of the seas. U.S. National Research Council, (Washington: NRC, 1985).

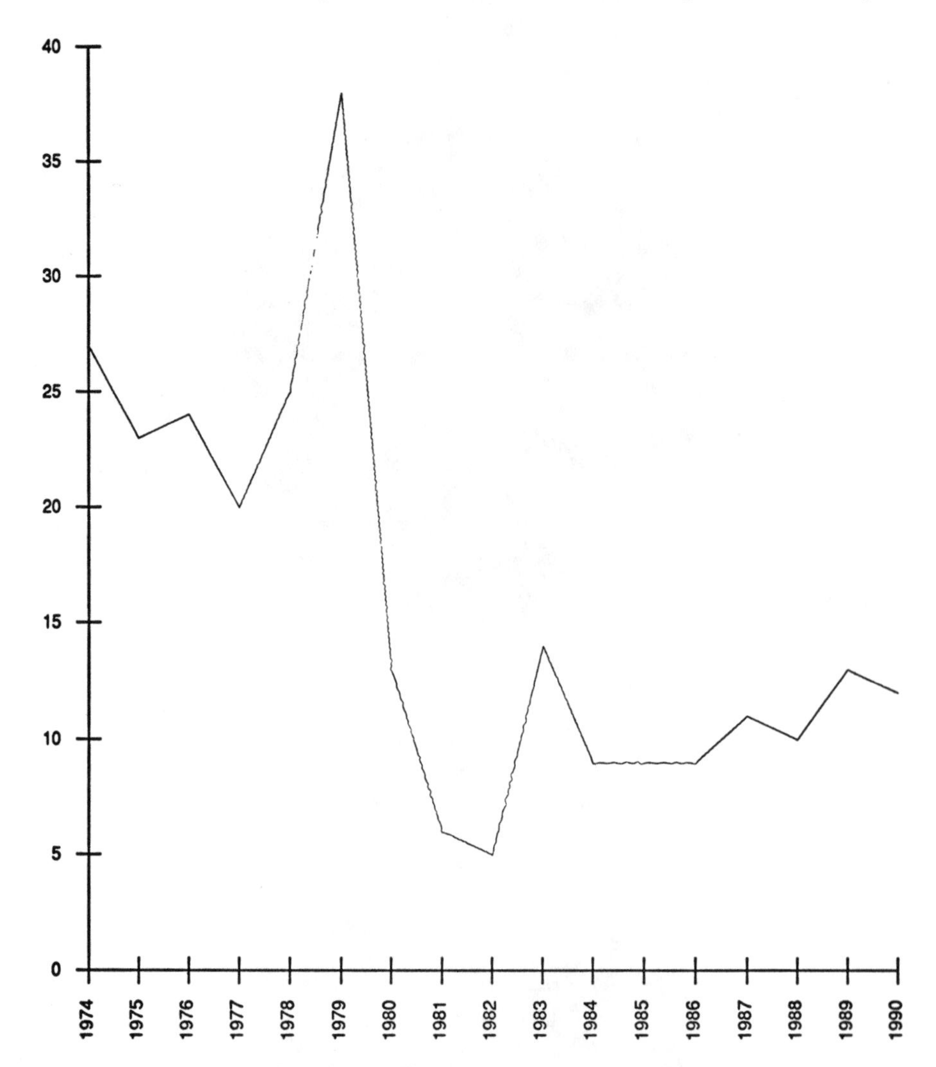

Figure 2–2 Accidental oil spills over 700 tons, 1974–1988. International Tanker Owners Pollution Federation ltd *Fate of Marine Oil Spills,* Technical Information Paper Noil. (London: ITOPF, 1990).

percentage of accidents among those accounting for the 50 largest spills between 1960 and 1989 was about equal for groundings and fires or explosions, closely followed by collisions. Although structural failure had a similar frequency as collision, it only accounted for about half as much in terms of spill amount.

Even though significant reductions in the number of tanker accidents—and even more importantly, in the reduction of oil spilled

TABLE 2–1 Tanker Spills and Casualties

	ACCIDENTAL TANKER SPILLS AND LOSSES							
			TOTAL LOSSES					
	NUMBER	TONS SPILLED	NUMBER	MILLIONS OF DWT	NUMBER OF DEATHS	NUMBER OF TANKERS AT RISK	MILLIONS OF DWT TONS AT RISK	CASUALTY RATE PER 100 TANKERS
1973	36	84,458	12	0.682	70	3,750	218.9	1.96
1974	48	67,115	14	0.536	94	3,928	253.6	1.89
1975	45	188,042	22	0.815	90	4,140	296.2	2.41
1976	29	204,235	20	1.172	226	4,227	336.7	2.60
1977	49	213,080	20	1.000	113	4,229	369.0	2.39
1978	35	260,488	17	0.913	148	4,137	380.4	2.44
1979	65	723,533	26	2.501	306	3,945	376.0	3.25
1980	32	135,635	15	1.703	132	3,898	375.7	2.14
1981	33	45,285	21	1.166	73	3,937	372.5	2.84
1982	7	1,491	16	0.818	72	3,950	364.7	1.84

SOURCES: Tanker Advisory Center, New York, 1983; and *IMO News* (London: International Maritime Organization), No. 3, 1984, p. 3.

TABLE 2–2 Tanker Accident Causes

Tanker Acidents Resulting in Oil Spills

CASUALTY TYPE	GREATER THAN 3,000 DWT 1969–1973	GREATER THAN 10,000 DWT 1976–1989	GREATER THAN 100,000 DWT 1979–1989	50 LARGEST SPILLS 1960–1989
Grounding	27	30	13	28
Collision, contact	38	29	27	22
Fire, explosion	11	10	19	24
Structural failure	21	31	15	22
Machinery failure	2	—	20	—
Other, unknown	—	—	6	4
Total	100	100	100	100

Tanker Spill Acidents: Distribution Based on Spilled Amount

CASUALTY TYPE	GREATER THAN 3,000 DWT 1969–1973	GREATER THAN 10,000 DWT 1976–1989	50 LARGEST SPILLS 1960–1989
Grounding	24	28	30
Collision, contact damage	20	30	25
Fire, explosion	10	34	30
Hull failure	36	8	14
Machinery failure	3	—	—
Other, unknown	7	—	1
Total	100	100	100

SOURCE: Lloyds Casualty Reports 1960–1989 (London: Lloyds Register of Shipping, Jan. 1990) and S. Kristiansen and E. Rensvik, *Human and Organization Factors in Safe Operation and Pollution Prevention.*

per accident—have been attained, total tanker or ship loss rates have obstinately remained nearly constant. Table 2–3 shows ship casualties for all ocean-going ships. Some ship registries show consistently better performance than others. Also, much of the oil spilled by tanker accidents is from spills caused by total tanker losses or sinkages of such ships.

Tanker accidents are only responsible for a small proportion of tanker-caused oil spills (Table 2–4). The bulk of spills (70% to 92%) caused by tankers (Table 2–5) are operational spills such as those during loading and discharging, bilge and fuel oil discharge, drydocking, oil ballast discharge, and other voluntary operations. Table 2–6 ranks the sources of tanker oil spills by amount spilled. Collision and grounding both end up with 8% (1975–1989), but these are the

TABLE 2–3 Casualties (percentage of number of ships owned and totally lost)

	1960	1980	1984	1986	1988	1990
United Kingdom	0.25	0.28	0.28	—	—	—
Greece	0.54	0.99	0.72	—	—	—
Japan	0.32	0.44	0.45	—	—	—
Liberia	0.92	0.50	0.52	—	—	—
Norway	0.44	0.44	0.26	—	—	—
Panama	1.48	1.12	0.89	—	—	—
World total	0.47	0.52	0.43	1.10	0.30	0.20

Tonnage lost by Number and Type of Ships (in Thousand of DWT)

	1986	1988	1990
Oil Tankers	4,342	1,138	178
Bulk Carriers	1,732	236	1,098
General Cargo Ships	749	432	317
Containerships	11	32	—
Other Vessels	76	67	87
Total	6,910	1,905	1,680
Number of Ships	358	271	175

SOURCE: Lloyd's Maritime Information Service Ltd. (London: Lloyds Register, Jan. 1991).

TABLE 2–4 Marine Spills of Hydrocarbons

	1973 ESTIMATE		1981 ESTIMATE	
SOURCE	METRIC TON/YEAR	PERCENTAGE OF TOTAL SPILLS	METRIC TON/YEAR	PERCENTAGE OF TOTAL SPILLS
Tanker operations	1.08	51	0.7	50
Drydocking	0.25	12	0.03	2
Marine terminals	0.003	0.1	0.02	1
Bilge and fuel oils	0.5	23	0.3	20
Tanker accidents	0.2	9	0.4	27
Nontanker accidents	0.1	5	0.02	1
Total spills	2.13	100	1.47	100

SOURCE: *IMO News* No. 3, p. 4. (London: Information Maritime Organization, Jan. 1984).

TABLE 2–5 Frequency of Oil Tanker Spills, 1974–1979

OPERATION	NUMBER OF SPILLS	RELATIVE FREQUENCY (%)
Loading and discharging	2,261	55
Bunkering	427	10
Bilge pumping	108	3
Tank cleaning	70	2
Ballasting	593	14
Internal transfer	106	2
Collision	114	3
Grounding, stranding	200	5
Other tanker accidents	235	6
Total	4,114	100

SOURCE: Lloyds Casualty Reports, (London: Lloyds Register of Shipping, Jan. 1984).

principal causes addressed by recent legislation (partly because tanker accidents are usually spectacular and newsworthy) and the most costly to prevent. Table 2–7A lists the most important tanker accidents from 1967 to 1989, while Table 2–7B lists major oil spills by magnitude.

Tankers are not the principal causes of oil spilled at sea. In fact, ocean oil deposition by atmospheric rainout, natural seeps, and urban runoffs contributed more oil spills to the ocean environment than all tanker-generated oil pollution and, in fact, all marine oil pollution (Table 2–8). Although the data are from the 1970s, the trend continues in favor of tankers, which have decreased their contribu-

TABLE 2–6 Ranking of Spill Sources

SITUATION	AMOUNT SPILLED (%)	SUBJECTIVE WEIGHT (%)
Loading and discharging	50	34
Tank Cleaning, ballasting	12	8
Fuel oil, bilge	8	6
Grounding	8	12
Machinery failure and stranding	2	4
Collision	8	12
Fire and explosion in cargo section	5	10
Fire and explosion in machinery	2	4
Hull failure	5	10

SOURCE: Lloyds Casualty Reports (London: Lloyds Register Shipping, Jan. 1984).

TABLE 2–7A Selected Accidental Oil Spills

DATE		NAME OF SHIP	FLAG	COUNTRY AFFECTED	QUANTITY SPILLED (metric tons)
1967	March	*Torrey Canyon*	Liberia	United Kingdom, France	121.2
1968	June	*World Glory*	Liberia	South Africa	45.0
	November	*Spyros Lemos*	Liberia	Spain	20.0
1969	November	*Keo*	Liberia	United States	25.0
	November	*Pacocean*	Liberia	Bahrain	30.0
1970	February	*Arrow*	Liberia	Canada	12.0
	March	*Ennerdale*	United Kingdom	Seychelles	49.0
	December	*Chrissi*	Panama	United States	31.0
1971	January	*Oregon Standard*	United States	United States	7.7
	February	*Wafra*	Liberia	South Africa	63.2
	March	*Texas Oklahoma*	United States	United States	35.0
	November	*Juliana*	Liberia	Japan	4.0
1972	January	*Golden Drake*	Liberia	Azores	31.7
	April	*Giuseppe Giulietti*	Italy	Spain	26.0
	June	*Trader*	Greece	Greece	35.0
	July	*Tamano*	Norway	United States (Maine)	3.6
	December	*Sea Star*	South Korea	Oman, UAE, Saudi Arabia	120.3
1973	March	*Zeo Colocoltroni*	Greece	United States, Puerto Rico	8.0
	June	*Napier*	Liberia	Chile	36.0
1974	June	*Imperial Sarnia*	Canada	Canada, United States	6.0
	August	*Metula*	Dutch Antilles	Chile	53.5
		Yugo Maru 10	Japan	Japan	50.0
1975	January	*Showa Maru*	Japan	Singapore	3.8
	January	*British Ambassador*	United Kingdom	Japan (Pacific)	45.0
	January	*Jakob Maersk*	Denmark	Portugal	84.0
	January	*Corinthos/E.M. Queeny*	United States–Liberia	United States (Delaware)	40.0
	April	*Spartan Lady*	Liberia	United States	25.0

TABLE 2–7A Continued

DATE		NAME OF SHIP	FLAG	COUNTRY AFFECTD	QUANTITY SPILLED (metric tons)
1975	April	*Shell Barge No. 2*	United States	United States	—
		pic Colocoltroni	Greece	France	57.0
		Mitsui Maru 3	Japan	Japan	5.0
1976	February	*Saint Peter*	Liberia	Colombia	33.0
	May	*Urquiola*	Spain	Spain	101.0
	June	*Nepco 140*	United States	United States, Canada	1.2
	July	*Cretan Star*	Cyprus	India, Sri Lanka	28.6
	October	*Boehlen*	German D.R.	France	11.0
	December	*Argo Merchant*	Liberia	United States (Massachu-setts)	28.0
1977	January	*Irene's Challenge*	Liberia	Japan	34.0
	January	*Borag*	Liberia	China	4.0
	February	*Hawaiian Patriot*	Liberia	United States (Hawaii)	99.0
	May	*Caribbean Sea*	Panama	Nicaragua	30.0
	December	*Venpet and Venoil*	Liberia	South Africa	26.0
	December	*Grand Zenith*	Panama	United States (Massachu-setts)	29.0
1978	March	*Amoco Cadiz*	Liberia	France	228.0
	May	*Eleni V*	Greece	United Kingdom	3.0
	July	*Cabo Tamar*	Chile	Chile	60.0
	October	*Christos Bitas*	Greece	United Kingdom	5.0
	December	*Esso Bernica*	United Kingdom	United Kingdom (Shetlands)	1.1
	December	*Andros Patria*	Greece	Spain	47.0
1979	January	*Betelgeuse*	France	Ireland	27.0
	February	*Antonio Gramsci*	USSR	Sweden, Fin-land, USSR	6.0
	March	*Messlaniki Frontis*	Liberia	Greece	6.0

TABLE 2–7A Continued

DATE		NAME OF SHIP	FLAG	COUNTRY AFFECTD	QUANTITY SPILLED (metric tons)
1979	March	*Kurdistan*	United Kingdom	Canada	7.0
	April	*Gino*	Liberia	France	42.0
	June	*Aviles*	Liberia	Arabian Sea	25.0
	July	*Atlantic Express*	Greece	Tobago	276.0
	August	*Ionnis Angelicoussis*	Greece	Angola	30.0
	September	*Chevron Hawaii*	United States	United States	2.0
	November	*Burmah Agate*	Liberia	United States (Texas)	40.0
	November	*Independenta*	Romania	Turkey	94.6
1980	January	*Princess Anne Marie*	Greece	Cuba	6.0
	February	*Irenes Serenade*	Greece	Greece	102.0
	March	*Tanio*	Madagascar	France, United Kingdom	13.5
	December	*Juan A. Lavalleja*	Uruguay	Algeria	40.0
1981	January	*Jose Marti*	USSR	Sweden	6.0
	March	*Ondina*	Dubai	Germany	5.0
	July	*Cavo Cambanos*	Greece	France	18.0
	November	*Globe Assimi*	Gibraltar	USSR	16.0
1983	August	*Castello de Belver*	Spain	South Africa	255.5
	September	*Sivand*	Iran	United Kingdom	6.0
	November	*Feoso Ambassador*	China	China	4.0
1984	January	*Assimi*	—	Oman	51.4
	December	*Pericles GC*	—	Qatar	46.6
1985	February	*Neptunia*	Liberia	Iran	60.0
	December	*Nova*	Liberia	Iran	71.1
1989	March	*Exxon Valdez*	United States	United States (Alaska)	35.0
	December	*Kharg 5*	—	Morocco	—

Inclusion criteria: over 25,000 metric ton of oil spilled by tankers or over $5 million of indemnity.

1986–1988: no major oil spills over 25,000 metric ton.

SOURCES: OECD, IMO, IOPC-Fund, ACOPS, IFP, TAC.

TABLE 2–7B Oil Spills by Magnitude

NUMBER	DATE	SPILL	LOCATION	MILLIONS OF GALLONS	REFERENCE(S)
1	1979–1980	Ixtoc 1, well blowout	Mexico	139–428[a]	a,b,g,h
2	1983	Nowrux Oil Field, well blowout(s)	Persian Gulf	80–185	a,b,
3	1983	*Castello de Belver*/broke, fire	South Africa	50–80[a]	a,b,e
4	1978	*Amoco Cadiz*/grounding	France	67–76	a,b,f,h,m
5	1979	*Aegean Captain*/*Atlantic Express*	off Tobago	49[a]	a,b,l
6	1980–1981	D-103 Libya, well blowout	Libya	42	a
7	1979	*Atlantic Empress*/fire	Barbados	41.5[a]	a,b.l
8	1967	*Torrey Canyon*/grounding	United Kingdom	35.7–38.6[a]	b,c,f
9	1980	*Irenes Serenade*/fire	Greece	12.3–36.6[a]	a,m
10	1972	*Sea Star*/collision, fire	Gulf of Oman	35.3[a]	b,f
11	1981	Kuwait National Petroleum Tank	Kuwait	31.2	a
12	1976	*Urquiola*/grounding	Spain	27–30.7[a]	b,f
13	1970	*Othello*/collision	Sweden	18.4–30.7	b,c,f
14	1977	*Hawaiian Patriot*/fire	N. Pacific	30.4[a]	b,f
15	1979	*Independenta*	Turkey	28.9	a
16	1978	No. 126 Well/pipe	Iran	28	a
17	1975	*Jakoc Maersk*	Portugal	25[a]	f
18	1985	BP Storage Tank	Nigeria	23.9	a
19	1985	*Nova*/collision	Iran	21.4	a
20	1978	BP, Shell Fuel Dept.	Zimbabwe	20	a
21	1971	*Wafra*	South Africa	19.6[a]	c,f
22	1989	*Kharg 5*, explosion	Morocco	19	q
23	1974	*Metula*/grounding	Chile	16	c,f
24	1983	*Assimi*/fire	off Oman	15.8[a]	a
25	1970	*Polycommander*	Spain	3–15.3	c

26	1978	Tohoku Storage Tanks, earthquake	Japan	15	a
27	1978	*Andros Patria*	Spain	14.6	a
28	1983	*Pericles GC*	Qatar	14	a
29	1985	Ranger, Texas/well blowout	Texas	6.3–13.7	b,k
30	1968	*World Glory*/hull failure	South Africa	13.5	b,c,f
31	1970	*Ennerdale*/struck granite	Seychelles	12.6	c,f
32	1974	Mizushima Refinery/tank rupture	Japan	11.3	c,d,f
33	1973	*Napier*	Southeast Pacific	11[a]	f
34	1980	*Juan A. Lavalleja*	Algeria	11	a
35	1989	*Exxon Valdez*/grounding	Alaska	10.8	i
36	1978	Turkish Petroleum Corporation	Turkey	10.7	a
37	1979	*Burmah Agate*/collision, fire	Texas	1.3–10.7[a]	a,b,c
38	1971	*Texas Oklahoma*, 120 mi offshore	North Carolina	9.2–10.7	c,f
39	1972	*Trader*	Mediterranean	10.4	f
40	1976	*Saint Peter*	Southeast Pacific	10.4	f
41	1977	*Irene's Challenge*	Pacific	10.4	f
42	1972	*Golden Drake*	Northwest Atlantic	9.5	f
43	1970	*Chrissi*	Northwest Atlantic	9.5	f
44	1969	*Pacocean*/broke in two	Northwest Pacific	9.2	f
45	1977	*Caribbean Sea*	East Pacific	9.2	f
46	1976	*Grand Zenith*/Disappearance	Northwest Atlantic	8.9	f
47	1976	*Cretan Star*	Indian Ocean	8.9	f
48	1969	*Keo*/hull failure	Massachusetts	8.8	b,f
49	1969	Storage Tank	New Jersey	8.4	b
50	1977	*Ekofisk Bravo*/well blowout	North Sea	4.6–8.2	b,f
51	1972	*Giuseppi Giulietti*	Northeast Atlantic	8	f

TABLE 2–7B Continued

NUMBER	DATE	SPILL	LOCATION	MILLIONS OF GALLONS	REFERENCE(S)
52	1977	*Venpet and Venoil*/collision	South Africa	7.4–8	e,f
53	1976	*Argo Merchant*/grounding	Massachusetts	7.7	b,f,h
54	1967	Humble Oil Pipeline/offshore leak	Louisiana	6.7	n
55	1973	*Jawacta*	Baltic Sea	6.1	c
56	1967	*R. C. Stoner*	Wake Island	6	c
57	1970	*Marlena*	Sicily	4.3	c
58	1970	Pipeline	Saudi Arabia	4.2	c
59	1971	Oil well	Persian Gulf	4.2	c
60	1980	*Tanio*/broke amidships	France	4.2	j
61	1988	Ashland Storage Tank/rupture	Pennsylvania	3.8	b
62	1969	Santa Barbara Channel/well blowout	California	1.4–3.4	d,f,p
63	1970	*Arrow*/grounding	Nova Scotia	1.5–3.1	c,h
64	1970	Storage Tank	Pennsylvania	3	c
65	1984	*Alvenus*/grounding	Louisiana	2.8	b
66	1970	Offshore Platform/well blowout	Louisiana	2.7	c

SOURCE: Congress of the United States, Office of Technology Assessment, "Coping with An Oiled Sea: An Analysis of Oil Spill Response Technologies," OTA-BP-0-61 (Washington, DC: U.S. Government Printing Office, March 1990), 70 pp.

Notes:
a. A list of the 20. . . , 1989.
b. Reuters, 1989.
c. Van Gelder-Ottway. . . , 1976.
d. A Basic Spill. . . , 1981.
e. Lord et al. . . , 1987.
f. Butler, 1978.
g. Woods and Hannah, 1981.
h. Teal and Howarth, 1984.
i. Caleb Brett, 1989.
j. Ganten, 1985
k. Quina et al. . . , 1987.
l. Horn and Neil, 1981.
m. Bao-Kang, 1987.
n. Tracey, 1988.
o. Ocean Industry, 1980.
p. NRC, 1975.
q. Journal of Commerce, 1/4/90.

Tanker spills from the Iran-Iraq War were not generally available.

[a]Fire burned part of spill.

TABLE 2–8 Worldwide Sources of Marine Oil Pollution, Annual Inputs to the Oceans (in millions of tons)

SOURCE	1973	1978
Load-on-top tanker	0.310	0.110
Non–load-on-top tanker	0.770	0.500
Bilges and bunkering	0.500	0.120
Terminal operations	0.003	0.001
Dry docking	0.250	0.250
Tanker accidents	0.200	0.300
Nontanker accidents	0.100	0.100
Total	2.133	1.381
Offshore oil production		0.060
Coastal oil refineries		0.060
Industrial waste		0.150
Municipal waste		0.300
Urban runoff		0.400
Natural seeps		0.600
Atmospheric rainout		0.600
Total		2.170
Overall Total		3.551

SOURCE: I. Cowell, U.S. National Research Council (Washington DC, NRC, Report 1979).

tion to ocean oil pollution significantly since then, while there has been no corresponding improvement in other sources of ocean oil pollution.

Oil inputs to the oceans have decreased slightly in recent years, due in part to a decreased frequency of large shipping accidents and spills. Oil pollution from continental origins (rivers, coastal activities, and the atmosphere) as well as from routine maritime transport, however, persists, and its effects on beaches and various forms of marine life continue.

Shipping safety has been the subject of discussions, conventions, and regulations for centuries. Oceangoing ships are classed by special "classification societies" that set rules for the construction and maintenance of vessels and to some degree, their operations. Most major maritime nations have a classification society; examples are Lloyds, American Bureau of Shipping, Norske Veritas, Bureau Veritas, NKK, Germanische Lloyd, and others. Each sets its own standards and, after inspection, issues certificates of class that determine qualifications for insurance. To maintain class and thereby insurability, a ship must be kept up as stipulated by the rules and be certified by the classification societies' surveyors. In recent years, the International Maritime Organization (IMO), a technical agency of the United Nations, has assumed responsibility for developing general safety standards for ships embodied in various Safety of Life at Sea conventions. But even with all the new conventions and changes in standards by classification societies, major disasters, such as the ferry capsizing in Belgium and the breakup of tankers at sea, continue.

The safety of shipping has not improved, even with all these safety activities, and about 0.3% of all ships at risk in any year are lost (Table 2–9), a percentage that has not changed since World War II. This is in contrast to aviation casualties, as a percentage of commercial aircraft at risk worldwide, being halved every ten years.

Major changes in shipping safety rules and standards usually only follow disasters and are, as pointed out by Rawson, usually "based upon design concepts and modes of operation which would be soon superseded."[1] As a result, new shipping technology, such as semisubmerged catamarans and hatchless container ships, is often introduced without proper standards or rules; they are seldom pre-

TABLE 2–9 Registration and Serious Casualty Figures for the Top 12 Nations

PERCENTAGE OF WORLD OWNERSHIP 1990		CASUALTIES 1985–1989: PERCENTAGE OF SHIPS AT RISK	
Liberia	12.9	Cyprus	2.91
Panama	9.3	Liberia	2.19
Japan	6.4	Panama	1.86
USSR	5.5	Greece	1.81
Norway	5.0	Denmark	1.65
United States	4.8	West Germany	1.55
Cyprus	4.3	United Kingdom	1.43
Greece	4.3	Philippines	1.40
People's Republic of China	3.3	Singapore	1.39
Bahamas	3.2	Sweden	1.30
Philippines	2.0	India	1.28
Italy	1.9	South Korea	1.24
Total	62.9	World Average Casualties as % of Ships at Risk	1.5

SOURCE: *Lloyds Casualty Reports* (London: Lloyds Register of Shipping, 1991).

[1]K. Rawson, "Whither Maritime Safety?" *Shipbuilding International* (London: Royal Institute of Naval Architects, 1991).

pared in time for the effective introduction of technological innovations.

Finally, another issue affecting the field today is a preoccupation with reducing the amount and impact of oil discharged in a ship or tanker accident and not with preventing ship or tanker accidents.

2.1.1 Oil Slick Spreading

Once a spill occurs, it is important to contain the spill for effective cleanup. In reality, an oil spill's spread often stretches over large areas before effective cleanup can be organized. Spreading is affected by (1) the size of the spill; (2) the type and viscosity of the oil; (3) environmental conditions such as surface, air, and oil temperatures, surface waves, currents, and winds; (4) time between spill and oil slick condition; and (5) emulsion characteristics.

Empirical models of spreading rates for oil slicks at sea assume that the instantaneous rate of spreading is proportional to the prevailing slick thickness. In general, three distinct spreading phases are identified. They are as follows:

1. the initial phase where spreading is controlled by gravity and inertial resistance forces,
2. the second phase when gravity and viscous drag forces control spreading, and
3. the third phase when spreading is controlled by surface tension and viscous drag forces.

A theoretical estimate of the length of surface tension spreading slick can be obtained using a formula that includes the effects of water density, time, and kinematic viscosity:

$$\text{length} = K\left(\frac{\sigma^2 t^3}{\delta^2 V}\right)$$

where

σ = spreading coefficient
t = time
δ = density of water
V = kinematic viscosity
K = constant with values of 1 to 10

Most film thicknesses will be 0.05–2.00 mm, but thicker water in oil emulsion layers may be found floating. The thickness of the slick will also depend on water temperature and waves.

The rate of evaporation of the oil will primarily depend on the vapor pressure of the oil at ambient temperature but will be enhanced by high wind speeds and rough seas that may promote aerosol formation. The typical loss of weight of a surface slick usually experienced is 20% to 30% every 8 hours, but this can vary appreciably with vapor pressure, wind speed, and surface temperature. In some cases, a 50% loss of weight is experienced every 8 hours. In other cases, weight loss was as little as 5% to 10% every 8 hours.

As lighter, more viscous components evaporate first, the remaining slick usually becomes denser and less viscous. Emulsification of oil in water will enhance surface oil slick persistence. Emulsification is largely a function of sea state and does not persist in moderate or calm seas.

Vertical dispersion of oil depends on the density and viscousness of the oil. Typically, 8 hours after discharge the top 5 m of water will contain 60% of the discharge, but this can be affected by waves, currents, winds, the viscosity of the oil, and water temperature.

2.2 RUNOFF AND DRAINAGE FROM RIVERS, FLOOD PLAINS, WASTEWATER, AND SIMILAR POLLUTION SOURCES

The largest amounts of pollutants discharged into the oceans are by runoff and drainage from land-based pollution sources. These sources are responsible for over 85% of the pollution of the Mediterranean Sea and similarly large percentages in other oceans and seas. Large rivers and flood plains are particularly large pollutant sources as they often drain heavily industrialized or agricultural production areas. Similarly, cities add to the problem through sewerage and other liquid outflows. These often introduce high nutrient levels that encourage widespread growth of phytoplankton. Marine contamination from metal compounds in the runoff or drainage also poses significant dangers. Generally, runoffs introduce also synthetic organic chemicals and trace metals, all extremely hazardous to the ocean environment.

Runoff and drainage effects are often amplified by irrigation that diverts river waters for agricultural purposes. This water is often mixed with fertilizers and chemicals washed out of the soils before reentering the runoff or drainage system. The resulting environmental issues affect

- salinity and waterlogging,
- sedimentation and catchment degradation,
- surface water and groundwater pollution,
- waterborne disease, and
- the habitat of wildlife.

Both surface water and groundwater pollution are affected by fertilizer pollution (primarily nitrates) and excessive use of pesticides. Similarly, the use of agrochemicals in irrigation systems is usually quite high. These chemicals introduce both metallic and nonmetallic elements (Ca, Zn, Pb, Cd, Cl, PO_4) in the drainage. Nitrate pollution, for example, is largely due to agrochemicals and seeping of sewage effluent.

The volume of fertilizer pollution has increased radically with the use of phosphatic and nitrogenic fertilizers; use of these has doubled worldwide since 1970. They are now used, particularly in developing countries, in much higher and often unnecessarily high concentrations. The use of pesticides and agrochemicals (antialgae, for example) has increased substantially and is now 80% above the volume used in 1970.

Although the use of DDT was suspended in the United States in the early 1970s, 50 million pounds per year are still manufactured in the United States for export. Although some DDT is even reimported on fruits and vegetables from Mexico and other Central American countries, most of it ultimately drains into the groundwater of the using countries or into the oceans.

It is estimated that the amount of sediments discharged as suspended solids from surface runoffs into streams, rivers, and ultimately into the oceans amount to about 4 billion tons per year in the United States and over 24.8 billion tons per year worldwide, of which 9.3 billion tons is natural sediment runoff and the rest the result of human intervention. At this rate, the land area of the earth decreases by an average of 2.3 in. in elevation every 1,000 years. Similarly, the amounts dredged and disposed of at sea amount to about 500 million tons per year worldwide, nearly 40% of which originate in the People's Republic of China.

2.2.1 Wastewater Pollution and Liquid Waste Disposal

Wastewater outflow causes one of the most damaging environmental impacts known. Although an increasing number of large cities in developed countries subject wastewater at least to primary treatment, many major coastal urban areas and all small communities in the developed world, and basically all coastal communities in developing countries, still discharge wastewater directly into the sea. When wastewater receives primary treatment, the input into the secondary treatment is sludge, which is usually diluted in such secondary treatment by a factor of 1:150 by mixing it in a special tank and allowing the bottom-admitted sludge to rise. When the sludge is discharged from a primary treatment plant into the ocean, larger particles will drift to the bottom and build up, changing the community at the bottom of the ocean. This, in turn, affects both the food chain—by introducing metals in inorganic form, which do not build up in with animals of higher tropic levels—and organic materials and PCBs, pesticides, and methyl mercury, which do.

Although organic pollution by wastewater discharge is rare, sewage usually contains a lot of phosphorous that either settles or is absorbed onto fine particulates or precipitates with iron, manganese hydroxide, or $CaCO_3$. Sediment also releases phosphorous when the $Fe(OH)_3$ coating that binds the sediment is reduced and dissolved to Fe^2. There are also concerns about the negative effects of Biochemical Oxygen Demand (BOD), ammonia, and pH on coastal waters, but these may be without merit because there usually is an ample amount of oxygen in the water. The main effects of wastewater pollutants are:

1. Sludge, which buries benthal organisms when suspended solids are deposited. This fouls gills of fish and filters of feeding organisms. It also reduces sunlight penetration.
2. Reduced dissolved oxygen, which affects survival of certain marine species, a result of discharge of biodegradable organics.
3. Pathogens, which can be transmitted to humans through contaminated seafood.
4. Excess discharged nutrients, which result in heavy growth of plankton and attached algae.
5. The bioaccumulation of toxic (persistent) organics such as pesti-

cides and PCBs to marine organisms and subsequent effect on humans who consume them.

6. Heavy metal deposition toxic to marine life, which accumulates it. It similarly affects humans who consume such contaminated seafood.

Unless effectively treated before discharge into the oceans, liquid wastes and wastewater cause major and often long-term environmental impacts, particularly in the fertile and productive coastal plains that form the principal breeding grounds for sea life and vegetation.

2.2.2 Effect on Fisheries and Aquaculture

Ocean pollution has had a devastating effect on fisheries and aquaculture in many parts of the world. In fact, fish consumption has become a real or potential health hazard, even in high-income countries such as the United States and Japan, because of the effects of ocean pollution on fish and other seafoods. Ocean pollution affects fish in many ways: biologically, chemically, and physically.

The seafood chain is dependent on energy flows up to trophic levels. Bioaccumulation primarily affects seafood consumed by humans. Humans constitute the top of the seafood chain and are most adversely affected by high concentrations of pollutants, which increasingly reach detrimental levels and cause toxic effects. This comes at a time when seafood consumption continues to grow. U.S. seafood consumption was 17.5 lb/year in 1990 and is expected to grow to 40 lb/year by the year 2000, while Japanese consumption of over 58 lb/year in 1994 is expected to grow to 200 lb/year by the year 2000. As a result, seafood—from both fishing and the aquaculture industry—continues to grow. Japan leads in seafood and seafood processing technology. For example, Japan is developing protein-rich products made from mechanically deboned fish that has a similar taste and texture as shellfish.

By reducing the catch or harvest and by increasing the health hazards imposed by seafood consumption and ocean vegetation, ocean pollution has detrimentally affected the development of an increasingly profitable and important seafood industry. Pollution (including oil spills) affects breeding and spawning, and oil spills and similar surface-introduced effects greatly affect the size and quality of fish catches. Also, plants and algae living on the seabed are often destroyed by oil spills and hydrocarbon residue settling on the seabed. Health hazards to human seafood consumption consist, among others, of the following:

- pathogenic bacteria in shellfish, causing illness or death in humans;
- diarrhetic shellfish poisoning (DSP);
- numbness or loss of sensation caused to saxitoxin (another marine toxin);
- blooms of diatoms cause concentration of domoic acid in mussels, which are said to have caused death and illness in humans who consume mussels;
- fish made smelly and tough by the aromatic hydrocarbons in oil, which may also cause health hazards; and
- free radicals that cause oxidation of fatty acids in fish to produce aldehydes.

As a result, ocean pollution by liquid waste discharge affects the economics and often also the viability of fisheries and aquaculture. Not only is growth and thereby production reduced, but a significant proportion of catches or harvests is infected, uninviting, unsightly, and often simply hazardous to health and therefore not sellable.

Ocean pollution in combination with overfishing (and the two are interdependent) have caused a severe shortage and, as a result, high cost of seafood at a time when seafood was expected to be a major source of cheap protein and ample nutrient supply for a growing world population.

2.3 SOLID WASTES AND HAZARDOUS MATERIALS POLLUTION

Solid waste is generated in everincreasing amounts by households, service industries, manufacturing, and construction. The amount of solid waste generated in the United States alone now exceeds 790 million tons per year; worldwide it is over 2.8 billion tons per year. This is nearly equal to the total volume of goods traded internationally. Solid waste now absorbs an increasing percentage of world transport capacity.

Until recently, most solid waste was deposited in landfills but now, as landfills fill up or refuse to accept solid waste from nearby or remote areas, an everincreasing amount is now discharged or dumped into the oceans. In addition, landfills, even when filled with nontoxic material, may pollute soils or groundwater by long-term chemical reactions or other processes. As a result, fewer and fewer landfill sites are available for the disposal of solid waste.

Similarly, as controls on land-side disposal become stricter, many hazardous materials are now disposed of directly or indirectly into the oceans. Although there are some examples of new low-cost waste recycling technology, more effective solid waste collection, sorting, consolidation, recycling, and other innovative measures designed to reduce the amount of solid and hazardous waste discharged must be developed to cope with the mushrooming problem of solid waste disposal.

Few of the potential gains have been achieved so far, as only about 15% of solid waste and 5% of hazardous wastes is now being recycled in OECD countries and less than 8% and 2%, respectively, worldwide. In some countries, such as Germany, household solid waste recycling is fairly effective and captures nearly 40% of solid waste; this compares with only about 4% in the United States. On the other hand, less progress has been made in recycling of industrial solid wastes, which account for 60% of the solid waste generated worldwide.

The use of existing technology, however, actually permits recovery of 80% of liquid waste solvents and 50% of metals in liquid waste streams. In fact, there are estimates that existing technology could reduce hazardous waste generated in the United States, for example, by as much as 15% to 30% by the year 2000. The problem of reducing hazardous waste disposal has become severe as many landfill sites and surface impoundments used for dumping hazardous wastes are found to leak corrosive acids, persistent organics, and toxic metals into the ground, which in turn pollute the ground, groundwater streams, rivers, and ultimately the oceans. Cleanup of severely polluted dumping sites in the United States is estimated to cost in excess of $100 billion. An even larger amount is needed for the rest of the world, with Eastern Europe and the former Soviet Union accounting for nearly $400 billion alone. At the same time, the industrialization of the developing world will result in an increase in solid and hazardous waste generation, as many developing countries are unwilling to spend the additional money to create cleaner, nonpolluting, or effective recycling plants.

The disposal of hazardous waste has always been a problem. In the late 1960s, incineration of such materials at sea on a large scale began. Many specialized incinerator ships and barges designed for offshore incineration of the substances and deep-sea dumping of the remaining ashes and residues, were built. In recent years, though, the practice was found to be environmentally unacceptable and in fact hazardous to ocean chemistry and marine biology. As a result, at-sea incineration has been largely halted and has been outlawed in several countries.

Dumping of high- and medium-level radioactive wastes in the oceans has been banned for years, but dumping of low-level wastes was permitted if such wastes were properly contained or effectively diluted. Since 1985, an indefinite moratorium on low-level radioactive waste disposal at sea has been suspended. This includes the disposal of such wastes into subseabed repositories. Most countries have maintained the terms of the moratorium, under pressure by public interest groups, and this voluntary moratorium is expected to result in outright banning shortly.

The volume of production and composition of municipal and industrial solid wastes can only be estimated because definitions of what constitutes solid waste differ and data are usually only available from OECD countries. Yet, because these countries are expected to contribute 80% to 85% of the solid waste worldwide, the data are useful.

Table 2–10 indicates the solid waste generated by OECD countries in the late 1980s. It clearly shows that industrial waste constitutes about 60% of solid waste generated. There are, however, major differences. For example, while the per capita generation of municipal waste in the United States is more than twice that of Japan and most other OECD countries, the ratio of industrial to municipal solid waste is comparatively even larger. Another interesting issue is the composition of municipal waste (Table 2–11), which shows that paper and cardboard wastes continue to grow in the United States and Japan, while plastic waste is now nearly constant.

Tables 2–12A and 2–12B present amounts of selected groups of industrial waste generated in selected OECD countries and provide important information regarding the relative contribution of various sources to the amount of industrial waste generated. When reading this table, one should bear in mind that the data do not represent all industrial wastes, nor the potential toxicity, and that the definitions for different groups of industrial wastes may vary from country to country. The table also shows that the United States generated nearly 80% of all the hazardous and special wastes disposed of by OECD countries.

Table 2–13 shows the production and movement of hazardous waste for selected OECD countries. It shows the importance of transfrontier movements of hazardous waste, as well as the use of the sea for its disposal. Although dumping and incineration at sea appear to be rather small, the data presented here may underestimate actual at-sea disposal, particularly because total exports are many times total imports even when reported imports into developing countries are also included. It is estimated that over 30% of hazardous and toxic wastes produced by industry worldwide end up in the ocean, a percentage that is on the rise. The total quantity of hazardous wastes worldwide continues to climb at a rate of about 4.2% per year. As a result, the amount of hazardous and toxic wastes deposited in the oceans may double by the end of the century from levels experienced by 1988, a development that would aggravate an already dangerous situation.

2.4 PORT AND INDUSTRIAL POLLUTION

Among the most important concentrated activities responsible for ocean pollution are ports and industrial facilities. Pollution caused by ports compares with pollution caused by more distributed activities such as agricultural and human-habitation–generated pollution. Ports pollute as a result of the construction and use of shoreside or offshore facilities, which often require major coastal construction or developments and the use of port facilities by ships and cargo operations.

The world is increasingly dependent on trade, particularly international trade, most of which is handled through ports. In fact, in 1991 the value of world trade was equal to nearly 30% of the world's GNP, or WNP or about $5.3 trillion, and was growing at a rate of 4.2%, or about 1.3% faster than the world's GNP. As a result, an ever-larger volume of raw materials, semifinished goods, and finished goods will traverse ports in the future. The total volume of world international trade handled through ports now exceeds 4 bil-

TABLE 2–10 Amounts of Solid Waste Generated, by Source, Selected Countries, Late 1980s (in 1000 tons)

COUNTRY	YEAR	MUNICIPAL[a]	INDUSTRIAL	ENERGY PRODUCTION
Canada	1989	16,400	61,000	12,400[m]
United States	1986	208,760	760,000[o]	99,247
Japan	1988	48,283	312,271[m]	19,828[m]
Austria	1983	2,700[f]	13,258[p]	707
Belgium	1988	3,470[t]	26,700[u]	1,069[v]
Denmark	1985	2,400	2,400	1,532
Finland	1987	2,500[n]	10,500	950
France	1989	17,000	50,000	
West Germany	1987	19,483	61,424	11,702
Greece	1989	3,147	4,304	7,680
Ireland	1984	1,100	1,580	130
Italy	1989	17,300	39,978	
Luxembourg	1990	170	1,300	
Netherlands	1988	6,900	6,687	1,482[l]
Norway	1989	2,000	2,186[j,k]	
Portugal	1987	2,350[m]	662	260
Spain	1988	12,546	5,108	
Sweden	1985	2,650	4,000[l]	550
Switzerland	1989	2,850		
Turkey	1989	19,500		
United Kingdom	1989	20,000	50,000	14,000
Yugoslavia	1989		7,164	
OECD[c,d]		423,000	1,430,000	

SOURCE: OECD Environmental Data, 1991.

[a]Wastes originating from households, commercial activities, and so forth and that are collected by municipalities or by order of them.

[b]Wet weight.

[c]Rounded figures. Includes western Germany only.

[d]Secretarial estimated.

[e]Include wastewaters that meet United States definitions of solid wastes.

[f]Data refer to 1988.

[g]Production of manure from livestock in intensive husbandry.

[h]Exclude sludge from chemical and physical sewage.

[i]Data refer to 1986.

[j]Data refer to 1980.

[k]Chemical industrial wastes only.

[l]Household waste only.

TABLE 2–10 Continued

AGRICULTURE	MINING	DEMOLITION WASTES	DREDGE SPOILS	SEWAGE/ SLUDGE	OTHERS
48,000[m]	10,529	1,540	7,540	500	38,500[m]
150,566	14,000	31,500		10,400	
62,690[m]	26,017[m]	57,886[m]		2,001[j]	
	466	390	2,100	1,350	
53,000[j]	7,069[j]	680[v]	4,805[v]	687[v]	2,830[v]
		1,500		1,263	300
23,000[f]	21,600	2,000	420	153	
400,000	10,000[q]			620	2,800
	9,488	11,826		1,750[h]	
90	3,900				1,200
22,000	1,930	240		570	860
29,830[j]	57,000[l]	34,374		3,500	1,985
		4,000		15	
86,000[g,r]	121[l]	7,700[f]	16,000[r]	252	664
18,000	9,000	2,000		100	
202	3,900[j]				
45,000	18,000[m]			10,000[m]	
21,000[o]	28,000	3,000[s]	600[j]	372	3,895
		3,000[d]		260	
250,000	23,000	25,000	37,000[f]	30,000[b]	21,000
20,597					

[m] Data refer to 1985.

[n] Data refer to 1989.

[o] 17,000 kt of this waste is fully recycled.

[p] Partial figure based on national survey data. Estimate for total industrial waste: 31,000 kt.

[q] Includes demolition waste.

[r] Amounts dumped at sea only.

[s] Includes nonchemical industrial waste.

[t] Data include 1982 figures for Brussels region, 1987 figures for Flanders region, and 1989 figures for Walloon region.

[u] Data include 1986 figures for Brussels region, 1987 figures for Flanders region, and 1989 figures for Walloon region.

[v] Flanders region only.

TABLE 2–11 Composition of Municipal Waste, Selected Countries, 1975–1989

		PAPER AND CARDBOARD				PLASTICS			
COUNTRY	REFERENCES	1975	1980	1985	1989	1975	1980	1985	1989
Canada		—	36.5	36.5	36.5	—	4.7	4.7	4.7
United States	b,c	32.5	29.7	34.7	—	3.0	5.3	6.7	—
Japan	d,f	30.9	27.4	38.3	45.5	8.9	12.3	7.7	8.3
Austria	h,k,m	27.2	30.7	33.6	—	6.0	6.1	7.0	—
Belgium	i,e	30.0	35.0	—	28.3	5.0	5.8	—	7.7
Denmark	j	35.0	34.0	38.4	—	4.0	7.0	3.4	—
Finland	k	—	—	40.0	—	—	—	8.0	—
France	i	35.0	28.0	27.5	27.5	5.0	6.0	4.5	4.5
West Germany	n,r	25.0	19.9	17.9	—	8.0	6.1	5.4	—
Greece		—	19.6	20.0	20.0	—	7.0	7.0	7.0
Ireland	j	33.0	35.0	24.5	—	4.0	11.0	14.0	—
Italy	a,q	20.4	22.5	22.3	—	5.3	6.8	7.2	—
Luxembourg	i	25.0	—	17.2	—	4.5	—	6.4	—
Netherlands	k	23.0	21.0	22.8	24.2	5.6	6.5	6.8	7.1
Norway	o	31.0	31.0	31.0	31.0	4.0	4.0	4.0	5.0
Portugal		—	18.9	19.0	—	—	3.2	3.0	—
Spain	g	—	15.0	15.0	20.0	—	6.0	6.0	7.0
Sweden	i	—	43.0	—	—	—	10.0	—	—
Switzerland	p	—	30.0	—	32.0	—	13.0	—	13.0
United Kingdom	s	30.0	29.0	—	—	4.0	7.0	—	—

SOURCE: OECD Environmental Data, 1991.

[a]1985 data refer to 1986.

[b]1985 data refer to 1984.

[c]1990 data fro "paper," "metals," and "organic substance" refer to 1978

[d]For 1975 and 1980, average of four cities (net base). 1985 and 1988 data refer to the sample figures for Tokyo in 1984 and 1988, respectively. Data for "glass" refer to glass and ceramics. 1989 data for "others" include textiles and wood product waste.

[e]Data include estimates.

[f]Data for "organic substance" refer to combustible components and water, derived from average of six cities.

[g]1989 data refer to 1988.

[h]Rough estimates. 1975, 1980 and 1985 data refer to 1973, 1978, and 1988, respectively. Data in 1985 column refer to Vienna only.

lion tons per year, with a nearly equal amount of domestic trade passing through them. To reduce the cost of transportation and distribution, more and more processing and manufacturing activities now locate next to ports, which has given rise to the concept of port-related industries and makes ports into major potential pollution generators. This trend is encouraged by the growth of free ports and free port industrial or trading zones established in many parts of the world to promote large-scale industrial and commercial concentrations around ports.

Although this trend enhances the use of ports and improves the efficiency of cargo transfer through ports, it introduces large concentrations of industrial pollution activities near the ocean. Some industries often attempt to use the port access to develop inexpensive

TABLE 2–11 Continued

GLASS				METALS				OTHERS				ORGANIC SUBSTANCE			
1975	1980	1985	1989	1975	1980	1985	1989	1975	1980	1985	1989	1975	1980	1985	1989
—	6.6	6.6	6.6	—	6.6	6.6	6.6	—	45.7	45.7	45.7	—	57.6	74.3	—
10.0	10.3	9.0	—	9.0	9.6	8.8	—	45.5	45.1	40.8	—	—	37.5	—	—
6.1	8.0	1.3	1.0	3.7	4.7	1.4	1.3	50.4	47.3	51.3	43.9	78.4	85.0	—	77.2
11.1	10.4	10.4	—	8.0	8.2	3.7	—	47.7	44.6	45.3	—	65.4	61.7	60.5	—
8.0	8.2	—	7.6	4.5	5.1	—	3.7	51.5	45.9	—	52.5	40.0	34.8	—	47.6
8.0	6.0	5.4	—	4.0	5.0	5.0	—	49.0	47.0	47.6	—	—	—	81.3	—
—	—	4.0	—	—	—	3.0	—	—	—	45.0	—	—	—	85.0	—
8.0	11.0	7.5	7.5	5.0	5.0	6.5	6.5	—	50.0	54.0	54.0	—	59.0	—	—
15.0	11.6	9.2	—	5.0	3.9	3.2	—	47.0	58.5	64.3	—	—	63.4	—	—
—	2.7	3.0	3.0	—	4.2	4.0	4.0	—	66.5	66.0	66.0	—	53.7	57.0	57.0
8.0	8.0	7.5	—	4.0	3.0	3.0	—	51.0	43.0	51.0	—	—	—	56.0	—
6.4	6.7	6.2	—	3.0	2.9	3.1	—	64.9	61.4	61.6	—	68.9	67.2	64.4	—
5.0	—	7.2	—	3.5	—	2.6	—	62.0	—	66.6	—	—	—	44.0	—
12.0	11.9	7.2	7.2	3.3	3.1	3.4	3.2	56.1	57.5	59.8	58.3	82.8	83.7	87.9	88.3
3.0	3.0	3.0	3.0	7.0	7.0	7.0	7.0	55.0	55.0	55.0	55.0	77.0	77.0	77.0	77.0
—	2.9	3.0	—	—	3.6	3.5	—	—	71.4	71.5	—	—	74.7	74.5	—
—	6.0	6.0	6.0	—	2.5	2.5	4.0	—	70.5	70.5	63.0	—	52.5	52.5	49.0
—	5.0	—	—	—	6.0	—	—	—	36.2	—	—	—	89.0	—	—
—	9.0	—	7.0	—	6.0	—	6.0	—	42.0	—	47.0	—	70.0	—	70.0
10.0	10.0	—	—	8.0	8.0	—	—	48.0	46.0	—	—	54.0	58.0	—	—

[i]1975 data refer to 1977.

[j]1975 and 1980 data refer to 1977 and 1979 respectively.

[k]Data refer to household waste only.

[l]Data for "paper" include separated fraction at source.

[m]1985 data for "organic substance" refer to 1983; vegetables substances accounted for 23.3%.

[n]1975 data for "plastics" include textiles.

[o]1975 and 1980; concerning surveys in 1973/74 and 1979–1981.

[p]1980 data refer to 1982.

[q]1985 data for "glass" and "others" refer to secretariat estimates.

[r]1980 and 1985 data refer to household waste only.

[s]England and Wales only.

methods for the disposal of their waste. This may involve development of special waste containment, treatment, and disposal facilities in the port. Many ports, for example, provide dirty oil or oily water reception and treatment facilities for ships, petrochemical plants, and refineries that are used by waterborne and land-based plants. The same applies to liquid, solid, and hazardous waste treatment and storage facilities.

2.4.1 Port Pollution

Ecological impacts of port construction and operations are pervasive. In the past, ecological factors, especially those relating to air and water quality, formed only a secondary design issue in ports,

TABLE 2–12A Industrial Waste, Hazardous Waste, and Special Waste[a]: Total Amount Generated by Type, Selected Countries, Late 1980s (in 1,000 metric ton)

COUNTRY	YEAR	CHEMICAL WASTE	NONCHEMICAL WASTE	TOTAL	HAZARDOUS AND SPECIAL WASTE
Canada	1980	—	196	61,000	3,290[c]
United States	1986	105,400	—	760,000[m]	238,327[m,i]
Japan[n]	1985	—	—	312,271	666[j]
Austria	1983	525	12,733[e]	13,258[o]	400[e,i]
Belgium[p]	1989	—	—	26,700	915[q]
Denmark	1988	—	—	2,400[f]	112
Finland	1987	—	—	10,500	230
France	1989	—	—	50,000	3,000[k]
W. Germany	1987	10,218	51,206[b]	61,424[b]	14,210[b]
Greece	1989	423	3,881	4,304	423
Ireland	1984	—	—	1,580	20
Italy	1989	—	—	39,978	3,640
Luxembourg	1990	—	—	1,300	742
Netherlands[g]	1988	624	6,063	6,687	1,500[h]
Norway	1989	2,186[l]	—	—	200
Portugal	1987	530	133	662	165
Spain	1987	—	—	5,108[j]	1,708
Sweden	1980	500	3,500	4,000	500[f]

Switzerland	1989	—	—	—	400
United Kingdom[d]	1989	—	—	50,000	2,200
Yugoslavia	1989	—	—	7,164	—
OECD[r]	1989	—	—	1,430,000	303,000

SOURCE: OECD Environmental Data, 1991.

Notes: [a.] Special wastes that are considered hazardous.

[b.] Secretariat estimates based on national definitions of hazardous and special waste.

[c.] Wet weight.

[d.] Fiscal year, commencing April 1.

[e.] Secretariat estimates.

[f.] Data refer to 1985.

[g.] Data refer to enterprises of more than ten employees. Office and canteen wastes included.

[h.] Excluding ship-cleaning residuals.

[i.] Data refer to 1987.

[j.] Data refer to 1986.

[k.] Amount of toxic or hazardous waste. The total amount of special waste is million metric tons.

[l.] Data refer to 1980.

[m.] Includes wastewaters managed in land-based operations.

[n.] By law (i.e., the Waste Disposal and Public Cleansing Law), industrial wastes are subjected to treatment by elutriation or content tests prior to classification and subsequent disposal. (The latter test is only for water-soluble wastes that are to be disposed of in the ocean.) Waste is classified hazardous, if after treatment, the substance exceeds its relevant concentration criteria.

[o.] Partial figure for industial waste based on national survey data from 1983. Estimate for total industrial waste: 31,000 kt.

[p.] Data refer to 1989 figures for Walloon region, 1987 for Flanders region, and 1986 for Brussels region.

[q.] Secretariat estimates for early 1980s.

[r.] Secretariat estimates. Includes western Germany only.

TABLE 2–12B Amounts Generated of Selected Groups of Industrial Waste: Selected Countries, Late 1980s (in metric ton)

	YEAR	WASTE OIL	WASTE SOLVENT	WASTE PAINT	CONCENTRATED ACIDS
Canada	1989	367,000[q]	262,000[q]	72,700[q]	—
United States	1986	3,575,559[d]	89,173,520[d]	630,000[e]	2,737,740
Japan	1985	3,672,000[u]	—	—	4,320,000
Australia[j]	1983	30,700	2,000	4,350	49,000
New Zealand	1983	900	50	10	1,000
Austria	1983	650,000[x]	7,000	5,800	1,266,000
Finland	1987	62,000	8,300	11,500	188,000
France	1989	250,000	285,000	90,000	—
West Germany	1987	859,456	454,489	225,525	1,266,599
Ireland	1980	25,000	13,500	—	—
Luxembourg	1990	10,700	818	898	1,276,678
Norway	1989	55,000	8,000	5,000	10,000
Netherlands	1986	150	—	10	—
Portugal	1987	—	3,088	756	49
Sweden	1980	180,000	33,000	20,000	72,800
Yugoslavia	1989	3,085	—	—	—

SOURCE: OECD Environmental Data, 1991.

[a]Data refer to 1980.

[b]Data refer to 1987.

[c]Data refer to 1982.

[d]Figure based on a survey of hazardous waste generators and therfore does not reflect the total U.S. volume.

[e]Hazardous wastes only.

[f]Wastes originating from metal plating only.

[g]Wastes containing silver or mercury.

[h]Data refer to 1977.

[i]1978 estimate.

[j]1983, state of Queensland only, data given in kl.

[k]Metal finishing wastes plus neutral salts.

[l]Oil-based inks.

TABLE 2–12B Continued

	WASTE CONTAINING					
METAL FINISHING WASTE	SILVER OR ZINC	MERCURY	PCBs	BIOCIDES	PLASTICS RUBBER, ETC.	PHENOLIC WASTES
186,200[q]	—	263,000	120,000[w]	4,500[q]	74,000[b]	19,100[a]
1,800,000[e,f,a]	—	8,762,561[d,g]	5,015,060[d]	12,000	161,000[e]	366,000[h]
8,877,000	—	—	—	—	2,894,000	—
12,300[k]	750[l]	—	50[m]	3,500	110[n]	42,000[o]
900	—	—	800[p]	30	—	—
1,394,000	270	163	1,900	39	102,000	131,000
6,000[c]	500[c]	—	1,780[c]	120	61,000	580
—	—	450[a,s]	17,000	—	—	23,000[i]
219,527	52,057	—	10,537	—	867,015	—
33,000	1,600	—	—	5	45,000	—
1,300	168	126	25	5	—	—
17,000[b]	—	3,000[b]	2,000[b]	440	100,000[q]	10[v]
140	11	—	—	—	75[q,r]	—
—	—	—	719	—	—	—
112,000	3,600	450	30	600	—	—
—	—	—	—	—	—	—

[m]250 kl being phased out.

[n]Bituminous emulsions.

[o]Organic chemicals.

[p]Estimated total of PCB-contaminated waste to be disposed of in the next 10–15 years.

[q]Data refer to 1985.

[r]Automobile tires.

[s]Containing more than 1% of mercury.

[t]Amounts treated.

[u]Includes solvent waste.

[v]Data refer to 1984.

[w]Includes 6,500 metric ton of high-level PCBs currently in storage in Canada and awaiting disposal.

[x]Includes refinery wastes containing mineral oils.

TABLE 2–13 Production and Movement of Hazardous and Special Waste

		HAZARDOUS AND SPECIAL WASTES PRODUCED[a]		IMPORTS	
	YEAR	METRIC TONS	PERCENT	METRIC TONS	PERCENT
Canada[b]	1980	3,290	100	120.0	3.6
United States[c]	1987	238,327	100	40.0	—
Japan	1985	666	100	—	—
Australia	1980	300	100	—	—
New Zealand	1982	60	100	—	—
Austria[b]	1987	400	100	—	—
Denmark	1988	112	100	—	—
Finland	1987	230	100	—	—
France[c]	1989	3,000	100	250.0	8.3
West Germany	1988	14,210	100	20.2	0.1
Ireland	1984	20	100	—	—
Italy	1989	3,640	100	—	—
Netherlands[d]	1986	1,500	100	—	—
Norway	1989	200	100	—	—
Spain	1987	1,708	100	—	—
Sweden[c,e]	1985	500	100	—	—
Switzerland	1989	400	100	—	—
Turkey[a]	1989	300	100	—	—
United Kingdom[f]	1989	2,200	100	34.2	1.5

SOURCE: OECD Environmental Data, 1991.

[a]Secretariat estimates.

[b]Hazardous waste produced: wet weight.

[c]Data on amounts imported and exported refer to 1988.

[d]Excluding ship-cleaning residuals.

but they are now considered major factors in specifying vessel design and operating conditions.

Ecological considerations in port design and operation include, among others:

1. disturbances in water motion (surface and subsurface) as well as resultant effects on sediment flow, siltation, and underwater and shore erosion, resulting from port construction and operations;

TABLE 2–13 Continued

EXPORTS		DUMPING AT SEA		INCINERATION AT SEA	
METRIC TONS	PERCENT	METRIC TONS	PERCENT	METRIC TONS	PERCENT
101.0	3.1	—	—	—	—
127.0	0.1	—	—	—	—
0.04	—	—	—	—	—
0.3	0.1	—	—	—	—
0.2	0.3	—	—	—	—
87	43.5	—	—	—	—
9.0	8.0	—	—	—	—
65.0	28.3	—	—	—	—
45.0	1.5	—	—	15.0	0.5
805.4	5.7	—	—	—	—
14.0	70.0	—	—	—	—
3.0	0.1	—	—	—	—
188.0	12.5	—	—	—	—
8.0	4.0	—	—	5.9	3.0
0.10	—	—	—	—	—
30.2	6.0	—	—	5.9	1.2
108.0	27.0	—	—	—	—
—	—	—	—	—	—
—	—	160.0	9.0[g]	5.5	0.3[g]

[e]Data on amounts incinerated refer to 1980.

[f]Fiscal year commencing 1st April.

[g]Data refer to 1988/89 total special waste (1762 kt).

[h]Data for export refer to 1983 (amounts and share). Production data refer to 1987 secretariat estimates.

2. changes in submarine bottom structure and effects of structural invasion, permanent or temporary, resulting from dredging;
3. resulting ecological changes and disturbances on fish, shellfish, and other marine life, particularly in breeding grounds that are close to shore;
4. oil spills through surface floating, flexible risers, and mechanically supported or submarine pipelines;

5. vessel collision, grounding, and leakage resulting in cargo spills;
6. waste disposal discharges and spills, both solid and liquid vessel wastes;
7. tank vessel leakage, rupture, and overflow or similar spills, including operational spills on connection and disconnection of vessel pipelines;
8. air pollution caused by effluents such as combustion, venting cargo gases, and dust resulting from dry cargo operations, such as cement and grain;
9. interference with recreation, fishing, and industrial uses of the sea as well as the nearby shore;
10. aesthetic interference;
11. regularly occurring operational spills on port facilities;
12. above subsurface noise and vibrations during construction and operation of port facilities and equipments;
13. effects on land use of terminal interface, particularly the pipe, conveyor, hose, or shore connection;
14. effects of vessel movement, maneuvering, and anchoring patterns on marine biology and the conflicting use of sea and coastal zones;
15. effects of dredging and reclamation on benthic organisms that are located on the subsea area affected;
16. disruptive effects at source location of foundation and ditch excavations as well as bottom sand and gravel removal;
17. environmental disturbances caused by the construction of separate port facilities and structures; and
18. relocation of fish and other marine life distribution, causing undue concentrations often near the structure while depleting marine life in nearby locations and resulting in an imbalance of marine populations.

The physical causes enumerated above affect changes in the chemical, biological, hydrodynamic, and geologic factors, in sediment flow, and in other factors that contribute to ecological problems. It is exceedingly difficult to quantify the effect of different interrelated or dependent ecological causes because they depend on the following factors, among others:

1. local physical conditions such as currents, water depth, wind, wind and current direction, salinity, waves, solids in suspension, seabed formation, and air and water temperatures;
2. chemical and physical properties of various cargoes such as petroleum or other potential pollutants;
3. rate of emission, propagation, or intensity of ecological factors such as pollutants and sediment movement;
4. physical form of onshore and offshore port facilities;
5. port operational policies and procedures;
6. navigational requirements;
7. types and volumes of cargoes handled; and
8. vessel types used.

The magnitude of pollution and other environmental impacts caused by port and port-related activities is difficult to quantify, but not insignificant, particularly because pollution usually occurs in restricted, sheltered waters.

To a large extent, the physical impact of a port depends on the type of marine works, channel configuration, structures, and operations used. For example, floating mooring systems or stable floating platforms have relatively little effect on impeding water or sediment motions. A large structure built on pilings or filled types, artificial islands, and so forth that involves sinking solid structures into the seabed and that may obstruct movements of sediment, current swells, and waves, however, often causes erosion of the seabed and nearby shorelands. Two effects of such action could be a reduction in the desirability of the beach for recreation and residential purpose and the possibility of more maintenance dredging caused by increased sedimentation in adjacent channels.

Considering the extreme impact possible with the buildings of an artificial island protected by a breakwater, a solid structure could alter the current and water circulation. The salinity and water quality as well as the seabed and shoreline could thereby be affected.

The severity of the shoreline effects is a function of the distance of a terminal from the shore. Similarly, aesthetic reasons will support a desire to move such facilities as far out to sea as economically and operationally feasible. Artificial islands or solid foundation–supported offshore ports cause effects resulting from:

1. the filling operation, which covers any marine benthic organisms that are located at the site of the facility;
2. the process of obtaining fill materials such as sand and gravel, which may have disruptive effects at the source location; and
3. fish congregating around the island, although this effect may not result in an increase in the overall fish population.

Various approaches to reduce the ecological impact of offshore port development are available. Unfortunately, the requirements for the reduction of risk of ecological damage from various causes are often in conflict. For example, although a solid breakwater enclosure provides the most effective means for containment and subsequent cleanup of oil spills at the offshore port, it also may introduce the largest ecological impact on the natural balance at the location in terms of physical and biological subsurface effects.

Various artificial island and floating terminal designs that attempt to minimize both the effect on the ocean bottom as well as the interface while providing safe port facilities and reasonable containment opportunities are available. Among these are floating stable platform terminals with submarine storage tanks, tanker ferry slips, and floating self-closing containment barriers. These designs usually have a very small waterplane area and, as a result, a minimal effect on the water motion. Conversely, they are hardly affected by water motions no matter how severe. The requirement for seabed attachments is insignificant, and this terminal can be free floating or relocatable. This characteristic also permits a terminal to assume a most favorable position for interfacing with large tankers under varying conditions of wind, waves, currents, and tanker technology or operating procedure. Various methods for spill containment are currently under development.

Although floating flexible barrier type systems now predominate, other systems such as rigid semisubmerged barriers may provide safer containment. Hydraulic and pneumatic breakwaters fed and sustained by hinged or flexible pipes maintained at a distance under mean water level sufficient to assure pipe submergence under all weather conditions may offer many containment advantages.

The effect of ship movements in port operations, in terms of the impact on currents, turbulence, water temperature, and surface waves that could have a direct effect on the shoreline, other vessels, and marine organisms, must be considered. Normal terminal and vessel operations generally result in a discharge of oil, in contaminated ballast water, and in shipboard waste residues. This aspect of oil and other liquid waste water pollution is significant because an estimated 34% of all pollution in the oceans and 70% of all oil pollution of coastal waters is caused by tank cleaning, bilge wastes, bunkering, and minor leaks.

In summary, the largest ocean environmental effect of ports is probably the impact of dredging and reclamation associated with port and navigational channel construction and maintenance. The total volume of port-related dredging is estimated for the whole world at:

- capital dredging 232–382 million m^3/yr and
- maintenance dredging 80–100 million m^3/yr.

About 30% of this is performed in the West Pacific, mainly near China. Although most of the dredging volumes or spoils are dumped at sea, some—about 15% to 18%—are used for reclamation or the construction of artificial islands. In addition, about 50–70 million m^3/yr are dredged directly for reclamation, port construction, or other needs for fill. The principal environmental impacts caused by dredging are shown in Figures 2–3 and 2–4.

Among liquid waste pollution caused by ports and related activities, oil spills, leakages, and other voluntary or involuntary discharge of oil substances are probably the most significant and environmentally objectionable. Oil spills are generally classified as chronic or catastrophic. A chronic oil spill is one with nearly continuous, low-level discharges. A catastrophic spill denotes a single spill of major proportions, such as one that might result from a tanker grounding or collision. Obviously, many occurrences fall between these two general definitions, which are difficult to quantify. Either type of spill can result in the same overall discharge. Distribution of concentrations may differ widely even among spills of the same type and magnitude.

Bulk carrier operations usually result in the chronic type of spill, with bunkers and pumping engine room bilges as the most frequent sources of pollution. Combination carriers, of course, are just as prone to catastrophic spills as tankers are. The biological effects of spills can be defined as follows:

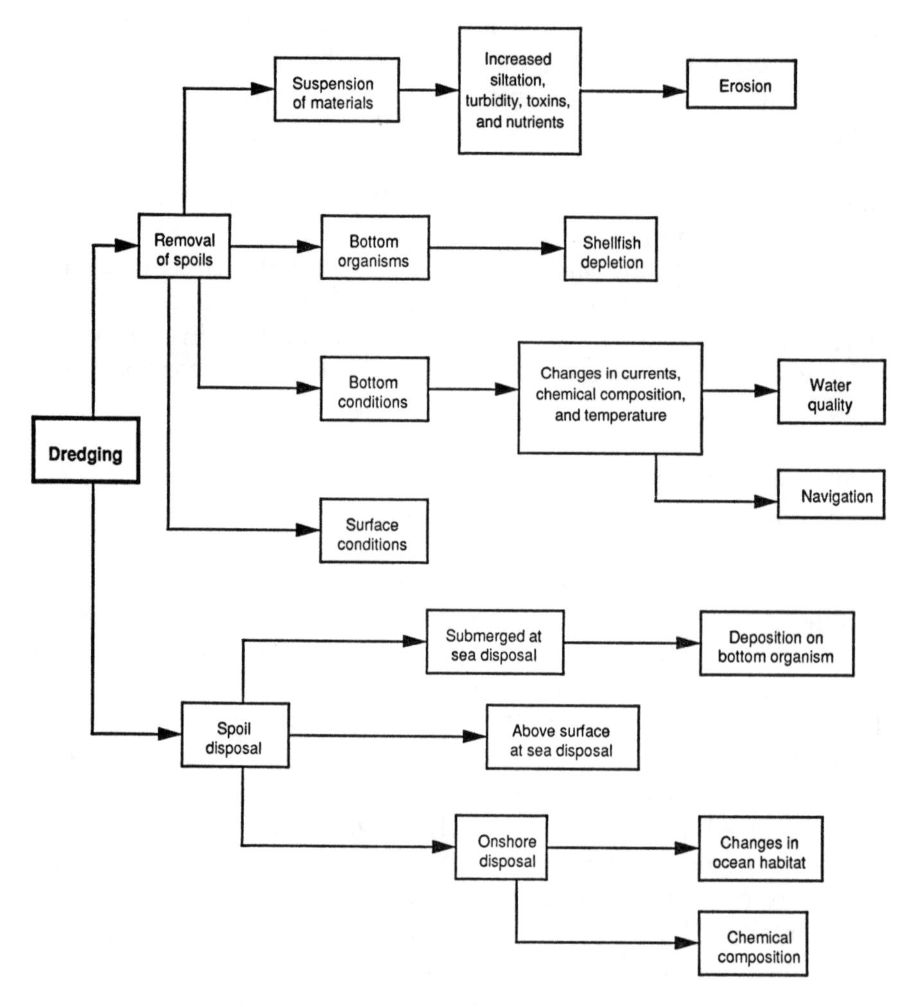

Figure 2–3 Environmental aspects of dredging.

1. *Immediate lethal toxicity:* This refers to the direct interference by hydrocarbons with cellular and subcellular processes, particularly membrane activities, leading to the death of sea life organism.

2. *Sublethal inhibition of sea life behavioral activities:* This type of impact, which can occur especially during feeding and reproduction of sea life, also refers to interference with cellular level processes, but its effects do not result in death.

3. *Lethal or sublethal effects by direct coating:* This effect, which may result in death of sea life, occurs when oil substances directly

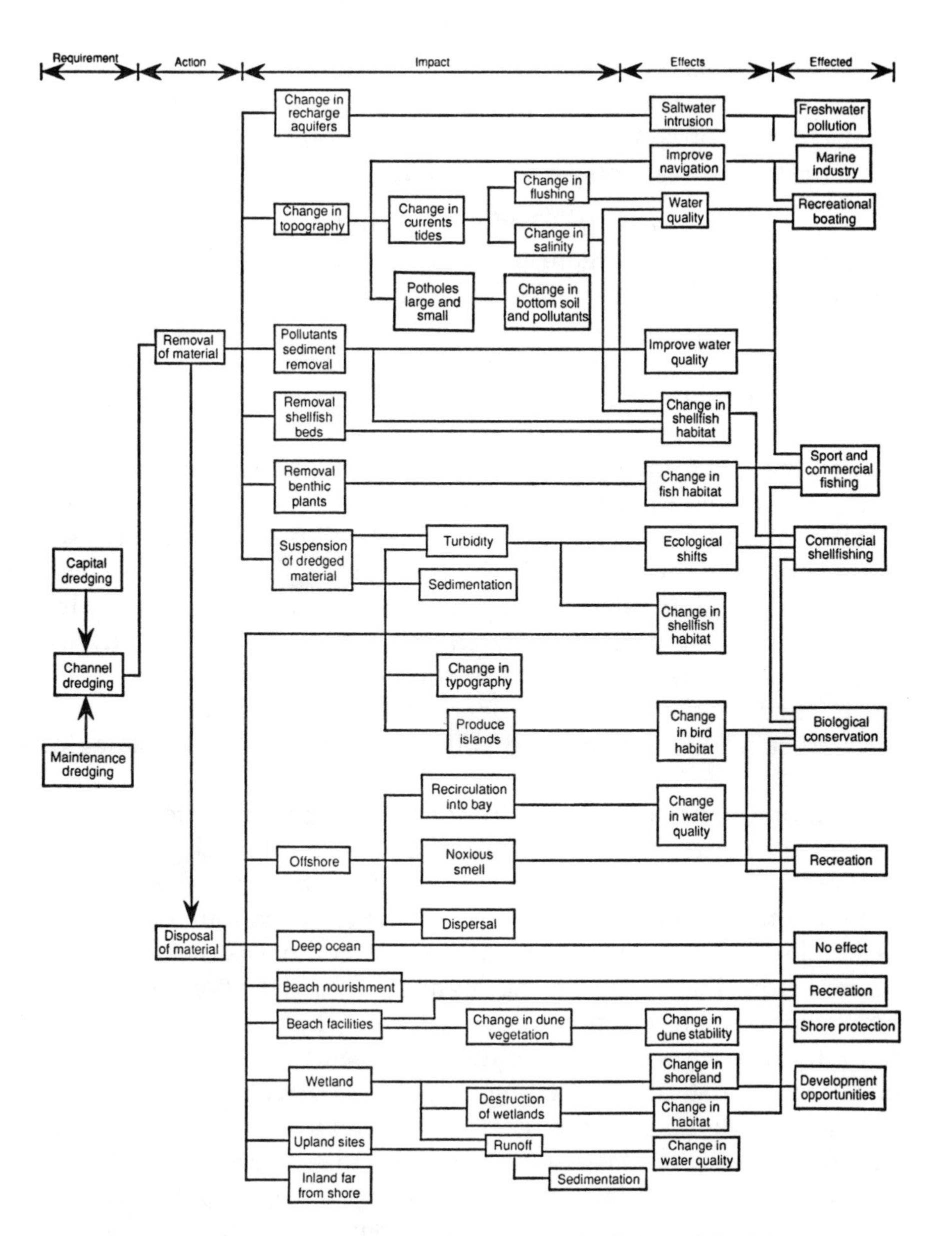

Figure 2–4 Environmental effects network of channel dredging.

coat sea animals. Death results from smothering (differentiating this impact from the lethal toxicity mentioned above).

4. *Incorporation of high boiling point polycyclic aromatic hydrocarbons (PAH) in the food chain:* The incorporation of hydrocarbons in the food chain is of concern because of the potential accumulation of PAHs, especially carcinogens, in various marine organisms.

5. *Changes in habitat:* Changes in habitat can occur, especially for attached (sessile) organisms, due to deposition of oil on rocks, sediments, or other substratas. These habitat changes, which include effects from both oil spill and non–oil spill events, consist of changes in the physical or chemical environment that cause significant shifts in species distribution in the region of concern.

In modeling the process of oil weathering, it was assumed that this process could be approximated by first-order decay. The large number of individual compounds in crude oil precluded the consideration of each one explicitly in the model. Consequently, compounds were grouped according to number of carbons and hydrocarbon type. One possible grouping, including the rate of physical and chemical constants for each fraction, is shown in Table 2–14. The six fractions chosen provided adequate flexibility in characterizing oil, particularly with respect to both short- and long-term biological effects.

An important conclusion from the research relates to the selection of port sites. It was concluded that in a relatively short time (24–48 hours), the highly toxic fractions (numbers 3 and 4 on Table 2–14) are reduced to very low concentrations. Therefore, it would be desirable to select a site such that spills could weather for 24–48 hours before impinging on the highly productive shore areas. The key factors in the selection of port sites are, therefore, not only distance from beaches or urban centers and coastal topography but also such characteristics as prevailing winds and currents.

In consideration of the types of hazards presented by bulk handling, it is clear that the distance required to separate bulk handling. Operations from environmentally sensitive areas is much smaller. Such a distance is determined by the volume of escaping dust and prevailing wind patterns. In fact, from the point of view of environmental damage by the cargo itself, little constraint is placed on the location of port facilities.

Other port emissions affecting water quality are sewage, solid

TABLE 2–14 Basic Data for Oil Spill Weathering Model

FRACTION	DESCRIPTION	PERCENTAGE BY WEIGHT In Crude Oil	DENSITY (gm/ml)	BOILING POINT (°C)	MOLECULAR WEIGHT	VAPOR PRESS at 20°C(mm)	SOLUBILITY (gm/10^6gm of distilled H_20)
1	Paraffin C_6–C_{14}	0+–25	0.66–0.77	69–253	86–198	110–0.01	9.5–0.003
2	Paraffin C_{15}–C_{22}	0±10	0.77–0.78	270–368	212–290	0.01–0	0.007–0.003
3	Cycle-Para. C_5–C_{11}	1–25	0.75–0.90	49–200	70–152	230–1	156–1
4	Aromatic (Monocyclic) C_{10}–C_{16}	0–5	0.88–0.90	80–204	78–136	72–0.34	1780–50
6	Residual	30–70	1.0–1.1	> 350	200–900	0	0

SOURCE: Stephen F. Moore, Robert L. Dwyer, and Arthur M. Katz, *A Preliminary Assessment of the Environmental Vulnerability of Machias Bay, Maine, to Oil Supertankers*, Report No. 162, MIT, Department of Civil Engineering, January 1973.

waste, washdowns of liquid or dry particles of residue (such as chemical or other cargo) clearing or removal of lifeless or diseased marine or other organisms, discharge of toxic or explosive materials, and others.

Because many ports are located in comparatively stagnant waters, such discharges pose definite environmental hazards and affect water quality at adjacent locations, often many miles upstream or downstream. Sinkage of liquid wastes often causes accumulation of a thick bottom layer of toxic and pollutant material, which eliminates the use of the water and waterfront for many desired activities.

Concentrations of those sinkages in many ports have eliminated marine life for a great distance from the port and have discouraged the use of adjacent areas for residences and recreation.

Air pollution, although not as important as water pollution, is another major environmental factor in port operations. The causes of air pollution are:

1. stack or exhaust emissions from ships, trucks, locomotives, port equipment, and the like;
2. dust emissions from dry bulk and similar cargo transfer and storage operations; and
3. fumes from vents, open tankage, spills, and so forth.

The concentration of air pollutants in port areas is usually larger than in many industrial plants, and in port areas the emissions are more haphazard and less controllable. Smoke discharge from ships is usually at a much lower height than comparative industry or utility station discharges and because of the location is often carried by downdraft into populated areas. Similarly, dust of various pulverized or open dry bulk commodities is often carried by wind or air currents in unacceptable concentrations.

Ecological impact factors for ports are summarized in Table 2–15. Although gaseous emissions can be significant, most detrimental emissions occur temporarily during soot blowing or intense maneuvering of vessels in port. It is difficult to quantify the ecological factors and the costs of potential damage to the environment, but it is usually possible to set general limits of acceptability that can be used.

TABLE 2–15 Ecological Impact Factors for Ports

CAUSE	EFFECT
Oil spills	Marine biology, including fish habitat
	Wildlife and birdlife
	Beach pollution
	Recreational use
	Air quality
	Structural corrosion
	Air-water interface
Seabed disturbances	Sedimentation
	Siltation
	Benthic organisms
	Bottom structure and geological formation
	Marine Biology and Fish Habitat
Hydrodynamic disturbances	Sediment flow
	Siltation
	Beach and bottom erosion
	Benthic organism
	Navigation and maneuvering
Gaseous emissions	Air quality (small effect)
	Structural corrosion
	Secondary effects
	Wildlife
	Navigation
Physical obstructions	Commercial Navigation
	Recreational use
	Use of the sea: fishing, underwater exploration, and exploitation
Physical form	Aesthetics and appearances
	Land use
	Recreational use

2.4.2 Industrial Pollution

Industrial pollution of the oceans is caused by "extractive industries" as well as by "discharging industries." Oil, gas, sand, gravel, shells, salt, phosphate, and various hard minerals are among the ocean or subsea resources extracted, largely in coastal waters, by a variety of methods, many of which cause environmental damage. Each extractive process, in fact, has a possibility for direct or indirect ecological impact through damage to the bottom layer, barging of breeding grounds, and dispersal of pollutants dug up.

Large-scale sand and gravel extraction, for example, may cause large increases in turbidity and sedimentation, a loss of productive ocean bottoms, and reduced plant life and breeding beds. Similarly, it may cause changes in the bottom topography and, as a result, ocean currents and sediment flows. Strip mining of shell beds (for cement making, poultry feed, and so forth) may cause large ecological damage to oyster beds.

Nonextractive industrial pollution consists largely of the disposal of liquid and solid process wastes that may be poisonous, toxic, or hazardous to the marine environment. Other such pollution may be heat or physical discharges such as high velocity flows, sediments, or other solid flows that may all pollute the ocean and in particular affect the sensitive balance of the coastal area.

Industrial pollution is usually generated by concentrated or point sources located in a small area, generating comparatively large amounts of pollutants. The most important industrial pollution sources are usually liquid residues from various processes. Not only are they large in volume, but they also contain toxic or other hazardous components in liquid or solid (sediment) form.

As a result, the major pollutant industries are process industries—such as petrochemical, refining, cement, and chemical industries—that convert large volumes of material, often using chemical and physical processes.

2.5 AIR POLLUTION

The pollution of the air above the oceans has many origins. Although most of the air pollution is transferred from on-land generated pollution by winds and air currents, there is a significant amount of air pollution caused by gas emissions from underwater vents, volcanic action, and various chemical interactions at sea or in the coastal interface. Such gases may come from the inner crust of the earth, may result from chemical reactions in the ocean waters, or may be caused, for instance, by biological (plant or animal) decay or by human activities such as burning fossil fuels at sea or on land.

The amount of pollutants in the air above the oceans has increased rapidly in recent years and now causes major changes in surface-water quality. The problem is particularly severe in coastal waters, confined bays, and river estuaries where land or inland water ocean interactions occur. This is usually amplified because coasts, bays, and estuaries provide preferred locations for the placement of heavy industries, ports, or other human activities with intense energy conversion.

2.5.1 Ship Air Emissions

Pollution from ship emissions is an increasingly serious problem. The total number of ships (1,000 DWT and larger) in the world is 64,820 oceangoing vessels, with a combined installed propulsion power of nearly 470 million horsepower, or just under 355 million kW. About 52% of this propulsion power is used on average or about 240 million horsepower (97.8% diesel) operates at sea at any one time, consuming about 160 million lb of diesel fuel per hour (or 1.7 million tons per day). Port consumption (mainly for electric power, heating, and cargo handling) is approximately 100,000 tons of diesel fuel per day. This generates nearly 2.8 million tons of effluents per day, effluents that contain large amounts of carbon oxides, unburnt carbon, various sulfurs, vanadium, and other impurities, which in part deposit in the oceans.

2.6 OTHER OCEAN ENVIRONMENTAL PROBLEMS

Although there is much attention on major environmental disasters, the environmental damage caused by routine activities is much greater. For example, 1.35 billion gallons of used motor oil are generated annually in the United States and about 80% of it is disposed of improperly, according to the *Environmental Business Journal*.[2] The volume of improperly disposed of used motor oil in the U.S. is the equivalent of 16 *Exxon Valdez* oil spills per year. Most of it ends up in sewage and drainage systems that ultimately enter the oceans.

U.S. municipal solid waste generation and carbon monoxide emissions have declined since 1982 and 1976, respectively, but pesticide use in agriculture continues at an ever-increasing rate. On a scale of 100 in 1975, municipal solid waste generation grew to 110 in 1982 and then declined to 100 again by 1990. Carbon monoxide emissions, on the other hand, decreased from 100 in 1975 to 91 in 1982 and 76 in 1990. But pesticide use grew from 100 in 1975 to 107 in

[2] *Environmental Business Journal* (Washington DC, Editorial comment, Jan. 1992).

1982 and then to 132 in 1990. Much of these pesticides ultimately wash into the oceans.

Land-based sources contribute three to four times as much oil to marine pollution as do ships and other marine activities, and although pollution by ships and offshore oil production is on the decline, that of land-based sources continues to increase.

Accidents (ships and offshore oil) contribute about 15% to total marine oil pollution and only about 5% of the total oil input to the sea. But massive concentrated releases of oil, such as from large ship accidents, have a much greater effect on the oceans than low-concentration operational discharges.

2.6.1 Transfer of Biological Poison

Scientists have known for centuries that human and animal populations in one part of the world can be decimated by the transfer of viruses and bacteria from other parts against which those populations have not developed an immunity. But only recently has research shown similar developments in the oceans. Australian research, for example, discovered that poisoning of marine organisms in Tasmanian waters was caused by the discharge of ballast water that ships had taken on in Japanese coastal waters. As yet, there is not much evidence of the transfer of biological poisons, but discoveries of red tide and other toxic developments in marine organisms in previously unaffected areas as well as new epidemics affecting marine species as never before give increasing weight to the theory that transfer of chemically or biologically polluted waters by ballast transfer may do much more damage than ever assumed.

2.6.2 Radioactive Wastes and the Oceans

Disposal of nuclear wastes in the oceans is becoming an increasingly critical issue, primarily because there are not many alternative disposal sites. Since World War II, over 1,200 nuclear tests have been conducted throughout the world, generating a large amount of nuclear waste material. Similarly, the 500 nuclear generators and power reactors in operation in 39 countries and the estimated 50,000 weapons deployed in 24 countries generate spent fuel rods and all kinds of other nuclear waste material.

Between 1946 and 1970, the United States alone dumped 107,000 containers of waste with estimated total activity of 4.3×10^{15} Bq.

(A Bq is a unit of radioactivity; 1 Bq = 1 nuclear disintegration per sec = 27.03×10^{-12} curies). Much of this material was deposited in U.S. coastal waters. Since then dumping of radioactive waste in U.S. coastal waters was discontinued.

Discharges of nuclear fuel from Europe are in the Atlantic Ocean at 45°50′N–46°10′N and 16°00′W–17°30′W, at a depth of 4,400 m. Little is known about the quantities deposited so far, but considering the size of the European nuclear industry, the quantities should be similar to those in U.S. coastal waters. It is estimated that the total α radiation-emitters worldwide (1967–1979) is 3.1×10^{15} Bq. The total β- and α-radiation emitters (excluding α-radiation) is 9.5×10^{15} Bq, and the total $\alpha = 9.7 \times 10^{15}$ Bq.

Radionucleotides of the earth's crust are transported to the ocean by runoff and winds and are often seeping upward through cracks in the seafloor. Similarly, cosmic activity produces radioactive elements that often find their way to the ocean by wet or dry precipitate. In addition, continental runoff is an important route for transferring water-soluble radioactive substances from the atmosphere into the ocean via rain.

Proposals for packaging of low-level radioactive wastes for sea disposal abound. Such disposal was a routine practice in the United States and most developed countries. The United States used canisters made of metals or alloys that resist corrosion and thermal damage for this purpose.

Some countries (the United States, France, Germany, Sweden, and others) have stopped the practice, but some continue to dispose of nuclear waste of low concentration in the oceans, particularly if such waste is "safely" shielded and diffused by binding it in matrices of cement or concrete. These matrices are then contained in a metal or reinforced concrete box and disposed of in the oceans, usually in special-prepared disposal pits that are then filled with a thick layer of sand or gravel.

One argument for the disposal of low-level radioactive material in the oceans is that seawater already contains a large amount of radioactivity (an estimated 5×10^4 curies) to which, by now, some hundreds of megacuries (1×10^8) have been added by nuclear explosions, as well as a few megacuries (1×10^6) by nuclear operations. It is therefore argued that nuclear waste disposal in the oceans can be effectively managed and, if properly diluted and diffused, that nuclear wastes cause no real increase in the ocean's radioactivity.

High-level radioactive wastes cannot be disposed of in the

TABLE 2–16 High-Level Radioactive Waste

TYPE	TOTAL AMOUNTS UPPER LIMIT (ci/y)	IAEA RECOMMENDED LIMITS (ci/ton)	IAEA SECRETARIAT LIMITS (ci/ton)	HALF-LIFE
α-emitters	10^5	1	10^{-2}	Very long
β- and γ-emitters	10^7	10^2	1	More than 6 months
Tritium and β-emitters	10^{11}	10^6	10^5	Less than 6 months

oceans in any form of containment and dilution. These are defined by the International Atomic Energy Agency (IAEA) in three categories as shown in Table 2–16, which shows that the IAEA limits recommended by its experts and its secretariat differ.

2.6.3 Ocean Pollution by Poisonous Algae

Toxic algae that are hazardous both to humans and fish often grow in oceans. In the North and Baltic Seas, for example, massive growths of blooms of planktonic (single-cell organisms) algae occur frequently and on several occasions have caused mass death of fish and other marine life. These algae also started to occur more frequently than usual along the North American Atlantic shores. There one alga is known as the "red tide" because of the discoloration of the water caused by it. Mussels, shellfish, and other seafoods that survive red tide are usually tainted by the toxicity, making them unsafe for human consumption.

Toxic algae is also a great threat to aquaculture and often causes havoc with marine farms. The growth of toxic algae is affected by the direction and strengths of ocean currents and the magnitude of land runoffs, particularly if these contain nitrogen nutrients from agriculture.

Large concentrations of such pollutants encourage the proliferation of toxic algae and similar growths that can disappear if the inflows are temporary and if there are adequate current movements. They often stay for long periods of time, however, particularly if nitrogen nutrient inflow continues consistently into stagnant waters.

3

Impact of Ocean Environmental Degradation

The various sources of ocean pollution deposit huge volumes of substances into the sea, and different substances have different impacts. Some cause temporary degradation but are absorbed biologically or chemically without any permanent detrimental effect. Others cause damage to marine life, marine fauna, and the physical marine environment, reducing it or making it nonusable. Some introduce radical permanent damage to the ocean's chemistry and physics. Although degradation is usually localized, it can become quite general such as in the Aral, Caspian, Mediterranean, and Baltic Seas, which in recent years have all been severely degraded or damaged. In the case of the Aral Sea, degradation may actually cause the complete destruction of the sea; since 1950, the sea has lost 60% of its water content, and it now contains largely brine. In some cases, all marine life—except the most primitive—is extinct. The pollutants introduced by the different sources can be divided into the following major categories:

1. *Sewage:* Sewage and oxygen-demanding wastes consist largely of carbonaceous organic material that can be oxidized to carbon dioxide and water. A standard test used is bio-

chemical oxygen demand (BOD), which measures (in mg/l) the amount of dissolved oxygen required to oxidize the material over a 5-day period. Septic conditions are low if O_2 is dissolved. Fully saturated H_2O has DO = 0.2 mg/l (at a temperature of 20°C). Chemical oxygen demand (COD) measures the amount of dissolved O_2 used to oxidize organic compounds that are not biologically degradable.

These pollutants produce odor, affect aquatic life, impair water supplies, produce scum, and prohibit the recreational use of coastal waters. Industrial water pollution from water-using factories discharging BOD load is estimated to be three to four times the load from sewered population discharges. Similarly, agricultural wastewater pollution from sediments, fertilizers, and farm and animal wastes causes a large amount of organic material discharge into the sea.

2. *Infectious agents:* Wastewater from municipalities, sanatoriums, slaughtering plants, and boats are sources of infectious agents such as bacteria and microorganisms.

3. *Exotic organic chemicals:* Surfactants in detergents, pesticides, various industrial products, or decomposition products, or in other organic composition of 1 part per million of phenol are toxic to fish. Many new chemicals are introduced each year without much knowledge of their effects on natural ecosystems.

4. *Inorganic material in water:* A number of industrial processes use mercury, which is disposed in effluents. Bacteria can convert it to CH_3Hg, which leads to mercury poisoning.

   When oil is drilled, brine is used in the operation in quantities three times amount of crude oil produced. Brine dumped into the sea contains large amounts of inorganic materials. Similarly, exposed coal mines come into contact with water and minerals containing sulfur from sulfuric acid and drain. Coal mines, particularly surface mines, wash the coal and drain the water into rivers and seas. Another important source is salt used on roads and sidewalks in winter, which also washes into rivers and seas.

5. *Radioactive substances:* Materials resulting from wastes of uranium, thorium mining, and refining from nuclear power plants are yet another source of ocean pollution.

6. *Detergents:* Surfactants used in detergents lower surface tension, thereby raising a detergent's ability to rise to the surface interface. The detergent then exchanges with the dirt, (surfactants are hydrophilic and soluble in H_2) plus oily or lipophilic groups. Commonly used surfactants are:
   (a) Anionic surfactants are alkyl benzene sulfonates or linear alkyl sulfonates (negative-ion surf).
   (b) Cationic surfactants are quaternary ammonium salts.
   (c) Nonionic synthetics are polyoxyethylene nonylphenol.
   Similarly large amounts of phenol, cyanides, and ammonium compounds are discharged into the oceans. Also, wastewaters from the phosphate industry contain elemental phosphorus.
7. *Rubber and plastic wastes:* Rubber and plastic wastes contain butadiene, styrene coagulated with acid brine solutions, and hydrocarbons, which all severely impact the oceans.
8. *Acidic wastes:* Wastes from metal industries—from coking coal, washing blast furnace flue gases, and pickling steel—are often drained into the seas. Such wastes are acidic and are loaded with cyanogen, phenol, ore, coke, limestone, alkali, oils, mill scale, and suspended solids.

Similarly, sediments that contain large amounts of excess nutrients or biologically contaminated materials, that are simply excessive, that grossly permeate ocean waters, or that cause large-scale turbidity serve as major pollutant factors and disturb or destroy the ocean's ecological balance.

Large-scale chemical, physical, and biological imbalances of any kind will cause environmental degradation and will reduce the productive capabilities of the oceans. Dredging, coastal development, reclamation, and similar activities can also cause severe ocean or coastal environmental degradation, not only by burying marine breeding grounds and other ocean-bottom biological activity and increasing the turbidity of the waters, but also as the result of high levels of toxins or other environmental poisons in the dredge spoils.

Although oil and other hydrocarbons are the most commonly identified pollutants, they are not the most dangerous or long-term toxic chemicals. Other pollutants have much more pronounced environmental impacts. Ocean environmental degradation affects all the different uses and resources of the oceans and ultimately may affect the biological, chemical, and physical balance of this globe. This planet depends on sensitive relations between land, air, and water to sustain life.

Accidental oil spills and their effects on fisheries, wildlife, and recreation may be among the most visible ocean environmental impacts, but there are many pollutants with much larger impacts. The principal sources of marine pollution and their effects are shown in Table 3–1.

The virtual elimination of marine life and related biological activity in the Aral Sea, or more recently in the Baltic, is not the result of accidental oil spills or other environmental casualties. Instead, the problems were caused by the sustained degradation of the ocean or water quality by a reduction in oxygen, a deviation of freshwater and sediment inflows, an addition of massive pollutants and excess nutrient inflows, and other gradual developments. For example, the eastern Mediterranean has suffered from a lack of sediment and nutrient inflows from the Nile River since the construction of the Aswan Dam. This, by the way, not only resulted in a reduction of fish growth but also of the fertility of Nile delta lands, which rely on irrigation by Nile water, for agricultural use.

3.1 DEGRADATION OF RECREATIONAL USES

The use of the oceans, particularly their coastal zones, for recreation has escalated to an extent where well over 30% of tourist and recreational expenditures today are related to ocean recreational or tourism activities. Cruising is a $24.8 billion industry, and coastal boating (including sport fishing) accounts for another $39 billion a year worldwide now. The coastal resort and hotel business in the United States alone is estimated to have revenues of well over $38 billion a year; worldwide the figure is nearly $100 billion.

The value of the use of the oceans for recreation and related activities worldwide now accounts for well over $250 billion per year, or about 30% of all recreational costs. The quality of the ocean environment has a major effect on recreational uses that, in many cases, provide the principal source of income (and employment). This is particularly true on islands, such as many island nations in the Caribbean Sea and South Pacific and Indian Oceans.

The impact of the ocean environment may affect not only the health and viability of ocean-related recreational uses, but also transportation and other support industries indirectly. Recreation and

TABLE 3–1 Sources and Effects of the Principal Marine Pollutants

TYPE OF POLLUTANT	PRINCIPLE SOURCES	ENVIRONMENTAL EFFECTS	EFFECTS ON LIVING RESOURCES
Organic wastes, including pathogens	Discharge of untreated or partially treated domestic wastewaters into rivers, estuaries, and the sea; some contribution from agricultural runoff and industrial watewaters	Polluted bathing beaches, inshore waters, and bays; organic deposits in bays and sea bottom, including seagrass beds; increased turbidity; reduced oxygen levels in water; damage to wetlands and submerged vegetation	Human disease, including typhoid, eye and skin infections, polio, cholera, and hepatitis A; contamination of shellfish
Excessive nutrients, including phosphates and nitrates	Agricultural runoff (fertilizers) and domestic wastewater (detergents) discharged into rivers, estuaries, and the sea	Eutrophication of lagoons, bays, and semienclosed gulfs, often manifested by excessive growth of algae; red and green tides; fouling of beaches by decomposing algae	Death of aquatic life owing to lack of oxygen in water; dermatitis from contact with toxic algae. (If properly dispersed, nutrients can be beneficial to fisheries.)
Industrial chemicals (heavy metals, organic chemicals, and the like)	Discharge of untreated or partially treated industrial wastewaters into rivers, estuaries, and the sea; some contribution from domestic wastewater, urban runoff, solid wastes, and ship discharge; diffuse input into the air from industrial sources on a continental scale	Locally high concentration in sediments and seawater	Accumulation in shellfish, fish, marine mammals, and birds of mercury (from chlor-alkali plants and natural sources), cadmium (from electroplating and other industries), and other metals and persistent organic chemicals; potential health hazards for human consumers

TABLE 3–1 Continued

TYPE OF POLLUTANT	PRINCIPLE SOURCES	ENVIRONMENTAL EFFECTS	EFFECTS ON LIVING RESOURCES
Pesticides and other agricultural chemicals	Agricultural runoff into rivers and estuaries; some contribution from airborne fallout	Polluted inshore waters and bays; deposits in bays and sea bottom, including seagrass beds; damage to wetlands and submerged vegetation	Accumulation of DDT and other persistent organics in fish, birds, and mammals, causing hazards to predatory birds; fish kills and hazards to humans as a result of local concentrations of organophosphates
Petroleum hydrocarbons	Discharge from ships and from shore facilities; some contribution from industrial and urban sources by way of rivers, urban runoff, and direct discharge	Oil slicks on water; tarballs on beaches; tainted seafood; tar stains on clothing, surfaces, boats, and so on	Tar on bathers' skin; injury to fish and marine mammals; death of seabirds
Litter, including plastics, floating debris, and organic materials	Coastal dumps, discharge from ships, local dumping on shores by tourists and residents; some contribution from agriculture and fisheries	Floating and suspended litter in water; accumulation of aesthetically offensive litter on beaches and in harbors; clogged intakes of power plants and desalinization facilities	Death of fish, turtles, birds, and marine mammals owing to ingestion and entanglement
Silt and mining wastes	Erosion of poorly conserved agricultural soils, deforested hillsides, mine tailings, and metal-rich soils	Siltation of lagoons and coastal waters; increased turbidity; elevated levels of mercury and other metals near mining areas	Loss of productive wetlands in lagoons and deltas; accumulation of mercury in fish, with health risks to consumers of large amounts of fish

SOURCE: H. S. Peters, "A Framework for Environmental Assessment in the Maritime Industries," World Bank Report 18–91.

tourism usually generate greater economic spin-offs than other economic activities and therefore have a greater effect on job creation and economic development, particularly in developing countries.

For many countries, recreation and tourism have not only become a major economic sector but often contribute significantly to foreign exchange earnings and employment. Worldwide recreation and tourism have grown at a rate of nearly 8.8% per year, or well over twice the rate of economic growth. A very substantial proportion of new recreational and tourist developments are oriented towards the use of the coastal zone and the oceans. Yet recreation and tourism are very fragile economic activities that can suffer long-term damage when the environment on which they are based is degraded. The control of environmental quality is most important, not only because the recreation and tourism industry is very competitive, with many locations offering similar advantages, but also because it is an activity of choice, not need, and people's selection is based largely on qualitative judgment and reputation. For example, a beach resort along a shore even temporarily polluted by sewage, other outflows, or floating debris may take years to regain its tourism market share.

Recreation and tourism have become particularly important for many developing countries in North Africa, the Caribbean, the South Pacific, and Southeast Asia. Most of this new industry, which often provides an important—if not dominating—contribution to the national economy, is coastal zone or ocean based. The maintenance of the ocean environment is therefore of great importance to developing countries and to many others that are quite unfamiliar with and unprepared for effective ocean environmental management.

As a result of uncontrolled algae growth, low- or high-intensity outflows of sewage or toxins, or persistent bottom deposits, coastal pollution may affect recreational use for long periods. There are many examples of continued impact, years after the basic source of coastal pollution was eliminated. Furthermore, coastal pollution can affect the coastal material balance. Beach nourishing or decretion and coastal boundary flows, which in turn may cause bottom scouring, also affect an ocean environment.

Offshore ocean pollution affects sailing and other offshore recreational uses of the oceans, such as sports fishing and boating. Ocean pollution may cause odors that make coastal areas unattractive and sometimes even uninhabitable, even though those areas often constitute the most valuable land.

The degree of environmental degradation depends on many factors and can be expressed in terms of recreational use degradation, economic value degradation, and social and development opportunity degradation. These are usually interdependent and affect each other.

Recreational use degradation implies the reduction of effective use that can be made for the principal purposes of the coastal area. Economic degradation is often a consequence of use degradation. In recreational terms, a small use degradation will usually cause an even larger economic value degradation, which in turn causes an even larger social and development opportunity degradation.

For example, a thriving beach resort infested by a flood of sewage resulting from a breakdown in an adjacent treatment plant may cause a temporary and quite local reduction of water and beach quality for recreational uses. These in turn may cause a percentage of normal users to depart or to not use the facility at all. The maintenance of baseload may require large discounting, which will reduce revenue disproportionately. At the same time, cleanup and containment will increase operating costs. Similarly, the value of development opportunities will decrease out of proportion of the environmental damage, even if the damage is only temporary.

Coastal pollution also affects beaches themselves, not only because of high levels of bacteria in water and noxious or sewage pollutants, but also as a result of solid and liquid wastes deposited on the beach itself. Most recently, medical waste has become an ocean beach pollution hazard that causes damage well beyond the immediate disposal site.

Ocean wastes disposed on beaches are often very persistent and not readily removed. Changes in the coastline or coastal bottom profile as well as various types of construction near shore or offshore often cause beach erosion, decretion, or simply changes in the beach physics that make such land less desirable or usable for recreational purposes.

Solid waste or litter is not only aesthetically unattractive; these wastes often dissolve, ooze chemicals, and deteriorate. They also settle on the ocean bottom, covering benthic communities and disturbing the substrata. This can lead to anoxia at the sediment surface. Similarly, litter and debris affect sediment movement on the ocean bottom.

Ocean littering has become a serious problem not only in coastal areas near major urban centers; today it is prevalent in many areas. Recreational boating is an increasingly important contributor. It is estimated that over 3.8 million tons, or 4%, of the total litter disposed in the oceans is caused by recreational boating.

The total impact of pollution on recreation worldwide is hard to determine. Yet it is increasingly evident that environmental degradation can have a devastating effect on the economics of coastal vacation areas. In a typical situation, an accidental discharge of sewage at a beach resort made the use of the beaches for swimming and water sports impossible for about a year and caused occupancy in hotels and motels to drop immediately from 85% to less than 40%; occupancy stayed at less than 60% of the normal level for nearly 3 years. The total loss in this area, with a normal tourist trade revenue from coastal recreation of about $400 million per year, dropped to less than 40% of that immediately. In this situation, the loss in Net Present Value (NPV) terms until the area recouped its normal level of tourist trade was in excess of $500 million, about ten times the cost of installing an effective treatment plant at the outset.

The effects of pollution on ocean recreation are mounting worldwide and are estimated to cost $268 billion, or nearly $20 billion per year today, an amount that is expected to rise unless radical measures are taken to prevent or reduce coastal pollution. In some areas, to assure a safe environment and reliable tourist trade, tourist industries are moving into artificial coastal recreational environments, such as contained or artificial lagoons with artificial waves, at great expense, but this is obviously not a large-scale or a long-term solution, particularly as demand for coastal recreation accelerates all over the world.

Beach or coastal erosion or accretion from changes in the coastal topography caused by humans result in further coastal environmental problems, when beaches vanish, protective dunes or dikes are penetrated or washed away. Conversely, deposits of large volumes of sediment can transform a coastal resort into a landlocked resort in a matter of a few years.

The economic and social impacts of the effects of coastal pollution on recreation are difficult to determine quantitatively. In addition to direct economic losses such as lost revenues are many secondary effects or spin-offs such as job loss, relocation of people, and evaporation of the economy. A number of studies have been undertaken to determine the value of effective coastal zone management in which a whole array of costs and benefits are considered. Several approaches to modeling the effect of ocean environmental management are presented in Chapter 7. All indicate the difficulty of not only identifying, but of quantifying, costs and benefits and of establishing their interdependence.

3.2 DEGRADATION OF OCEAN RESOURCE EXPLOITATION

Although ocean pollution affects the exploitation of the oceans for food, such as fish, shellfish, and ocean vegetation, the production of other resources is affected as well. In some activities, such as the mining of sand or gravel for construction or fill, the relation between pollution and value of production is direct; polluted construction material has little or no value. Similarly, the value of ocean water used for cooling and process purposes is decreased if it is polluted or oily. In fact, such water may not only be useless; it also may damage heat exchangers in power or process plants. Distillation of ocean water is greatly affected by pollution. Some ocean uses are only indirectly affected by ocean pollution, such as transportation. Transportation is affected because ships use ocean waters for cooling in their power plant and hotel services, as well as in freshwater distillation. Although many resource exploitation activities, such as offshore oil production and deep-water mining, are not affected by pollution itself, they have become unknowing accessories because existing pollution may in part be blamed on or related to these activities.

3.2.1 Effect on Fisheries and Aquaculture

Ocean pollution has had a devastating effect on fisheries and aquaculture in many parts of the world. In fact, fish consumption has become a real or potential health hazard in many places, even in such high-income countries as the United States and Japan, as a result of ocean pollution. Ocean pollution affects fish in many ways and often influences significant parts of the marine food chain.

The seafood chain is dependent on energy flows up trophic levels. Bioaccumulation primarily affects seafood consumed by humans. This constitutes the top of the seafood chain and is most adversely affected by high concentrations of pollutants that increasingly reach detrimental levels and cause toxic effects. This comes at a time when seafood consumption continues to grow. As a result, the seafood (fishing and aquaculture) industry continues to grow, with Japan leading in seafood and seafood-processing technology. For example, Japan is developing protein-rich products made from mechanically deboned fish that have a similar taste and texture as shellfish. Other food sources being developed use products that were previously wasted in fish processing.

By increasing the direct or assumed health hazards posed by seafood consumption, ocean pollution has detrimentally affected the development of this increasingly profitable and important industry. In addition, oil spills, surface pollution intrusion, and other developments have greatly affected the size and the quality of fish catches. Important plants and algae living on the seabed, particularly in coastal habitats and breeding areas, have often been destroyed by oil spills, dredging, dredge disposal, or other polluting activities. Health hazards to human seafood consumption consist of:

- pathogenic bacteria in shellfish, causing human illness or death;
- diarrhetic shellfish poisoning (DSP), a toxin made from dinoflagellates;
- numbness or loss of sensation caused by saxitoxin (another marine toxin);
- blooms of diatoms, which cause a concentration of domoic acid in mussels and is said to have caused death and illness in some humans who consume mussels
- fish made smelly and tough by the aromatic hydrocarbons in oil; and
- free radicals, which cause oxidation of fatty acids in fish to produce aldehydes.

In addition, pollution (including oil spills) affects breeding and spawning grounds.

Fishing and related activities are more sensitive to ocean pollution, even if the pollution is localized, than most other activities. Ingested pollutants will often be carried and spread over large areas and thereby will infect fishing or mariculture over a much larger area than that affected by the original pollution.

Furthermore, pollution-caused damage usually passes through the whole food chain and may affect many generations over a long period. Similarly, breeding and nursery grounds, migratory patterns of species that traverse polluted waters, and unique habitats are affected.

Ocean pollution creates long-term exposure to benthic systems. To determine biological effects of ocean pollution, chronic bioassays are usually used. Field bioassays should preferably be carried out on the natural population. Bioassay measurement of short- and long-term effects should be supplemented by bioaccumulation studies of the effect of specific elements on compounds of organisms. This should particularly be done in fish used as human food.

Fish require oxygen, which as shown in Figure 3–1 is introduced by photosynthesis as well as by discharges into the oceans. Large volumes of sediment or turbidity in the near-surface waters can greatly reduce the effectiveness of solar radiation and oxygen production, which in turn affect fish breeding and growth.

There is now pervasive evidence showing the effects of polluting materials on the reproductive behavior and physiology of marine life and its growth, health, and survival. Although most serious pollution is still isolated in some areas of the world, there is now an increased risk of widespread pollution with a related danger of extinction of some fish or marine species, and alteration of others.

Toxic chemical buildup in sediment that saturates many ocean

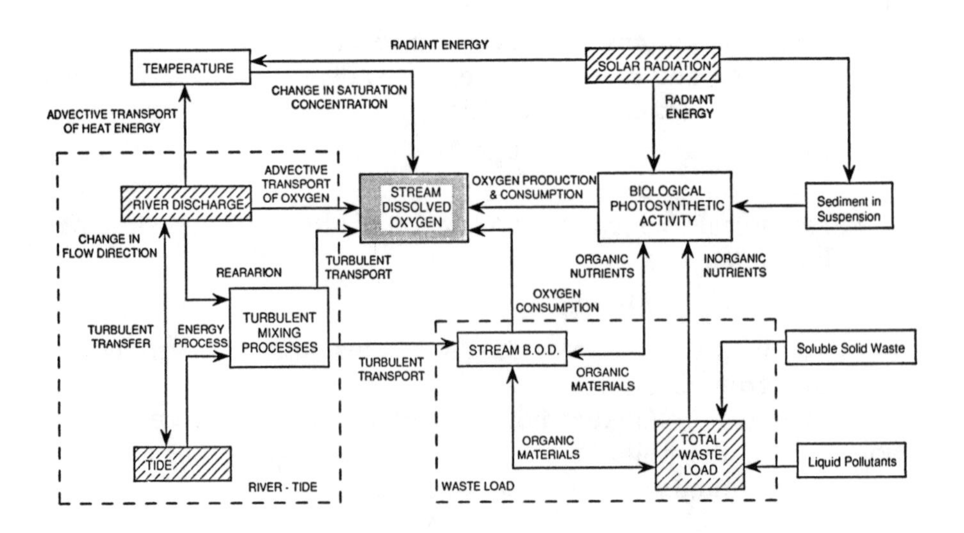

Figure 3–1 Factors affecting dissolved oxygen concentration in coastal waters while impeding fish breeding and growth.

waters has grown and is persistent, particularly in coastal waters where it is often mixed with other chemical and fertilizer intrusion through runoff. At the same time, these are particularly fertile, yet sensitive, areas that also provide the bulk of world fishing resources.

Overfishing, natural phenomena, and other factors influence fish population as well. In many parts of the world, and particularly in coastal areas, pollution has had severe effects on the size of fish population, on the health of fish, and on the size and reproduction capacity of fish. It is estimated that pollution and related environmental impacts account for at least half the reduction in catches worldwide, but much more in local areas, such as the Baltic, Black, and Mediterranean Seas where pollution from humans accounts for basically all the reductions in catches. In fact, in the case of the Baltic Sea, the catch is very low indeed.

The total impact of pollution on fishing worldwide is difficult to determine or even estimate in monetary terms, particularly because fish populations and fish catches are affected by many developments in addition to pollution caused by fishing. One estimate, however, is that the reduction in the value of fish catch caused by pollution is about $16 billion per year, a figure derived from extrapolating fish population growth and fish catch between 1930 and 1962 and today, based on the assumption that most ocean pollution occurred since 1962.

The determination of the cost of pollution on fish production, such as fisheries and resource economics, is usually addressed in capital theoretic terms (or a capital theory) in which fish population or biomass is considered the capital stock that is assumed to be capable of yielding sustainable consumption or production over time. Fishery management traditionally addresses fish production problems by determining their impact on the stock level, considering reproduction rates as affected by environmental condition. This is a dynamic problem in which changes in consumption as well as in the environment affect both future consumption or production volumes. Although environmental conditions were assumed to change slowly and in general to support or at least not affect fish population growth, their impact in the past was assumed to be only gradual and not very important over the short run.

The increasing rate of ocean pollution combined with excessive fish harvesting have radically altered the equation. Now the environmental impact of ocean pollution has become an important factor in determining sustainable fish production. The use of the capital theory cast as a dynamic resource production, growth, replenishment, and destruction or depletion model in recent years has been found to be an effective approach to estimating the cost of ocean pollution, at least in defined seas such as the Baltic and Mediterranean.[1]

According to the U.N. Food and Agriculture Organization (1992), the cost of catching the $70 billion worth of fish in the world's oceans is in excess of $124 billion. The difference is largely met by government subsidies and losses by fishers. This is a recent phenomena; fishing was both abundant and profitable until quite recently. Overfishing, lack of effective management of fishing resources, and most importantly the effects of ocean pollution are the attributed causes of this.

As lack of controls and management of fish resources spreads to as yet unaffected and abundant fishing grounds and as pollution of coastal breeding grounds continues at an accelerating rate, the situation is expected to worsen. The pressure for increased fish production is mounting, not only in response to population growth but also as a result of the search for potentially lower-cost and healthier sources of protein.

World protein production has fallen behind population growth, and commercial fish farming is hoped to make up the difference. Fish farming is expected to provide a more efficient method for the production of protein than farming of beef, pork, and poultry, if the fish can be protected from pollution.

3.2.2 Environmental Degradation by Port Activities

Physical activities in port construction and operations may cause chemical, biological, hydrodynamic, geologic, and other impacts that contribute to ecological problems in the port area. These problems may impact the effective use of the port, related facilities, and both adjacent ocean and land areas. Preventive measures, if they can be used to reduce environmental impact, are usually more desirable than reactive containment and cleanup, but the probability of ecological damage resulting from unexpected accidents or exposure will always remain. It is exceedingly difficult to quantify the effects

[1]C. W. Clark and G. R. Munroes, "The Economics of Fishing and Modern Capital Theory: A Simplified Approach," *Journal of Environmental Economics and Management* 2 (1975):92–106.

and probability occurrence of the different potential environmental impacts caused by ports. They usually depend on some of the following factors:

1. local physical conditions such as currents, water, depth, wind, wind and current direction, salinity, solids in suspension, seabed or inlet formation, and air and water temperatures;
2. chemical and physical properties as well as the form of cargoes handled;
3. configuration of port facilities;
4. rate of emission, propagation, or intensity of ecological factors such as pollutants and sediment movement;
5. methods of cargo handling, transfer, and storage;
6. interface and feeder technology;
7. operational policies; and
8. social environment.

Most of these factors are independent and vary with time.

Oil spills, leakages, or other voluntary or involuntary discharges of oil substances are probably the most significant and environmentally objectionable emissions. They occur as a result of ship accidents such as groundings, hose ruptures, ineffective pipe disconnections, and tank or hose leakages.

Oil spills are generally classified as chronic or catastrophic. A chronic oil spill is one with nearly continuous, low-level discharges, such as hose or pipe leakage. A catastrophic spill denotes a single spill of major proportions, such as one that might result from a tanker grounding or collision. Obviously, many occurrences that are difficult to quantify fall between these two general definitions. Either type of spill can result in the same overall discharge. Distribution of concentrations may differ widely even among spills of the same type and magnitude.

The toxicity of crude petroleum and other possible discharges depends on the source. Source-related variations occur in physical and chemical properties such as acidity, volatility, boiling point, and viscosity. These variations account for the differing impact of oil pollution: the contrasting widespread destructive effects on marine life in some cases compared with a lesser effect and rapid regeneration of marine life.

In the past, port developments and operations have degraded

the port's waters. Because most ports are located in sheltered bays or estuaries, such degradation has often caused serious secondary effects to groundwater, quality, recreation, the coastal zone, and inshore fisheries. Particularly damaging is usually the persistent effect of repeated operational oil spills.

The physical and chemical effects of such oil spills depend largely on the environmental conditions of the locality, the rate of spilling, and the following:

1. **Surface Effects**

   - Surface tension effect on wave motion and two-phase or air and water interphase, including the effect on oxygen content of subsurface water.
   - Effect on surfacing or surface using marine and bird life. (Clinging to wings causing death of seabirds by coating and so on.)
   - Corrosion effects on surface piercing and floating structures.
   - Shore and floating-body coating.
   - Aesthetics.
   - Effects on near-shore aquaculture.
   - Effects on hydrodynamics (water motion, waves, and so forth).

2. **Above-Surface Effects**

   - Air pollution and odors resulting from volatility, flammability, toxicity, and corrosiveness of resulting gases.
   - Corrosion effects on above-surface (solid or floating) structures.
   - Fire hazards from volatile gases and flammability of lighter petroleum components.

3. **Subsurface Effects**

   - Corrosive effect on submerged structures.
   - Salutive and coagulating effects, especially of hydrocarbons and soluble impurities that affect water chemistry.
   - Effects on subsurface water motion resulting from changes in viscosity, surface tension, and so on.

If the oil spilled contains tar and heavy components, it will settle on the bottom and cause continuous impacts.

Serious environmental impacts are also caused by port construction and particularly by capital and maintenance dredging. This not only causes polluted soil to be excavated and often deposited in an area where it may bury breeding grounds and pollute or even poison bottom conditions, but the dredging and dredge disposal process itself often causes large amounts of polluted spoils to go into suspension in the surrounding waters.

Another issue is spillage or leakage of dry or liquid cargoes, on piers and in port storage areas, that drain or are washed into port waters. Similarly, ships in port discharge effluents and often waste or sewage, and even though this practice is unlawful, some port approaches are difficult to police. Port pollution also often includes hazardous or poisonous materials dropped or spilled into port waters.

Because most port waters are contained and often nearly stagnant bodies of coastal waters, the effects of pollution sometimes build up and reach dangerous levels of concentration. This not only causes extinction of all marine life in such waters but also makes it hazardous for other purposes. For example the use of the waters for process or cooling may not be viable because of the water's corrosive properties.

In the United States, where most ports (84%) are located in river estuaries or bays, most port waters are severely polluted. Boston, in Massachusetts Bay, used to have the distinction of the most polluted body of coastal water in the United States. This has now changed, and the water quality in Boston Harbor has significantly improved as a result of a determined and costly cleanup supplemented by strict enforcement of inflow restrictions.

Pollution of port waters is often greatly increased by the discharges from port-related industries that locate adjacent to the port, such as petrochemical and other material processing plants. In the Mediterranean, for example, recent investigations show that most pollution originates in port waters. Ports are often located in densely populated urban areas, and in fact a majority of the major cities of the world grew around ports, so the quality of coastal ocean waters is often severely affected by ports. As a result, the use of coastal waters for cooling, processing, fishing, and recreation is severely constrained in many port cities, as may be the use of construction material such as sand and gravel if mined from polluted port waters. Similarly, port-related industries may discharge toxins or chemicals that affect the smell of the water.

The degradation by ports of coastal water, bays, or estuaries on which they are usually located has become so serious that many ports have been forced or elected to move to alternative sites that, in an increasing number of cases, are now artificial reclaimed offshore islands. Some major Japanese ports, such as Kobe, Osaka, Yokohama, and Tokyo, have all been relocated to offshore islands. Rotterdam, New York City, and other ports have moved principal activities to open sites away from major population concentrations.

Because most (about 80%) coastal cities with populations in excess of 100,000 are port cities, and because nearly half the world's urban population resides in coastal cities, water pollution by ports and related activities affects a large proportion of the world's population in many ways. Waterfront and marine construction of piers, breakwaters, and seawalls and land reclamation cause major changes not only in the bottom contour and water and sediment flow demand, but also affect breeding areas, distribution of settlement of sediment, bottom boundary conditions, and coastal currents. These changes are caused by introducing new structures or by removal of bottom material or deposition on the bottom. Unfortunately, in most port areas spoils dredged up or deposited are often highly polluted or even toxic. For example, according to the Environmental Protection Agency (EPA), bottom materials at major U.S. ports and harbors contain large quantities of contaminants. Among these ports and pollutants are:

- Massachusetts Bay/Boston Harbor: organic materials;
- Charleston Harbor, South Carolina: dioxins;
- Chesapeake Bay, Maryland: polyaromatic hydrocarbons and PCBs;
- New Bedford Harbor, Massachusetts: PCBs and heavy metals;
- New York/New Jersey Harbor: PCBs, heavy metals, and DDT;
- San Francisco Bay, California: PCBs, heavy metals, and hydrocarbons; and
- Puget Sound, Washington: PCBs and heavy metals

In other words, the harbor and related coastal bottoms are highly contaminated, and any dredging or other submarine earthworks bring many of those contaminants into suspension, to the surface, or in contact with other soils.

Dredging always results in resettlement and suspension of sediments and coverage of marine breeding grounds. It may also result in increased saline intrusion into freshwater or groundwater. The volume of dredge spoil exceeds the volume of all other solid waste materials discharged into the ocean.

In the United States, with dredge spoils averaging 14.2–27.8 million tons per year (1980–1990), nearly one-third are estimated to have been polluted, based on measurement of sample compositions. Discharges from ships, both in terms of liquid and solid waste into the water, have been reduced significantly as a result of strict enforcement in major ports of developed countries, although they remain a major issue in the ports of some developing countries.

The major exception to discharge reduction is involuntary discharge of oil from loading and unloading operations (overflows, pipe ruptures, pipe disconnections, and so forth) and deck and other cleaning operations. Cracked and corroded tanks (both ship and shore storage tanks) also cause significant spillages.

Port operations also cause the deposition of solids or liquids from piers, docks, and storage areas washed into the water by rain, washdown, or drainage or carried by the air. Dry bulk commodities (cement, fertilizers, and so forth) usually emit thick dust clouds during cargo operations, with solids largely deposited on the surrounding water. Vessels and port equipment emit pollutants into the air as exhaust from engines, boilers, and motors.

The amount of pollutants discharged by a typical ship per day generating 400 kW during port operations is about 15 lb of CO, 50 lb of sulphur dioxide, and 120 lb of nitrogen oxides. Considering that ports often accommodate hundreds of ships at one time, the amount of air pollution generated becomes quite substantial.

In addition, ports often attract port-related industries that benefit from the association not only in terms of access to efficient transportation but also quite often attempt to use such colocation to discharge some of their environmental impacts.

3.2.3 Environmental Degradation by Ocean Mining

Activities involved in ocean mining affect the ocean environment in different ways. Exploration, construction of mining equipment and facilities, extraction, processing, and transportation (including transfer) influence the physical, biological, aesthetic, and chemical composition and balance of the ocean environment.

Although some explorations are purely passive, obtaining geophysical and geological information by seismic and similar techniques and involving simple towage of instrument assemblies, sensitive organisms may be harmed by high-intensity acoustic energy. Most environmental damage in mineral exploration is the result of explosive devices that are often used to reveal the structure of mineral deposition by seismic refraction. Bottom-surface testing and sampling, as well as soil coring, often harm benthic organisms and other bottom life.

The use of radioisotopes for sediment flow tracking and bottom sediment movements can harm benthic and pelagic organisms, and extraction is usually much more harmful to the ocean environment than tracking. Ocean mining usually consists of dislodgement, lifting, and then onboard preprocessing. Dislodgment, which can be performed by dredging bucket, bucket and ladder, or suction, or by dragline or drag bucket, affects the seafloor's protective layer and bathymetry. Dislodgment methods also generate large amounts of silt that is carried into suspension and that may cover large areas outside the immediate dredging or mining zone. In other words, dislodgment causes

- destruction of the active bottom layer,
- suspended solids and turbidity,
- oxygen reduction by sediment dispersion,
- nutrient dispersal,
- metal and pesticide release, and
- covering of marine organisms.

Various dredging methods cause different effects. Some methods involve deep holes or craters on the ocean floor that often fill with silt and clays and then possibly become anaerobic.

Ocean mining, particularly for sand and gravel, may reduce coastal accretion or erosion. The lifting of minerals will usually result in a large discharge of mineral dust or fines and other solids that cause sediment suspension and turbidity dispersion.

The lifting of mineral often involves a mixture of mineral and water or a slurry, and the water must be drained from the minerals before they can be preprocessed and stored on the vessel. This turbidity and silt release reduces sunlight penetration in the water column, which affects the amounts of phytoplankton and zooplankton.

Also, sediments discarded may absorb oxygen as they descend to the ocean bottom.

Trace metal and nutrients are similarly released from mining operations, but probably more so from trailings discharged into the water. The large clouds of descending sediment and fines have a very detrimental effect on marine organisms in the water column as well as on breeding activities on the ocean bottom.

Processing on board is often the most readily controllable, yet potentially most environmentally hazardous or impacting, of ocean mining operations. Few vessels have large tank capacities for the storage of waste, and as a result it is often discharged into the water. Some claim that the discharge of concentrated volumes of mineral processing waste is less damaging than descending sediment clouds, but investigations show that these wastes usually break up into sediment clouds anyway. As a result, mining sites often become waste sites in which all marine life is extinct, at least temporarily. For example, rock-handling processes, such as crushing, generate large amounts of suspended emissions that are usually dumped into the sea. Although ocean mining is still a rather small industry, the environmental effects are already noticeable in many parts of the world.

Ocean mining of minerals suspended in the sea is assuming some importance in some parts of the world. This activity can be severely affected by the presence of pollutants in the water. Extraction of suspended minerals is often a side product of freshwater distillation from seawater, performed on a large scale in many parts of the world. Both surface pollution, such as oil spills, and suspended or dissolved pollution affect the effectiveness of distillation and the quality of freshwater produced. As a result, coastal pollution can add appreciably to the cost of producing freshwater from the sea.

3.2.4 Effects of Port and Coastal Pollution on Mangroves and Beaches

One of the most effective methods of beach reconstruction and coastal rehabilitation is by mangrove trees, both natural and planted by humans, that not only stabilize the shore but prevent it from washing away. The roots of the mangroves not only capture sand, shells, and sediment but trap as well as reinforce the shore by root branch growth. Mangroves also build land and solidify it against attacks by waves and currents.

Mangroves also offer homes and shelter for many animals, such as crabs, oysters, and shrimp. Mangrove seeds sprout before dropping into the water and float until taking root in soils or even in floating sediment. They grow very quickly, often as much as 2 ft per year, if the environment is right and if the water and sediment are not polluted.

During recent years significant mangrove stands have been depleted both by humans (for fuel) and by pollution, which affected the nutrients in the sediment, altered the chemistry of the water, or affected the flow patterns. As a result, shorelines protected by mangroves in Southeast Asia, Africa, and some parts of South America are now eroding. This not only causes a loss of land and beaches but also results in a severe reduction of breeding ground and subsequently a reduced catch or production of shrimp, crabs, and other coastal seafood species.

3.3 THE COSTS OF OCEAN POLLUTION

Ocean pollution results in ever-increasing economic costs, many of which are deferred or cause delayed economic impacts but are economic costs nevertheless. Some, such as the cost of the loss of tourism and fish catch, can be estimated, and the added costs of mining for sand at remote versus nearby locations can be determined, but many costs can only be vaguely evaluated because the costs or disbenefits cannot be clearly identified or because they will only materialize at some future time. These costs also depend on future demands or uses of ocean resources by humans, on the development of technology for cost-effective ocean resource exploitation, and on the availability and cost of land-based resources that ocean resources will replace or substitute. There are also indirect and sometimes intangible costs, such as health effects, impacts on coastal air quality, smell, aesthetics of the ocean waters (such as color and surface conditions), and more. Although the cost of ocean pollution is in the hundreds of billions of dollars per year and growing in terms of actual definable losses, it is difficult to establish an accurate estimate of all the direct and indirect costs introduced.

4

Physical and Operational Ocean Pollution Prevention, Containment, and Cleanup

4.1 PHYSICAL OCEAN POLLUTION PREVENTION

Ocean pollution is produced by short-term point sources, such as a grounded tanker, or distributed sources, such as the temporary failure of an area's sewage treatment plants. Point sources can also be planned sources, such as power plants or industrial outflows. Similarly, unplanned, distributed sources, like the eruption of Mount Pinatubo, whose environmental effects were felt halfway around the world (although only for a short time), are distinct from long-term distributed sources, such as large river estuaries. For example, the Nile River carries pollutants into the sea for long periods of time.

Pollution sources can be specific and exude particular pollutants, or they may be general or diffused and emit a large variety of different pollutants. Pollution can be planned, accidental, and involuntary or unplanned. It may be part of a continuous operation or of a temporary, often unplanned, activity.

Ocean pollution occurs in a variety of forms, originates from many different sources, and assumes many characteristics. These all require different approaches to prevention, containment, and cleanup where possible. In recent years, attempts have been made to develop methods for pollution prevention as well as reduction and, where inevitable, for containment and cleanup. In this chapter some of the most important methods are described.

4.1.1 Prevention and Mitigation of Pollution by Port and Harbor Activities

Ports cause environmental impacts on the land, in the air, and in the water. Water impacts are caused by dredging, construction, ship discharges, spills, and operational damage. Land impacts may be caused by port-related industries located on or near the water, runoffs, waste spills, reclamation, and drainage, while air impacts are caused by fugitive emissions, hazardous materials and cargoes, ships' exhausts, other material handling, and cargo air emissions, as discussed in Chapter 5. Table 4–1 lists some mitigating measures proposed by a World Bank study group for each port or harbor activity with a potential ocean environmental impact.

Although many preventative or impact reducing measures have been introduced by the major ports in developed countries, ports and related activities continue to expose the ocean environment to many impacts. To prevent these impacts, port and harbors worldwide are now subjected to increasingly more stringent requirements that include

1. restriction of construction and dredging to environmentally safe waters using acceptable (nonpolluting) methods, materials, and equipment;
2. discharge ship wastes only into proper reception facilities equipped with effective treatment processes; and
3. perform cargo transfer or related operations in an environmentally acceptable manner that assures not only elimination of pollution (air and water) by the cargo transfer operations, but also elimination of pollution from post–cargo transfer cleanup activities.

In the United States, countries of Europe, and Japan, as well as in several other countries, ports must file an environmental impact statement and get approval for any dredging and construction proj-

TABLE 4–1 Environmental Impacts of Port and Harbor Facilities

POTENTIAL NEGATIVE IMPACTS	MITIGATING MEASURES
Direct	
1. Project location (e.g., enhancement or development of a waterway) may affect sensitive habitats and/or valuable fisheries resources or otherwise significantly degrade environmental quality.	1. Perform screening analysis of site environs and ecology and select an area that is not adjacent to sensitive habitat and would not displace valuable fisheries resources.
2. Repositioning of "null zone" in port vicinity.	2. Perform analyses to establish "controlling channel depth" that represents an equilibrium between flow-associated transport energy and sediment supply.
3. Removal and disturbance of flora and fauna at the dredging site.	3. Plan for minimizing impacts on local flora and fauna and screen for the presence of rare, threatened, or endangered species that are indigenous to the project location.
4. Interference of stationary dredging equipment with other maritime traffic	4. Prepare a program in advance to coordinate and reduce interference to other waterway users.
5. Possible disturbance or damage to stationary installation such as underwater cables, piplines, and outfalls.	5. • Identify and document locations of stationary installations. • Modify dredging process/disposal plans to accommodate presence of such structures.
6. Objectionable noise to nearby residents, especially at night.	6. Reduce noise level by decreasing operating level during quiescent periods in the local community.
7. Increased short-term turbidity at dredging site causing decreased light penetration and associated photosynthetic activity.	7. Reduce turbidity by efficient use of less intrusive dredging equipment, silt curtains, timing to coincide with low flow.
8. Alterations of bottom surface, which may be unfavorable to the success of indigenous benthic flora and fauna.	8. Plan for minimizing impact on important or sensitive benthic fauna and flora through ecological investigation during project planning.
9. Partitioning of natural and/or anthropogenic contaminants from sediments to the water column.	9. • Perform physical and chemical analysis of sediments prior to disturbance. • Locate potential "hot spots" and prepare plan to minimize sediment resuspension in these areas.

TABLE 4–1 Continued

POTENTIAL NEGATIVE IMPACTS	MITIGATING MEASURES
10. Modified bathymetry causing changes in tidal bore, river circulation, species diversity, and salinity.	10. Perform project area investigation, sampling, and characterization so project planning can yield a design that minimizes impacts.
11. Generation of turbidity plumes.	11. Use technologies such as temporary dams and/or barriers to lessen the transport of suspended material away from the project area.
12. Loss of shoreline integrity.	12. Evaluate shoreline geology and hydrology prior to project design to ensure deepening will not cause modifications such as slumping and increased erosion.
13. Upland disposal of dredged material would modify terrestrial habitat.	13. • Evaluate disposal options and select one with least impingement on important habitat. • Require reclamation plans for terrestrial sites.
14. Short-term sir quality degradation resulting from dredging-related operations.	14. Monitor local air quality and reduce operations if unacceptable quality arises.
15. Projects may result in stress on local cultures.	15. • Evaluate local sociocultural environment prior to project implementation. • Develop specific mitigation measures with community involvement.
16. Covering of potential archaeological sites with dredge spoil.	16. • Evaluate disposal area for presence of important artifacts. • Modify design or salvage or protect artifacts.
17. Spills associated with increased maritime commerce.	17. • Develop spill prevention and cleanup plans. • Train a team to handle spills.
18. Covering of valuable benthic species (e.g., mussels, clams) by sediment.	18. • Monitor turbidity and maintain concentration below 2 grams/liter. • Limit dredging activity during critical spawn-and-set periods for shellfish.
19. Increasing saltwater intrusion to groundwater and surface water.	19. • Major modification to channel depth and cross section should consider the effect on saltwater encroachment. • Analysis of effects on tidal bore and river flow will be helpful.

TABLE 4–1 Continued

POTENTIAL NEGATIVE IMPACTS	MITIGATING MEASURES
Indirect: Dredging Processes/Disposal	
20. Uptake and accumulation of resuspended and partitioned sediment contaminants by biota.	20. • Physical and chemical analyses permits proper planning prior to project implementation, thus minimizing sediment resuspension through proper selection of dredging equipment • Implement long-term biota tissue monitoring program.
21. • Occupational health effects on workers from sediment handling operations. • Accidents occur at higher than normal frequency because of lower level of skill or labor.	21. • Train employees to be aware of potential occupational hazards and establish a facility program on safety and health that includes all of the following: • site characterization and analysis • site control • training • medical surveillance • engineering controls, work practices, and personal protective equipment • monitoring and informational programs • handling raw and processed materials • decontamination procedures • emergency response • illumination • sanitation at permanent and temporary facilities
22. Impacts of possible land disposal on groundwater, surface runoff, and/or land use.	22. • If land disposal is the selected option, contaminated wastes should be contained in an engineered structure that minimizes leachate generation and release to local aquifers. • Uncontaminated sediments have some practical uses; however, wetlands reclamation is no longer considered an environmentally sound option.

TABLE 4–1 Continued

POTENTIAL NEGATIVE IMPACTS	MITIGATING MEASURES
Indirect: Dredging Processes/Disposal	
23. Transit patterns disrupted, noise and congestion created, and pedestrian hazards aggravated by heavy trucks transporting materials to/from port and harbor facilities.	23. • Proper site selection can mitigate many of these problems, but special transportation sector studies should be prepared during project feasibility studies to select best routes to reduce new shorezone facilities/industries. • Develop emergency contingency plans to minimize risk of accidents during transport. • Initiate discussions on transport regulations where none exist.

SOURCE: J. P. Davis, S. MacKnight, and IMO staff, "Environmental Considerations for Port and Harbor Developments," World Bank Technical Paper No. 126, Transport and Environmental Series, Washington D.C., 1989.

ect, as well as for the introduction and use of new or different cargo handling or processing equipment.

Most ports must now acquire or establish safe dredge spoil disposal sites, install liquid waste reception and treatment facilities, and have separate safe hazardous cargo storage and handling capabilities. Otherwise, they may not dredge their facilities, handle petroleum and other liquid cargoes, accommodate ship traffic, and transfer hazardous cargo.

Similarly, ports control port approaches by ships and other vehicles and regulate ship and vehicle emissions in the areas under their jurisdiction. In many countries, ports must be equipped to contain and clean up spills and prevent or mitigate environmental pollution of all kinds. On the prevention side, they are responsible for assuring that ships and other vehicles calling at their facilities for service are equipped to discharge, store, and load cargoes safely, have effective waste storage and transfer facilities, and are equipped to control all potential environmentally harmful emissions to the required standards.

In the United States, the Coast Guard assumes most of these responsibilities; in most other countries, port authorities and affiliated agencies exert these controls. In fact, various international agreements provide the port state control, where ports are authorized to act on behalf of flag states in enforcing applicable national and international agreements, conventions, and standards.

In many countries, ports are now also required to maintain effective vessel traffic control systems to reduce the potential for ship groundings or collisions. Often they are required to establish effective spill and pollution response plans and to provide both the equipment and trained staff to combat, contain, and mitigate the effects of pollution caused by port users and port operations.

4.1.2 Safe Tanker Design and Operations

Tanker accidents that cause spillage of oil, particularly crude or residual oil discharge, have been in the limelight in recent years. Both national and international conventions and laws have been introduced to change tanker design and to reduce or eliminate the discharge of oil after underwater hull rupture or penetration as a result of grounding or collision.

The International Maritime Organization (IMO) Marine Environmental Protection Committee, the international body responsible for developing measures to prevent pollution of the seas from ships, introduced the International Convention for the Prevention of Pollution from Ships 1973, as modified by the Protocol of 1978 relating thereto as International Convention for the Prevention of Pollution from Ships, (MARPOL 73/78). This convention came into force in 1983 and has been updated several times, most importantly in March 1992. The changes were largely influenced by the *Exxon Valdez* accident in 1989, when that tanker ran aground in the Prince William Sound, in the approaches to the port of Valdez in Alaska, and spilled about 30,000 tons of oil.

In response to this accident and the large damage caused to the environment, the U.S. Congress passed the 1990 Oil Pollution Act (OPA-90), which mandates double hulls for tankers of all new ships visiting U.S. ports, with a phase-in period for existing ships in service. This act was a unilateral decision that contradicts the collective international approach favored and advocated by the IMO and many nations. The action was also criticized because many felt that double-hull designs were not the best approach for the prevention of spillage and the resulting pollution from grounding and collision accidents.

Not only is there a question about the most effective hull design to prevent pollution, but also about the role of humans in both preventing accidents and reducing spillage. There are a number of alternative proposals for safe tanker design, such as the following:

1. *the vacuum method,* in which the cargo tanks are tightly sealed and a vacuum is maintained between the oil and the top of the tank to prevent cargo escape on tank bottom damage;
2. *a hydrostatic balanced design,* in which the static head of the oil is always the same (or less) than that of the water outside the hull to prevent oil outflow if the bottom is damaged;
3. *double-hull designs;* and
4. *midheight* deck designs.

An alternative to expensive double-hull tanker construction or conversion, especially in older tankers, has been developed by Reidar Wasenius (patent rights Unitor) and consists of simple equilibrium arrangements that introduce the effects of a virtual or imaginary double bottom. Estimates for converting an existing large crude tanker to this spill prevention system are $100,000, which is a fraction of the cost of installing a real double bottom. Cargo tankers are filled with seawater to 1.5–2.0 m prior to loading cargo (the height of the seawater loading depends on the specific gravity of the cargo to be loaded, the height of the cargo tanks, and the loaded draft of the vessel). The seawater is specially treated to reduce any possibility of mixing with the top-loaded oil cargo. The chemicals are both emulsion preventing and rust inhibiting.

A bottom-hull rupture, such as experienced on grounding, would result in the discharge of part of the specially treated seawater until an equilibrium head is achieved.

The only installation required of Wasenius's design is a chemical storage and delivery system, which can usually be done in a few days. The chemically treated seawater is environmentally harmless and can also be used as part of the ballast requirements for the vessel. The main drawback is a 5% to 10% reduction in the cargo-carrying capacity of a tanker that, although significant, is lower than that experienced by a double-bottom or double-hull equipped vessel.

Similar systems in which a floating, high-surface tension skin is introduced above the ballast water to separate it from the lower-density top-loaded oil cargo provides another alternative to the virtual double bottom.

Although OPA-90 only applies to vessels trading in U.S. waters at this time, many foreign owners may abide by its requirements even if they do not serve U.S. ports because the MARPOL 73/78 Convention may, if adopted, also include many of the OPA tanker construction requirements.

The MARPOL (13F–13G) amendments for new and existing ships, respectively, include many of the OPA requirements. But the inclusion of the double-hull requirements of OPA-90 is not assured.

There are indications that the middeck tanker design developed by Mitsubishi Heavy Industries may be preferred by many other nations. Many now claim that the middeck design offers better protection under conditions of large damage to a ship's bottom, although the double hull is superior when smaller damage is experienced. As long as the damage resulting from grounding does not extend to the position of the middeck about 35–50 ft above the keel, oil will not be discharged if the oil has a specific gravity less the seawater and the draft of the ship is equal to the height of the middeck or if the draft is larger than the height of the middeck. There may be some oil discharge resulting from the dynamic effects of the ship movements in the water.

Although these safe tanker concepts are designed to reduce somewhat the damage of a tanker involved in a grounding or collision, their major advantage is in somewhat reducing the outflow of cargo, and thereby the resulting ocean pollution, after an accident. Most tanker accidents are caused by

- navigational errors, operational congestion, and inadequate navigational aids;
- inaccurate charts and data;
- human factors, as well as a decline in seafarer skill, training, or experience; and
- inadequate ship or navigational maintenance.

Most tanker accidents occur in port approaches. Therefore, more effective marking of navigational channels and control of traffic in these channels may reduce ship or tanker pollution much more effectively than changes in design would. Similarly, in an attempt to reduce ship accidents caused as a result of human error, a lack of skill, or a lack of experience, ship management procedures that may include the effective use of expert systems are under investigation. A lack of experience is often less the result of inadequate professional experience, but experience on a particular ship or in a particular port or navigational environment. Ship crews, like aircraft crews, change more frequently than they did in the past, and few crew members stay a sufficient time on a particular ship to get to know its behavior fully.

4.1.2.1 Other ship-caused pollution. Although accidental or operational oil pollution is the most important ship-caused ocean environmental impact, ships cause other pollution as well. Atmospheric pollution (NO_x and particulates) by exhaust gases from main propulsion and auxiliary machinery, dust and evaporation of cargoes, gases from paints, solvents, and detergents and emissions of freon and halogens are just a few gaseous pollutants caused by ships. These pollutants are reduced or prevented by strict control of emission standards. Similarly, liquid wastes such as cargo and ballast or tank and cargo compartment washing water discharges may cause serious ocean pollution if not transferred into special separating and reception facilities. The same applies to bilge water and fuel or lubricating oil waste or washing disposal.

Recent investigations show that antifouling coatings used to protect the underwater hulls of ships can emit serious pollution and can poison various marine organisms. The shipping industry has become quite responsible, and recent amendments to Safety of Life at Sea Convention (SOLAS) prohibit the use of halogenated hydrocarbons on new ships. Similarly, machinery exhaust emissions must now be strictly controlled. Tank overfill and overflow warnings must similarly be installed, and sewage and other ship-generated waste must be placed into treatment or holding tanks. New antifouling paints no longer contain Toxigenic Bacteria or similar toxins, and cleaning agents used on board must be environmentally neutral. Ballast water is separated before discharge, and residues are stored in holding tanks for transfer to safe, specialized shoreside facilities.

4.1.3 Safe Navigational Channels

Intelligently managed navigational channels use a collection of technologies to manage the flow of ship traffic through them, to assure the safety of vessels traversing the channel, and to increase the volume of traffic capacity. Such a system can be largely advisory by controlling the status and information and by transmitting it to the manually navigated passing vessels, or it may be fully automated, in which case all the vessel functions are controlled by the navigational channel management system. In practice, a manual system with an automated emergency override is probably the most effective and acceptable system.

Although such systems are available or feasible today, few ports and authorities responsible are willing to commit themselves, leaving themselves open to the risks of unmanaged channels. An intelligently managed channel has an integrated navigational aid, traffic control, and movement demand system that can accommodate all feasible changes in traffic, weather, or physical conditions. Such a system can physically guide each ship through the channel or at least tell the captain or navigator at each moment what action is required. The system can then check to make sure that appropriate action has been taken, and if not, permit an override, which could be automatic or advisory.

Sensors and monitors, navigational aids, and interactive ship controls, all interlinked to central computers and communication links, provide an intelligent or expert ship navigational control system for the passage of ships through such channels. The technology for such systems exists and is in fact simpler than that under development for intelligent road vehicle highway systems. The system could take control of the ship or could provide real time guidance. In either case, it would significantly improve ship safety in port approaches and thereby reduce ship accidents and the resulting oil pollution.

Ship traffic control systems that provide not only visual or electronic guidance for ships but that actually control ship speed, course, and related operations could now be installed. Automated landing of aircraft has been employed for many years and has improved the safety of flying. Similar technology is now available to improve the navigational safety of ships in port approaches. Furthermore, such an approach would furthermore increase the capacity of navigational channels by reducing the safe intership distance and would thereby increase port revenues while saving port (dredging) improvement investments. It can be readily shown that such systems would more than pay for themselves and would significantly reduce port access and turnaround time of ships.

An intelligently managed channel will control not only the passage of individual ships in terms of their speed, route (or steering), operating conditions, and separation distance, but will also assign ship passage sequences based on maximizing channel utilization, value or cost of ship delay time, ship arrival or departure commitments, and other factors. In a way, the system will mimic automated aircraft approach and landing systems and will also include some expert systems to control the ship's own shipboard operation.

The intelligently managed channel consists of a system that links channel sensors, monitors, and navigational aids through a computer control system to interactive onboard navigational control systems operated by an expert system that automatically and intelligently responds to all external directives.

The operational advantage of intelligent and managed navigational channels are numerous. Vessel separation distances, greater average speed, more effective stacking of vessels with different speeds and stopping distances (or size), and obviously greatly increased channel capacity and operational safety are just a few of the advantages such systems offer. They may also offer significant improvements in navigational channel design and, as a result, the cost of both capital and maintenance dredging. The system may also replace many of the largely manually maintained and sometimes controlled navigational aids that are usually expensive to maintain.

4.1.3.1 Effect of reduction of oil spills. The overwhelming majority of ship groundings and collisions causing accidental oil spills occur in navigational approaches to ports and waterways and are in most cases the result of

1. inadequate navigational aids,
2. lack of vessel traffic control,
3. insufficient or out-of-date hydrographic information,
4. human error and incompetence,
5. ineffective design of navigational channel, or
6. lack of traffic separation.

Most of these causes of vessel accidents would be eliminated or greatly reduced by the installation and mandatory use of intelligent and managed navigational channels. The technology is available now, and there is no reason not to install it and enforce its use. The system's costs and costs of onboard equipment are a small fraction of the added cost of spill damage insurance and spill reduction systems. In fact, the installation of such a system may result in a reduction in insurance rates, which would pay for the investment in a relatively short time.

4.1.3.2 Vessel traffic management systems (VTMS). A vessel traffic system (VTS) is designed to provide routine information on vessel movements. VTSs monitor compliance with rules, provide advice or guidance, and regulate ship and boat traffic to ensure safety for all users while ensuring effective use of the available waterway. They vary widely from general guidance to highly complex vessel traffic management systems (VTMS). Although in use or under trial in some places since the early 1970s, only now, with the availability of new positioning, tracking, communication, control, and guidance systems, can a VTS or VTMS be designed to achieve its full potential of vessel traffic management and control in congested and restricted waters.

In addition to damage by oil spills, loss of property damage in navigational channels resulting from ship collisions or groundings averaged nearly $5 billion per year in recent years. This cost is obviously reflected in insurance premiums, which in turn are usually passed on to freight rates.

Increased traffic density, competing and multiple use of navigational channels, increased size and speed of ships, and the new complexity of shipboard systems require more effective vessel traffic management than traditional human response systems can achieve. Response times have become much shorter and the decisions required are often too complex for shipboard staff to react in an effective and timely manner.

Furthermore, human judgment is often incapable of responding to complex situations that require expert systems for effective decisions. In 1991, for example, 23% of ship accidents in navigational channels were the result of violation of the rules of the road, in most cases because watchkeepers overestimated responsiveness. Excessive speed and an inability to judge stopping distance or turning radius were other factors.

In other words, it is no longer possible to rely totally on the competence of watchkeepers. The need for formal, mandatory vessel traffic management systems is increasingly pervasive, and such systems can be readily introduced at a fraction of the costs of passive spill reduction systems. The major breakthrough in the development of VTMS is the availability and capability of global positioning systems.

4.1.3.3 Positioning and position tracking systems. Although a U.S. global positioning system (GPS) has been in use for some time, the U.S. Navy degrades the signals for commercial use to an average positioning accuracy of only about 300 ft. This distance is fine for most open sea navigation but completely inadequate for narrow channel navigation by very large tankers or very fast container and other vessels. It is similarly insufficient for survey and alignment work.

To counteract this, differential GPS (DGPS) has been introduced by the U.S. Coast Guard in a number of U.S. locations. DGPS uses radio signals to transmit corrections by relating a GPS signal to a known fixed position. In the United States, DGPS is now commercially available with accuracies of 5–20 ft, according to the service providers.

With 51 (including 21 GPSs and 3 new Inmarsat) satellites available for navigation by the year 2000, GPS users with integrated receivers will have a large number of satellites in view at any one time. Accurate position and velocity information will therefore become available everywhere and will permit highly accurate navigation. The next step is effective ship routing, track identification, ship movement control, and ship collision and grounding prevention. GPS is already developed enough to provide not only accurate position and velocity but also course or tracking information.

GPS makes visual navigation with compromising accuracy obsolete. One issue that often affects navigational accuracy is the reliability of charts, including the maintenance of up-to-date changes on charts. Few charts are currently maintained at the accuracy required for GPS navigation, which is capable of updating positions every few seconds. To take full advantage of GPS for ship navigation and ship traffic control requires the use of electronic chart displays to show ship positions dynamically without manual charting. This is particularly important in navigating large ships (200–300 m in length) in restricted waters. There, some time may be lost in plotting the position as well as the orientation of the ship, and this delay may be critical, particularly when navigating in a narrow, curved channel.

As suggested in a recent article in *Marine Log,*[1] a scale model of the outline of ships in a channel on the electronic chart display

[1]R. I. Nijjer, "GPS Takes Navigation from the 18th Century into the 21st," *Marine Log,* Vol. 98, No. 7 (July 1993): p. 29.

would provide a realistic, real-time presentation to ship and shore navigation. DGPS-based systems will be designed to complement radar-based VTS because although the GPS-based system is cheaper, complementary radar is useful to detect all the traffic in an area.

Future VTMSs will include shore and shipboard integrated DGPSs, electronic charts, support radar, vessel traffic systems, and operating systems with onboard expert systems. The onboard expert systems incorporate knowledge of ship-operating characteristics, such as loading conditions, turning radius, and stopping distances, and advise the DGPS and electronic chart display in real time of

1. the ship's outline, position, speed, and course;
2. the stopping distance under prevailing speed and current conditions and bank and shallow water effects;
3. the rate of turn and turning circle under prevailing or different speed, current, and channel conditions;
4. the relative position, speed, and course of other ships in a channel, crossing channel, or approaching channel; and
5. the prediction of potential conflicts (collisions, groundings, and so forth) and the expert system's plan of deviation to eliminate risk, including measures imposed on other ship or ships.

All the technological elements of such a system exist, including effective communication links and expert systems. This system is really not very different from those used by aircraft controllers and aircraft navigation and landing management systems, with the exception of the DGPS.

Such a VTMS would be mandatory and in the first few years would become a directive system where VTMS controllers direct all vessels in a navigational channel and its approaches. Ships would inform the central VTMS of their characteristics or special requirements so that controllers could compute optimum operating procedures that take the requirements or capabilities of the various vessels in the system into account. Actual ship management, however, remains under control of the ship's crew. In the future, though, the whole system could be automated, and ship (like airplanes), land, or traverse navigational channels would automatically be under the guidance and control of the central VTMS.

An integrated DGPS/electronic chart/radar VTMS system with ship and shore expert systems' support may make visual and audible navigational aids largely obsolete. In addition, navigation in fog, darkness, and congested waters would be safer than under current systems.

4.1.3.4 Ship management responsibility. Ship management has become an increasingly important issue, particularly now that human error or lack of crew competence has been shown to be the major factor in ship accidents. Lack of training, inadequate definition of responsibilities, and ineffective shipboard management and organization appear to be major causes of problems of ship safety. Most human errors onboard ships are found to be the result of a lack of clarity about responsibility, a lack of effective communication, and a lack of well-defined operational procedures, routine, and duty plans. Similarly, where meaningful procedures and plans exist, they are often not followed because there is really no effective control and feedback.

THe IMO is introducing a mandatory requirement for an International Safety Management Code by 1998 that is designed to resolve some of these issues. Yet to be really effective, it will require the mandatory installation of a "black box" that records all relevant events and actions or responses. Therefore, the box can not only be used to reconstruct all events by cause, action, and effect, but also can supply valuable information or input into effective expert systems to improve ship management. Such a system would have a major effect on the quality and discipline of ship management.

The P&O Group pioneered the development of such a voyage event recorder and should be lauded for this contribution to ship safety. It is unfortunate that the IMO is not fully supportive of this approach even though the IMO admits that human error and competence are major issues affecting ship safety.

4.1.3.5 Effect of DGPS-based VTMS on tanker accident prevention. Statistical analysis of 107 collisions and groundings in navigational channels in the United States between 1987 and 1990 indicates that the principal causes (72%) of these accidents were navigational and human errors. The former type of error was largely the result of inadequate or wrong position fixing, while the latter was the result of misjudgment, incompetence, inadequate watchkeeping, or overconfidence. Inaccurate charts or charting accounted for 18% of the accidents. In other words, up to 90% of these tanker accidents could have been prevented or reduced in scope by an effective, integrated positioning, by a VTMS, and by an updated electronic chart system. Over 70% of the accidents occurred in only ten navigational channel systems; New York and New Jersey alone accounted for over 20%.[2]

Similarly, a study of worldwide tanker accidents indicated that over 78% of tanker accidents occurred in fewer than 30 navigational channels or navigational areas, such as the Straits of Malacca, the English Channel, the Strait of Gibraltar, and the Strait of Hormuz. Risk analysis of integrated DGPS vessel traffic management systems, with a positional accuracy of 5–10 m, shows that if such systems were installed and compliance was made mandatory for ships larger than 10,000 DWT, with communications links only installed on vessels more than 10 years old, over 85% of accidents in these channels could be prevented. At the same time this would improve channel management, which in turn would improve channel capacity and average ship passage time.

4.1.4 River and Runoff Pollution Prevention

Preventing ocean pollution by rivers, drainage, and other runoffs has become a major issue in ocean environmental management. In many countries, river pollution is addressed by strict regulation of agricultural fertilizers and chemicals as well as by control of industrial and residential outflows and waste disposal into rivers. Policing of agricultural, industrial, and commercial and residential outflows is not easy, and progress in cleaning up river pollution has been very slow. This is not only because of long and often difficult riverside and bank configurations, but also because the origin or source as well as the composition of pollutant discharges into moving rivers are sometimes hard to identify. Moving rivers often contain a lot of silt and various chemical and organic impurities. Some are introduced by pollutant discharges, while others may be the result of natural interactions or emissions from the surrounding soils or riverbanks or from submerged vegetation.

In some rivers, barriers, such as dams, have been introduced for hydroelectric power generation, flood control, improved irrigation, or navigation. Such damming of rivers often reduces the flow of sediment and sediment-imbedded pollutants into the ocean, yet dissolved or other liquid pollutants are not contained behind the dam. Other methods for removing solid waste from rivers include separa-

[2]"Polluting Incidents in and Around U.S. Waters" (Washington, D.C., U.S. Coast Guard, Department of Transportation-CG487, 1987, 1988, 1989, and 1990).

tion ponds, sediment traps, and filters. Dams may interfere with the migration of anadromous and catadromous fish, and thus such obstructions are often discouraged.

Separation ponds consist of submerged river dams or simply the enlargement of the river by widening so as to force a reduction in flow velocity and settlement of suspended materials. Submerged dams often achieve the same results as regular dams. Sediment traps, which are simple bores dredged in the bottom of a river across its whole width, are sometimes used for this purpose. Another method designed to cause settlement of suspended impurities is to train the river by introducing dams that require the river flow to change direction and to discharge some of the suspended material.

Wetlands are usually receiving basins for surface runoff from surrounding areas that, if used by agriculture or industry, may cause contaminants and pollutants to collect and ultimately to enter the coastal waters of oceans. Therefore, wetlands often serve as sinks for pollutants.

4.1.5 Offshore Resource Exploitation Pollution Prevention

Offshore oil and mineral production is of increasing importance and now occupies large areas of the oceans. Today, technological developments in exploration, preparation, and production of offshore oil wells ensure a high degree of safety and a very low risk of oil spillage during these operations. In particular, offshore wells are now equipped with automatic shut-off devices that activate fail-safe well closure in case of fire or pipe rupture that would cause a lowering of pressure.

Similarly, offshore mining of sand and gravel, which was often performed in a haphazard, unregulated manner, is now regulated in many countries. Such mining is often restricted to areas with little or no biological activity and where changes in the sea bottom have little or no effect on submerged flows, erosion, or accretion.

4.2 SPILL CONTAINMENT AND RECOVERY

Various approaches to spill containment are now in use or are under development. Floating or floatable booms or barriers, some of which are inflatable, are the most common methods used. Some systems rely on air or water currents or sprays to contain or move surface slicks. Containment of oil spills by floating booms is effective when the specific gravity of the oil is less than that of the water, but in freshwater or when the oil is very dense (extra heavy crude oil, for example), other methods must be used. Such oil will not float on the water but instead will sink in globules to the bottom or will stay in neutral suspension below the water surface.

Similarly, in rough water, not only does oil disperse more quickly and without maintaining a coherent slick, but typical floating containment barriers are not effective if the wave height exceeds the normal draft of the barrier. Under such circumstances, other usually dynamic methods of containment must be used. Such methods may use air and water sprays or liquid floating barriers. These are only now being developed, and their use is currently only experimental.

Chemical spills are often much more difficult to contain because the chemicals are water soluble, their viscosity is very low and they spread rapidly, their vapor pressure is low, or their specific gravity is high, or because of a combination of such characteristics that makes it difficult to contain chemical spills with physical or air barriers.

4.2.1 Oil Pollution Containment and Recovery

Oil spills are usually contained by physical floating barriers called booms, which come in various forms and are made of various materials. Their purpose is to prevent oil from spreading, and they permit the collection or reflection of oil from sensitive intakes or other areas. Types of booms include solid floatation, inflatable, fence, pneumatic barrier, net, weir, and trailing-booms. Oil containment booms can be made from anything that floats, as long as it is oil and water resistant, is durable, and has adequate elasticity and tensile strength.

Booms are deployed in a number of ways. They can be employed to encircle the source of the spill or to waylay the spill, or as reflection, towing, free-drift containment, multiple-setting booms, or netting booms. The methods used depend on the strategy of containment adopted, the methods of recovery, if any, to be used, the type and quantity of booms available, weather conditions, and the type of oil spill to be contained. Similarly, the process of mooring and storing booms is often a major issue because they are long and unwieldy.

Once the oil is contained by booms, cleanup must begin. To recover oil off the sea surface, recovery devices consist of suction devices, devices using oleophilic material, induction devices, and devices using other physical principals. In suction devices, oil is drawn into a tank and water is separated by gravity or surface tension (viscosity) methods. Oleophilic devices use an oleophilic material to which oil adheres and from which it can be readily removed into a recovery tank. Some of these work as discs, drums, belts, or endless adhesion rope systems. Oleophilic brushes are also often used. Induction devices mechanically collect oil and water in storage tanks and then separate the oil from the water, usually by gravity. Induction devices include the multiple weit, the inclined plane, and the hydrocyclone system. Other recovery systems include screw pumps, vortex skimmers, nets, vacuum trucks, mechanical grabs, and manual recovery.

For the effective containment and cleanup of spreading oil, oil recovery vessels are employed to sweep with booms. The single- and multivessel systems are two such sweep systems.

Booms are not always employed, particularly when high-capacity recovery vessels are available, when booms are not available, or when weather and current conditions are unsuitable. In these cases, specialized oil recovery vessels are often employed in fleets. These include the suction type, the absorption separation type, the induction type, the weir skimmer, and the scissor ship.

When oil recovery with specialized devices is difficult because the spill consists of small, floating oil slicks—for example, when a spill occurs in very shallow water or is quite inaccessible—sorbents or absorbent materials are often used instead of skimmers or vessels. Sorbents are classified into inorganic, synthetic organic, and natural organic types. Care must be taken for the proper distribution, collection, and storage and disposal of sorbents. In other cases, chemical dispersants are more effective.

Oil containment booms are usually dispensed from floating platforms, as shown in Figure 4–1, or from reels carried on floating craft or land vehicles.

A typical oil boom is defined by size (medium or large) and by diameter, height, density, skirt height, skirt thickness, faceboard, draft, and wind assistance, as shown in Table 4–2.

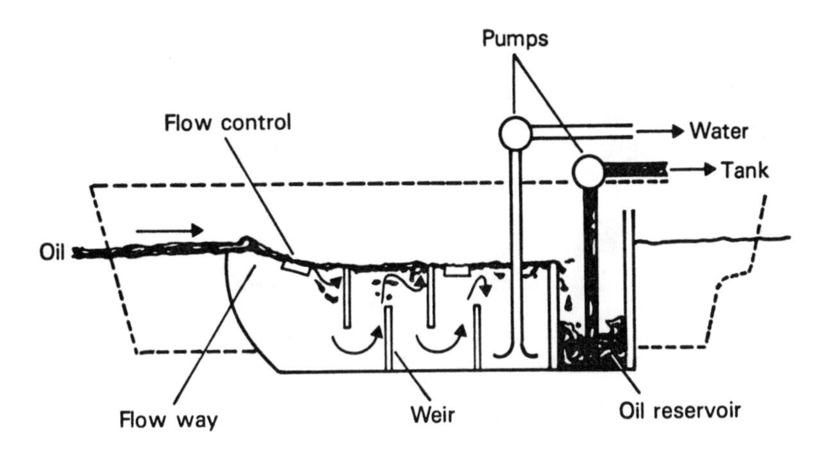

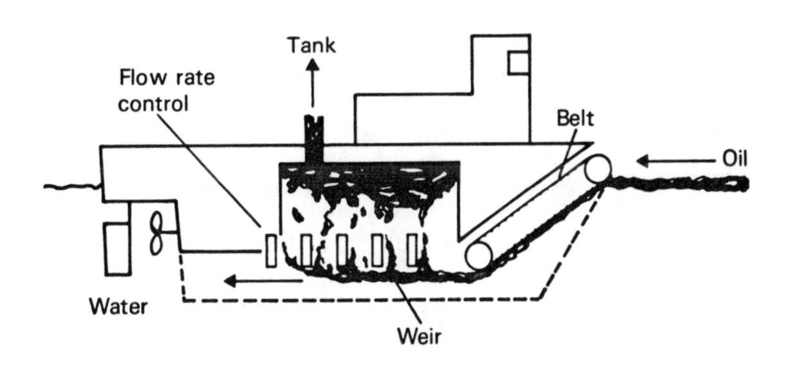

Figure 4–1 Oil Gathering and Collection Systems Source: IMO—Manual on Oil Pollution, Section IV Combating Oil Spills (London–IMO, 1988, pp. 92–93).

The boom platform (horizontal) reel or vertical barge or vehicle reel is usually equipped with brushes for cleaning oil from the boom when rewinding for storage.

Figures 4–2 and 4–3 show popular types of oil containment

TABLE 4–2 Typical Specification of Oil Boom

	MEDIUM SIZE	LARGE SIZE
Diameter	6 cm	10 cm
Height	75 cm	95 cm
Skirt height	65 cm	85 cm
Skirt thickness	≈ 1 mm	≈ 1 mm
Wind resistance	40 km/h	100 km/h
Freeboard	25 cm	35–37 cm
Draft	40 cm	50–48 cm

SOURCE: Manual on Combating Oil Pollution, Port of Shuweik, Kuwait (Kuwait, 1989).

booms, the netting type and the inflatable type, both of which are used in the Port of Shuaiba in Kuwait.

Oil skimmers usually rely on mechanical (suction and separation) systems. Figure 4–4 (see p. 143) shows frame, dragonfly, and vortex skimmers. Skimmers can be self-supporting with their power supply and operating system or can be supported by a mechanical arm from a barge or support vessels, as shown. Their capacities vary widely with size, surface condition, and thickness and type of oil spilled. Large skimmers have hydraulic capacities of 2,000–10,000 gal of oily water/h and can handle viscosities of 100–3,000 centistoke and oil layers 2–20 cm thick.

Figure 4–5 (see p. 144) shows typical vortex and belt skimmers. The latter is usually built into a tank barge that serves as the reception facility. When absorbents are used, various collection methods, such as special absorbent sweeping booms, mechanical trapping booms, or simple chemical recovery systems, may be appropriate. Recovery devices for oil on the ocean surface are usually of one of four types:

1. suction devices,
2. induction devices,
3. friction devices or devices using oleophilic materials, or
4. devices using static adhesion.

Suction devices consist of a head or mouth, a pump, pipes and storage tanks and work by sucking oil through restricted orifices to limit the amount of water intake. Oil trawling systems are also often used when a large weir-type, open-ended horizontal funnel is towed over the water surface.

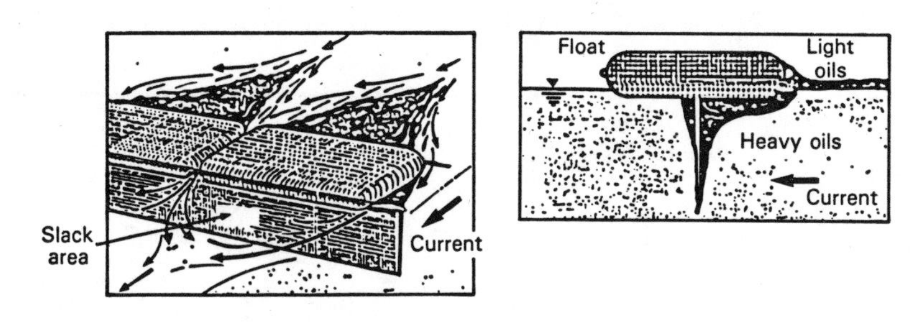

Net Booms and Netting System of Purse Seine Type (p. 97)

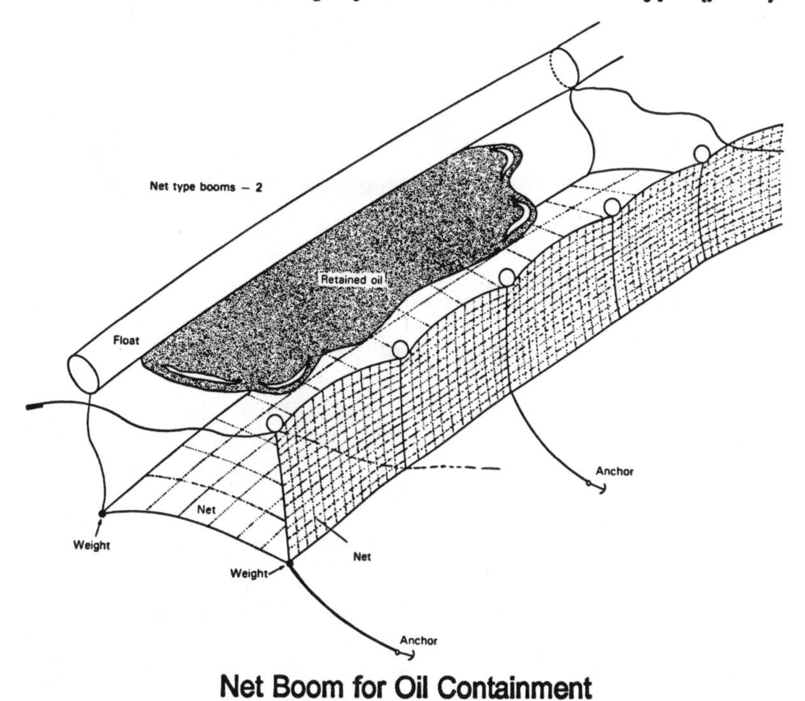

Net Boom for Oil Containment

Figure 4–2 Oil Booms Types. Source: IMO—Manual on Oil Pollution, Section IV—Combating Oil Spills (London–IMO, 1988, p. 70 and p. 97).

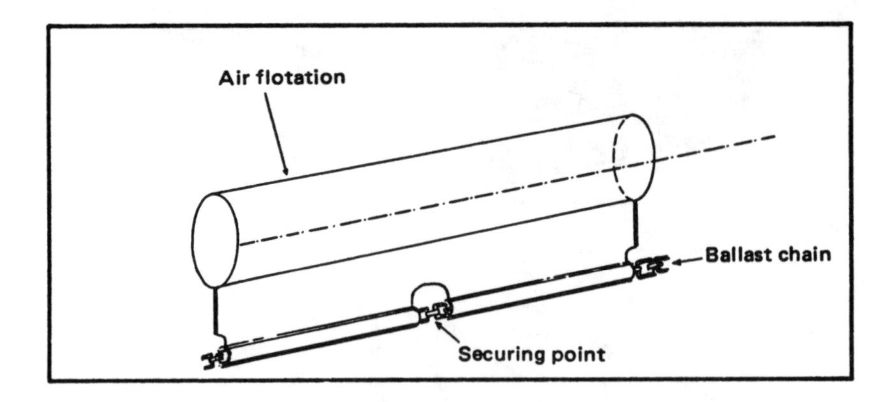

Inflatable Boom

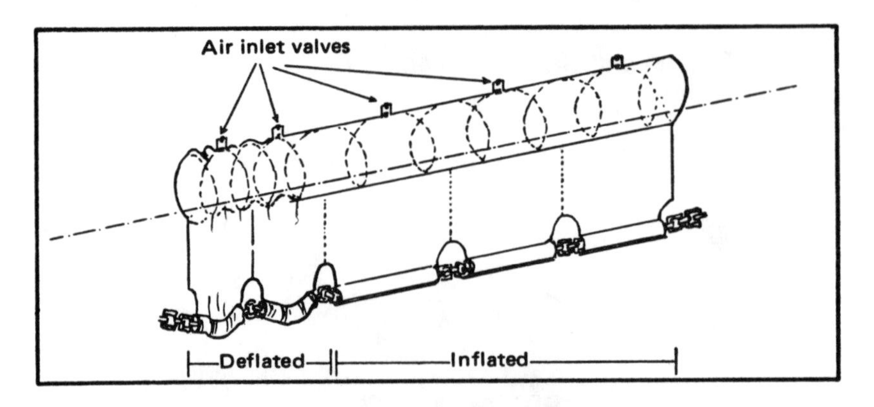

Self-inflating Boom

Figure 4–3 Inflatable and Self-inflating Booms. Source: IMO—Manual on Oil Pollution, Section IV—Combating Oil Spills (London–IMO, 1988, p. 51 and p. 53).

Disc skimmers, drums with fins, and belt skimmers are examples of the friction type of oil recovery devices. Oleophilic material can be used in rope or belt skimming devices. Inclined plane skimmers use friction or oleophilic characteristics. Other recovery systems, such as hydrocyclones, screw pumps, and vortex skimmers, which draw oil-laden surface water into a separating system, are largely mechanical.

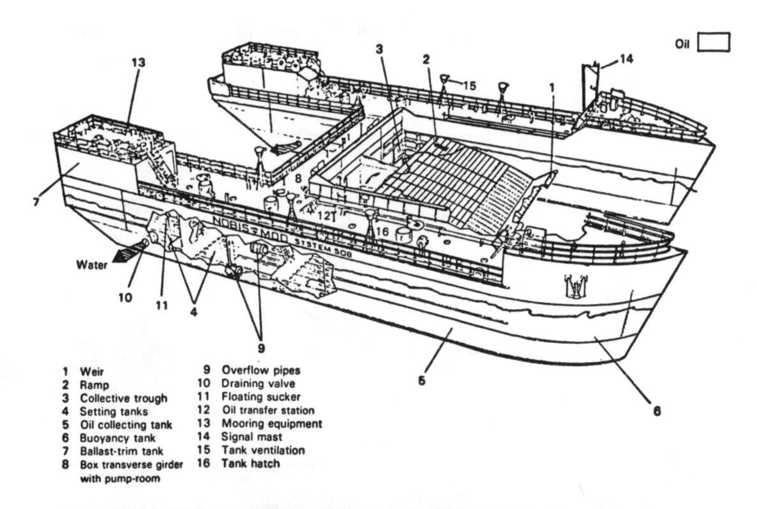

Twin hull weir skimmer

Figure 4–4 Mechanical Oil Skimmers. Source: International Maritime Organization.

Recovery is often facilitated by concentrating oil spills using sweeping booms towed by vessels. Specialized recovery vessels often combine sweeping, skimming (recovery), and storage. Sorbents or materials used to recover oil through absorption are sometimes useful but are usually applied in cleanup, not recovery, operations. Sorbents consist of inorganic materials; vermiculite, synthetic organic materials such as polypropulene, or natural organic materials such as peat, pulp, cotton, or pine bark are examples of such materials. The sorbents with the most absorbing capacity are synthetic organic materials such as polyurethene and urea form, which work best both with low- and high-viscosity oil spills.

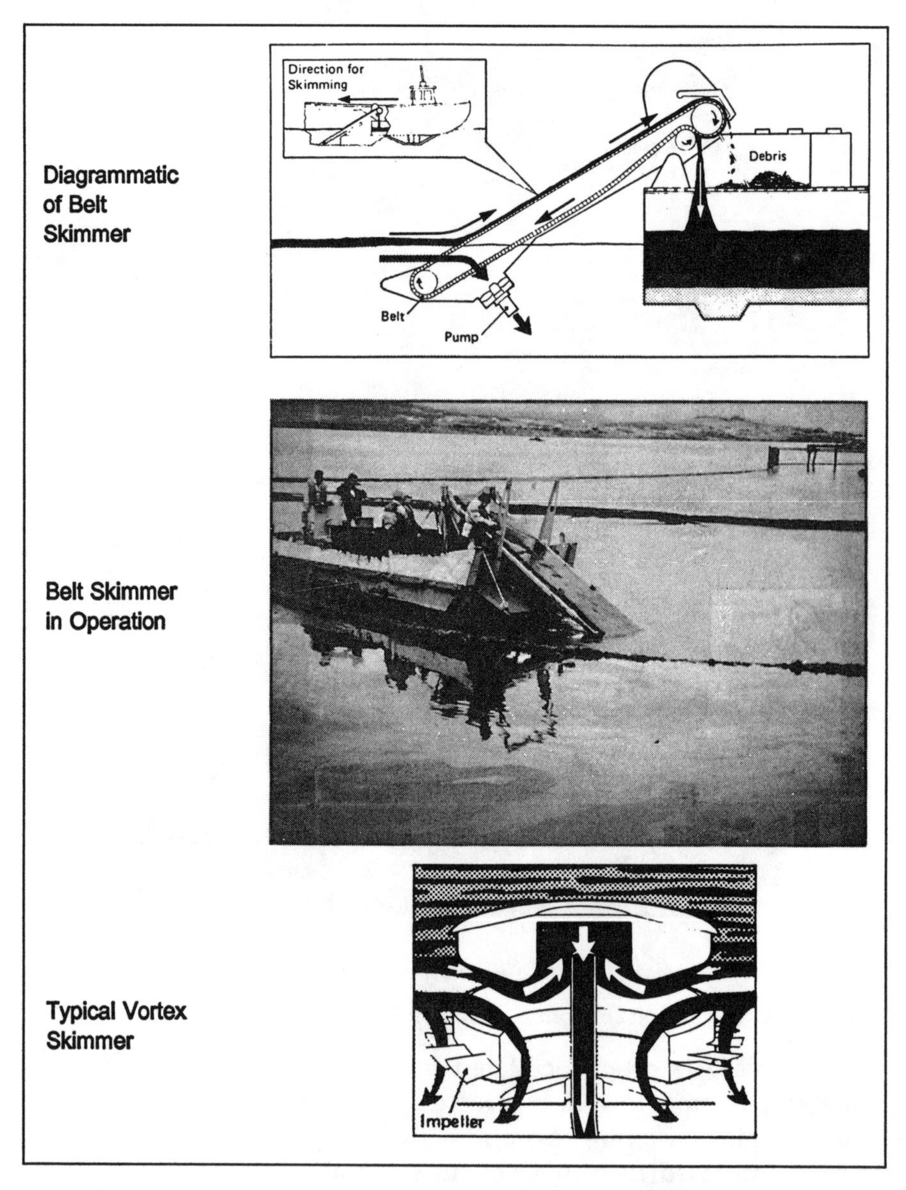

Figure 4–5 Typical Vortex and Belt Skimmers. Source: IMO—Manual on Oil Pollution, Section IV Combating Oil Spills (London: IMO, 1988, p. 88).

4.2.2 Chemical and Radioactive Pollution Containment and Recovery

Chemical and radioactive pollution is much more difficult to contain than solid waste and oil pollution because it combines chemically with water, dissolves in water, or makes water and impurities in water radioactive. As a result, such pollution usually spreads rapidly and widely and cannot readily be reversed. Furthermore, chemical and radioactive pollution affects marine organisms quite rapidly and often irreversibly. Although some methods for cleanup of chemical spills have been developed, most rely on dilation or neutralization of the adverse chemical effects.

4.3 POLLUTION CLEANUP METHODS

After containment and recovery of an oil spill, pollution cleanup, if feasible and economically attractive, can be performed using mechanical means, sorbents, chemical dispersants, or organic ingestors. Each of these works differently and is used under particular conditions.

Shoreline cleanup is usually performed using mechanical means and sorbents, while chemical dispersants or organic ingestors are more commonly used in open waters. Dispersants are chemical agents that affect the physical character of the oil on the surface. They usually consist of surface active agents and are commonly dissolved in a penetrating solvent. They are designed to reduce the surface tension of the oil on the sea and thereby to increase droplet formation. This causes the oil to disperse and gives much larger surface areas, which in turn accelerates degradation of the oil.

Chemical dispersants are usually sprayed on the oil-covered surface by boom sprayers extended over the sides of tugs or special dispersant-spraying vessels. Under some circumstances, airborne dispersant spray may also be used. Dispersants should be sprayed uniformly and in front of an advancing tide and should have some time (hours) to soak the oil slick.

Although dispersants are not effective in cleaning up beach pollution, they may be useful in final cleanup of remnants of oil. Dispersants should be used cautiously because they may be harmful to ocean life, birds, and humans if ingested in concentrations. Some dispersants may also cause skin damage. Dispersants are aqueous or hydrocarbon solvents, and their effectiveness is usually restricted to lighter crudes and distillates. Dispersants are also used to control fire hazards resulting from oil spilled on ocean surfaces or shores.

4.4 OPERATIONAL OCEAN POLLUTION PREVENTION

The major emphasis in ocean pollution prevention is now on planning, preparedness, and prepositioning. In other words, industrial concerns, port authorities, ship operators, offshore companies, and others involved in ocean-based or related activities that may result in ocean pollution are now required in many countries to acquire not only the necessary equipment to prevent ocean pollution (or to reduce the acceptable levels), but also to prove that they are effectively organized and have adequate plans and well-trained personnel. In addition, they need prepositioned or readily accessible containment and cleanup equipment to respond effectively to ocean pollution.

In fact, many organizations have established specialized groups whose principal function is to update their preparedness plans continuously, to train personnel, and to develop improvements in operating procedures. The preparedness measures employed vary widely but always include training of personnel, contingency planning, and positioning of materials and equipment.

4.4.1 Operational Tanker Pollution Prevention

International conventions such as OILPOL 1954, MARPOL 1973/78, and subsequent amendments define procedures and requirements for operational tanker pollution prevention (Appendix B). Operational tanker pollution occurs during loading or transferring of oil, bunkering or discharging of oil mixtures, and various other operations. A major operational pollution risk occurs when ballasting and deballasting of tanks is used alternatively for fuel oil and water ballast. Similarly, handling and discharging of bilge and wash water, particularly water waste from washing cargo tanks, presents a serious operational oil pollution risk. Other sources of oil pollution are the water discharge from oily water separating and from oil filtering equipment. To prevent operational oil spills, defined procedures must be followed in all the above-named operations.

On completion of any oil loading or discharge, cargo tanks and lines must be thoroughly drained and air must be blown through to ensure the discharge of oil from lines or pipes before they are disconnected. This may also require reverse or suction pumping to make certain that the pipe is empty before breaking the pipe flanges for disconnection. Oily wash water must be collected in slop tanks for safe discharge to special shoreside facilities.

Dirty ballast water must be given time to settle before discharge and may only be discharged to the "clear" level. Crews must be trained and certified to perform these operations and must be familiar with the "safe" requirements for tank washing, loading and unloading, the disposal of ballast water, and the discharge of slop tanks and bilge and wash water. Plans of operations must be prepared and exchanged between the oil tanker and the terminal facility.

Fines for contravention of MARPOL conventions are severe, and many ports use jurisdiction to enforce these and other pollution and safety regulations and conventions.

4.4.2 Oil Spill Response Plans

Under the Oil Pollution Act (OPA) of 1990, to be allowed to operate in U.S. waters after August 18, 1993, all tank vessels and certain oil handling facilities must prepare and submit for each ship vessel response plans (VRPs) with the U.S. Coast Guard. The plan must identify personnel and equipment sufficient to remove three levels of spills, ranging from average to worst-case scenarios. This can be done by listing the resources available and showing the capability of containing, removing, and storing spilled oil. Resources can be made available by oil response service operators who control floating equipment, booms, skimmers, storage vessels, and other equipment and trained personnel. VRPs can be computerized. Such response plans show compliance with government and IMO requirements and are also used for spill response management.

Development of an effective oil response infrastructure is not just a matter of assembling oil spill containment, cleanup, removal, and storage capability and placing it in strategic locations. It also requires training competent personnel, organizing response teams, and managing systems for effective response. Most importantly, it requires an overall response structure in line with search-and-rescue response systems in which, with Coast Guard leadership, all capable resources are marshalled when an emergency arises.

A similar response system is required to battle oil spills. When a major ship disaster occurs, it would be unfortunate if an oil spill response is limited to the capability of the oil response organization under contract with the ship operator, particularly if such contractor is not the closest one to the disaster site. A national or international response capability organization, controlled by a worldwide computerized response planning system in constant satellite communication, should be able to require response by the most strategically located and most effective response capability.

The United States has bilateral and multilateral agreements and joint contingency and response plans with neighboring countries to address notification of and response to oil spills. The Canada/United States Joint Marine Pollution Contingency plan covers emergency response activities in a basic plan. A similar agreement of cooperation exists between the United States and Mexico as well as between the United States and Russia (formerly the USSR) against pollution in the Bering and Chukchi Seas.

The federal oil spill response program established under Section 311 of the Clean Water Act is the primary instrument in the United States, but states play an important role and many have developed coordinated response plans. Similarly, local port authorities have oil spill contingency plans.

4.5 OUTFALL AND DREDGING-INDUCED POLLUTION PREVENTION

Outfalls or large pipe conduit discharges into the oceans are used for diluted and treated sewage disposal, the discharge of cooling water, and sometimes the discharge of diluted industrial waste. These pollute oceans chemically, physically, and thermally and often cause significant biological damage over a large area, particularly if the outfall ends in fairly shallow water subject to littoral currents. To prevent or reduce outfall pollution impacts, it is often advisable to lead the outfall into deep waters so that the discharge is into an ocean abyss not subject to surface currents. This will usually also result in greater dilution and a reduction of damage to breeding grounds.

Similarly, dredging should be done in an environmentally safe manner that reduces or eliminates a large buildup of sediment in suspension, damage to bottom layers (including large-scale coverage of the ocean bottom by dredge spoils), and dredging or opening up of toxic or polluted materials. Dredge spoil disposal must also be done in an environmentally safe manner because damage to the ocean environment can be significant.

4.5.1 Sewage and Cooling Water Disposal by Outfalls

Sewage outfalls that discharge a high concentration of biodegradable organic matter in the coastal zone affect the intertidal domain by the accumulation of nutrients and pollutants associated with particulate matter. In turn, microbial activity and primary production are increased.

Secondary effects—for example, the dissolution of calcium carbonates by carbon dioxide and concentration of pollutants, such as heavy metals—greatly affect the biological capacity in the zone.

Outfalls should always be well below the lowest low-water level, and effective means for the proper mixing must be provided, particularly where little or no bottom current exists. Long diffuser pipes terminating in deeper water well below the tidal levels are usually effective. Preferably, residual solids in outfalls should be discharged separately from the effluent after anaerobic digestion and screening. A diagram of a modern sewage treatment plant is shown in Figure 4–6.

Residual solids may require separate treatment and screening before discharge. When deep-water discharge is not possible, diffuser pipes for diluted and treated sewage should not only be long but should include venturies to increase the admixing with seawater before discharge.

Cooling water outfalls should also incorporate diffusers and admixes to equalize outfall and coastal water temperature before actual discharge and thereby to reduce thermal gradients to a biologically acceptable level.

4.5.2 Safe Disposal of Dredge Spoils

Increasing concern for the effect of the disposal of dredge soils and the performance of dredging in the oceans has led to the implementation of regulations controlling dredging and the open-water disposal of dredged sediment. Sediments from both capital and maintenance dredging projects often contain contaminated materials

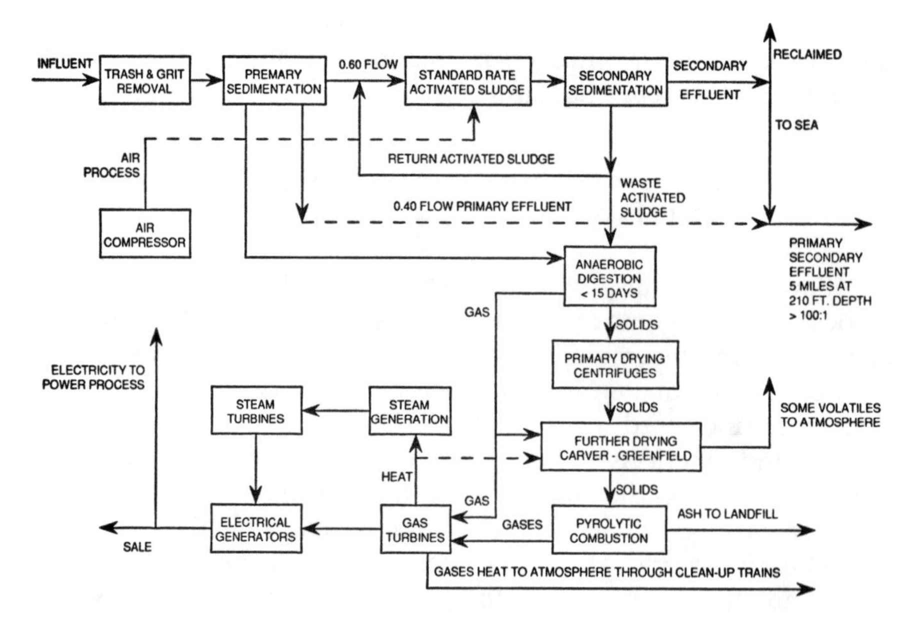

Figure 4–6 Treatment at the Hyperion Facility, City of Los Angeles, after 1986. From: W.F. Garber, "Environmental Laws and Environmental Improvement," *Water Science Technology* 18, no. 11 (1987).

due to pollution from a variety of sources, such as outfalls, runoffs, and waste disposal.

These sources often contribute chemical substances that poison the marine environment. In addition, dredging and dredge spoil disposal cause turbidity, cover breeding grounds, and impact the bottom topology. The average amount of maintenance dredging performed per year between 1980 and 1984 was[3]

Netherlands	50 million m^3
Germany	45 million m^3
France	35 million m^3
United Kingdom	27 million m^3
United States	166 million m^3
Mexico	20 million m^3

[3]J. G. Villot, *Terra et Acqua,* Journal of International Association of Dredging Companies, (Amsterdam November 30, 1985).

Brazil	7 million m^3
Philippines	6 million m^3
Indonesia	22 million m^3
India	37 million m^3
	415 million m^3

In addition, China is estimated to have dredged an average of 140 and other countries 75 million m^3, for a world total of 630 million m^3 per year. Capital dredging volumes vary much more than maintenance dredging volume. Estimates put the average at 250 million m^3 per year during the same period (1980–1984). In other words, nearly 900 million m^3 is dredged per year worldwide on average in recent years.

In 1990 the Netherlands reported that of the 60 million m^3 to be dredged that year, 17% to 33% was considered so badly polluted to require disposal within confined disposal facilities.

Beginning with the 1974 Oslo Convention for the Prevention of Marine Pollution by Dumping from Ships and Aircraft and the so-called London Dumping Convention, which entered into force in 1975, standards for the safe disposal of dredging spoils were set. By June 1989, 63 countries had ratified or acceded to the convention, with the IMO designated as its secretariat.

Dredging equipment consists of intermittent grab or clamshell dredgers, dipper dredgers, and backhoe dredgers as well as continuous suction, cutter suction, and mud cat pumping-type dredgers. The right choice of equipment depends on dredging depth, material composition and cohesion, and dredging quantities and environmental conditions. Similarly, the disposal site location and method of disposal affect the choice.

Spoil disposal options vary from simple release from split or hopper barges to deposition in confined areas. Uncontained open-water disposal is the cheapest and most popular method, but open-water disposal with capping (coverage with clean material) is becoming more popular (Figure 4–7).

Environmental concerns affect the design of the dredging project, the selection of dredging equipment, the method of dredging and use of the equipment, the timing of the project, the method of transportation of dredge spoils, the method of disposal of spoils, and the method of containment of dredge spoils if containment is deemed to be necessary. There is concern that unless all these as-

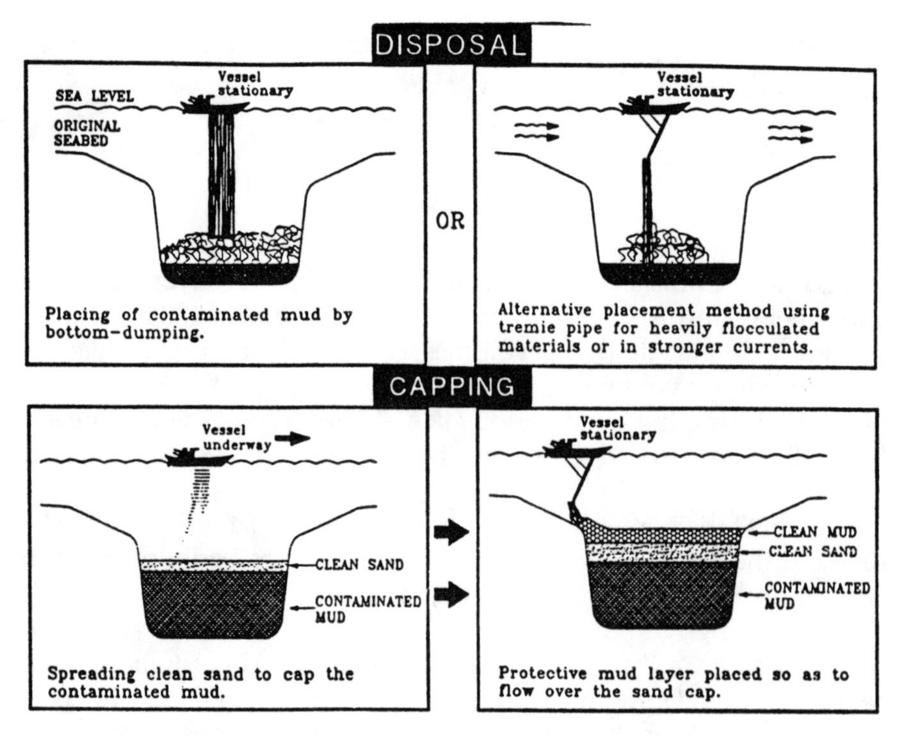

Figure 4–7 Disposal and Capping of Contaminated Mud from Victoria Harbor, Hong Kong. From: S. B. Reed. *Environmental Asset or Liability* Port 2000 Conference, Hong Kong, May 1993.

pects of dredging are effectively planned and controlled, serious and irreversible damage to the environment may occur.

Dredged materials must be tested prior to and during dredging, and the quality must be evaluated to affect both safe dredging and the transport and disposal of spoils. Where the quality of the spoils is in serious doubt, confined or container disposal is often required. Containment is usually constructed of dikes, and their permeability is restricted or prevented by the use of geotextiles or other types of surface treatments.

4.6 NUCLEAR AND TOXIC WASTE POLLUTION CONTAINMENT AND PREVENTION

The safe, permanent disposal of nuclear waste has been a longstanding problem and is becoming a major issue. There is an increase of nuclear waste resulting from the depletion of nuclear reactor fuel, disarmament in nuclear weapons, and an increasing use of radioisotopes and nuclear materials for tests and other operations. Early after the emergence of nuclear fission as an explosive and power source (soon after World War II), nuclear waste was often dumped at sea in metal-shielded containers under the assumption that salt water provided adequate shielding at great ocean depths.

Only recently has the error of this approach been discovered. Now efforts are under way to try to recover such waste off the New England coast and elsewhere lest it contaminate fish and other marine animals. More recently, "safe" disposal of low-level radioactive waste is claimed to provide a relatively safe permanent disposal method for such pollutants. In one method, the waste would be cast into concrete gravel and after mixing with sand is emplaced in reinforced concrete encasement blocks of about 1 m^3 for placement into deeply excavated lined ditches offshore; the ditches would then be filled with sand and capped. A number of variants of this encasement method of disposal have been suggested.

4.6.1 Nuclear Submarine and Disarmament Waste in the Oceans

Neutralizing the hazards of nuclear wastes in the oceans, such as those posed by accidental sinkage of nuclear submarines, is of great importance. Since the 1989 fire of the *Komsomolets,* 150 mi north of Norway's northern coast (a rich fishing areas), several other nuclear submarines sunk or were sunk in waters northeast of Murmansk, Russia.

One suggested solution to neutralize the wastes is to fill the sunken submarines with a gel that would harden and prevent leakage of radioactive waste while at the same time permeating or reducing leakage of radioactivity to ocean waters. The gel has never been used, but tests proceed to perfect it and to develop effective delivery methods.

Although significant radioactivity is leaking from sunken nuclear submarines and some other reactors now, leakage of nuclear materials such as plutonium from missile warheads has not been discovered. There is a great urgency to devise an effective method for neutralizing potential hazards, but as yet no technology exists for the recovery of these submarines, some of which, such as the *Komsomolets,* lie in water depths of about 6,000 ft.

Nuclear disarmament of Russia (the former USSR) and the

United States is causing a particularly difficult environmental problem. In the former USSR, most of its nuclear waste was dumped into the ocean, but in the United States, nuclear waste is stored in special depositories on land.

Environmentally, an important issue is land-use planning for severely contaminated areas. Technologies do not yet exist to return these areas to safe levels of habitability. The United States lacks an overall regulatory framework defining standards of "how clean is clean?" in terms of nuclear and toxic contamination. For example, at the Department of Energy's Hanford site in Washington State, over 440 billion gal of radioactive and toxic liquids—enough to create a poisonous lake the size of Manhattan and over 80 ft deep—were poured into the soil. Some of these liquids may have drained into groundwater or the aquifer. There is a lack of standards to determine how to process or manage (recycle or put in landfills) these contaminants. Without such guidelines, it is impossible to dispose of these contaminants.

In Russia, not only are tremendous areas severely contaminated, but also facilities continue to generate fissile materials to maintain jobs, with much of the waste going into the ground, into rivers, or into ocean waters. This may have serious long-term effects, because much of this waste cannot be readily contained, treated, or neutralized.

4.6.2 Use of the Abyssal Ocean for Waste Disposal

The use of the deep seafloor for waste disposal has been proposed for some time, although little is known of both the engineering problems involved in such a venture and the long-term impact of such disposal. Some have suggested burying solid wastes in specially prepared subfloor depositories, while others have suggested dropping waste into ocean floor cracks and fissures for probable disposal in the crust of the earth's mantle.

Disposal of organic material has also been considered, although there has always been a concern about the effect of organically rich disposals on the sea bed. Such disposals may produce anoxic conditions that could produce significant changes in the benthic conditions and marine life on the seafloor, which is known to be quite active even at great depths. Additions of chemicals are known to perturb the benthic environment, particularly at great depths where water motions or currents and, as a result, mobility of polluted sediment or chemicals is often limited.

The abyssal ocean consists largely of plains at depths of 4,000–6,000 m (which represent about 80% of the area of the world's oceans) and deeper valleys, trenches, and faults, many of which are tectonically active. The abyssal plains, hills, and shallow valleys are usually covered with sediments of oxidized clay and calcareous material formed from deposits of planktons and similar organisms. The temperature of abyssal ocean waters is usually a few degrees above or below freezing point and varies from about –3°C to +3°C. Dispersal of contaminants on the bottom is made difficult by the high water column and the low flow velocities experienced at these depths.

4.6.3 Ocean Island Geological Nuclear and Toxic Waste Repositories[4]

The use of a geological repository for the deposition of stabilized nuclear, toxic, and poisonous waste has been considered for some time now. Such a repository could be constructed under the seabed and could be covered by a large ocean island and shielded on all sides by thick layers of sand and other materials.

Although this approach offers many advantages—such as safety of isolation; effective shielding by many meters of rock, gravel, and sand; and being surrounded by large oceans, away from groundwater and other resources consumed by humans, and separated from human activities that may cause fires and explosions—certain issues cause reservations to be raised. One is that oceans, particularly deep oceans, are extraterritorial areas under the jurisdiction of humanity and not particular nations. Furthermore, oceans are mobile and dynamic environments that readily transport suspended particles over large distances. Therefore, any leakage of polluted particles or radiation that radiates sediment may affect even remote areas of the globe.

The idea now being advanced is to mix liquified nuclear or toxic waste with a cement or concreting mix so as to form small blocks or stones of concrete. These are next surrounded by dense

[4]C. Forsberg, "An Ocean Island Geological Repository—A Second-Generation Option for Disposal of Spent Fuel and High-Level Waste," *Nuclear Technology* 101 (January 1993).

sand or nonpolluted small blocks of stone and inserted into a precast reinforced concrete box. The box has outside dimensions of about 1 × 1 × 1 m with a 10–20 cm shell thickness and a cover that both contains and shields the waste. This reinforced concrete would be designed to be strong enough to resist any breakage or fracturing.

4.7 ENVIRONMENTAL GEOTECHNICAL ENGINEERING

Structures to control erosion, protect reclaimed land or slopes, and reduce scouring of channels as well as the toes of breakwaters, piers, or dikes usually consist of large stone armor, gravel, or even concrete surfacing. In some cases, such methods also use geotextiles, separately or in combination with the above-mentioned methods.

Even though some of these methods are environmentally benign, they all have some environmental impact. In recent years biological methods, particularly the use of plants or vegetation for slope protection, for reducing erosion, or for scouring, have become a meaningful alternative to structural protection. Biotechnical soil stabilization techniques have been perfected to provide reliable, environmentally attractive, self-regenerating solutions whose initial and maintenance costs are usually well below those of more traditional approaches.

5

Ocean Environmental Regulation

Ocean pollution prevention has relied mainly on extensive, yet often impractical, regulation of operations and other activities in the oceans. Technical solutions and methods for the satisfaction of guidelines and regulations often do not exist. As a result, these rules have often become simply unenforceable and sometimes only meaningless documents. Instead of preventing pollution, such regulations then become a shield for polluters who are protected by unenforceable laws. In many cases, environmental laws have become political instruments designed to further local, national, or international interests. Their meaning is often diffused and their enforcement lax.

For environmental laws to have any meaning on the national and international level, they must be built into policy making. Environmental considerations must be part and parcel of the policy-making process and not be added as an afterthought. They must be included in economic, social, educational, health, and strategic policy making, and environmental impact must form an integral part of policy analysis.

For national policy makers, impact on the population must be given priority. When weighing the environmental impact of policies, both local as well as national effects must be considered. Although policies and laws dealing with environmental impacts that affect human health and well-being should obviously be given priority, the impacts are not always very clear. Indeed, many are secondary or tertiary impacts resulting from chemical reactions, processes that are transmitted down or up the food chain, or are physical reactions caused indirectly by unrelated phenomena.

Policy changes and resulting laws usually cause obstacles or barriers to be erected by various interest groups. Similarly, public opinion will often tend to influence policy making on dramatic newsworthy environmental issues that may be marginal from a broader perspective. As a result, the most important environmental issues are often ignored. To be effective, solutions to ocean environmental problems usually require a partnership between public and private entities and among national and international agencies.

Increasing pressure for the use of ocean resources imposes not only new potentials for conflict, but also greater possibilities for ocean pollution. International agencies, national governments, and state and local authorities have introduced environmental laws and regulations. On the international level, the Law of the Sea Convention, which was first proposed in 1972 and was formalized in 1982, in 1993 had 55 of the 156 signatories required for ratification to bring the convention into force. The convention has been an exercise in "preemptive lawmaking and an effort to codify existing rules and create incentives for the observance of new ones."[1]

The convention is not only designed to safeguard national and user rights in the oceans, but also to protect the marine environment in a more effective approach taken by existing or proposed international agreements. These agreements cover mostly or exclusively ship-induced pollution, ignoring all land, coastal water, river, and air-carried pollution deposited in the oceans.

An internationally accepted law of the sea would not only contribute to the improvements in ocean environments by protecting it more generally. It would add to the achievements of security or defense objectives as well as improve the fair economic use of the oceans by providing a known, and possibly enforceable, body of laws that identify specific rights and duties. The Law of the Sea

[1]Elliot L. Richardson, Chairman of the Council of Ocean Law, at Council of Ocean Law Meeting, Washington D.C. May 1993.

Convention would establish a new international order that would not only protect the ocean environment comprehensively but would also provide incentives for more effective fishery management and exploitation of other ocean resources.

The convention would generate large new investments in ocean exploration, and later ocean resource exploitation, by formally establishing the rules under which ocean resources could be used. Even though the economic advantage of ocean mining may be far in the future because of the relative costs of ocean mining, fish farming and many other ocean industries may offer near-term economic opportunities that may resolve or diminish major problems with access to adequate food and other resources so abundantly available in the oceans.

The increasing dependence of nations and the world on international trade makes the passing of the Law of the Sea Convention a particularly urgent matter that, when resolved, will benefit all by establishing defined rules for the use of humans' greatest resource, the world's oceans.

Degradation of the ocean environment—depletion of fish stocks, wildlife, marine aquaculture and mariculture, coastal zone habitats, and recreational environments, as well as the oceans' ability to perform its natural absorptive and evaporative functions—has led to many laws, agreements, and regulations designed to reverse this trend.

At the same time, the increased uses of the oceans introduce economic factors and interests that often counteract these ecological pressures. In this chapter, the major trends in environmental law and rule making and their effects both on the national and international level are described. In particular, the effect of conflicts in political, economic, and environmental terms that affect not only rule making but also interpretation and enforcement are discussed.

While the gathering of scientific information to support many of the environmental laws continues, it is more and more evident that for such laws to have a real impact not only is effective control and enforcement needed, but also economic rationale.

Environmental laws and regulations are often introduced reactively both to respond to an increasingly important environmental impact and to reduce the impact instead of preventing the accident or phenomena that causes the impact. Under these circumstances, such laws or regulations are usually designed to prevent or reduce the impact or occurrence of a past accident, which may never recur because the conditions that caused it may have been unique. Instead, reasonable scenarios of the whole range of possibilities should be used to design laws and regulations that will prevent or reduce the impact of all possible accidents.

5.1 INTERNATIONAL OCEAN ENVIRONMENTAL REGULATIONS

The International Maritime Organization (IMO), a technical agency of the United Nations, has become the principal agency for international ocean environmental regulation. The International Convention for the Prevention of Pollution from Ships, 1973, as modified by the Protocol of 1978 (MARPOL 73/78), has received widespread acceptance.

Implementation of these instruments is credited with a major reduction in oil and other pollution of the oceans by ships. The IMO has developed a long-term strategy to ensure continued improvements in the ocean environment, not only by regulation but also by technical assistance.

The IMO program is composed of subprograms under (1) the Marine Safety Committee (MSC); (2) the Marine Environment Protection Committee (MEPC); (3) the Legal Committee; and, (4) the Facilitation Committee. Each addresses particular areas of concern.

The IMO's programs are directed towards achieving ocean environmental protection objectives and, according to the secretary general of the IMO, are oriented toward the following areas.

1. *Prevention of marine pollution from shipping activities (that is, from operational discharges)*. The principal means by which this problem is tackled is MARPOL 73/78.

2. *Marine pollution emergency response*. Notwithstanding international efforts, accidents will continue to occur, and the 1990 International Convention on Oil Pollution Preparedness, Response and Cooperation was adopted to provide a global framework for cooperation in emergencies. Developing countries are often heavily reliant on marine resources while at the same time lacking the capacity to combat marine pollution incidents that threaten them.

3. *Management of waste disposal at sea*. For many countries, dis-

posal at sea of certain categories of waste, such as dredged materials and sewage sludge, will continue to be the best practicable option. The 1972 London Convention (London Dumping Convention), for which the IMO provides secretarial functions, is the global instrument for dumping.

4. *Liability, compensation, and intervention issues.* Developing countries require assistance to understand and strengthen environmental legislation relating to rights and compensation in the event of damage arising from marine pollution caused by ships. These are set out in the Civil Liability, FUND, and Intervention Conventions.

5. *Baseline information.* The lack of adequate baseline data for the identification and assessment of marine pollution problems is acutely felt by developing countries.

These problems and their objectives are shown in Figure 5–1.

These programs are largely financed by voluntary contributions by donor countries and organizations such as the European Economic Community, (EEC), the U.N. Development Program, (UNDP), the U.N. Economic Program, (UNEP), oil industry bodies, and others. A major goal of the IMO's program is to equip participating contracting nations with the technical skills, equipment, and resources for effective implementation and control of the conventions and regulations.

IMO-administered regulations are, in most respects, quite specific and are designed to permit cooperating country agencies to enforce them. For example, control of discharge of oil from ships is governed by MARPOL and specifies discharge limits as shown in Table 5–1. Cooperating countries are expected to assist in the enforcement of these standards.

5.1.1 International Ocean Sewage Disposal Regulations

In 1978, the IMO developed a convention governing the discharge of sewage into the ocean. Various sewage handling and treatment methods have since been developed to handle sewage discharge, particularly within a distance of 12 nautical miles (n mi) from the shore. The standards of discharge are defined as follows:

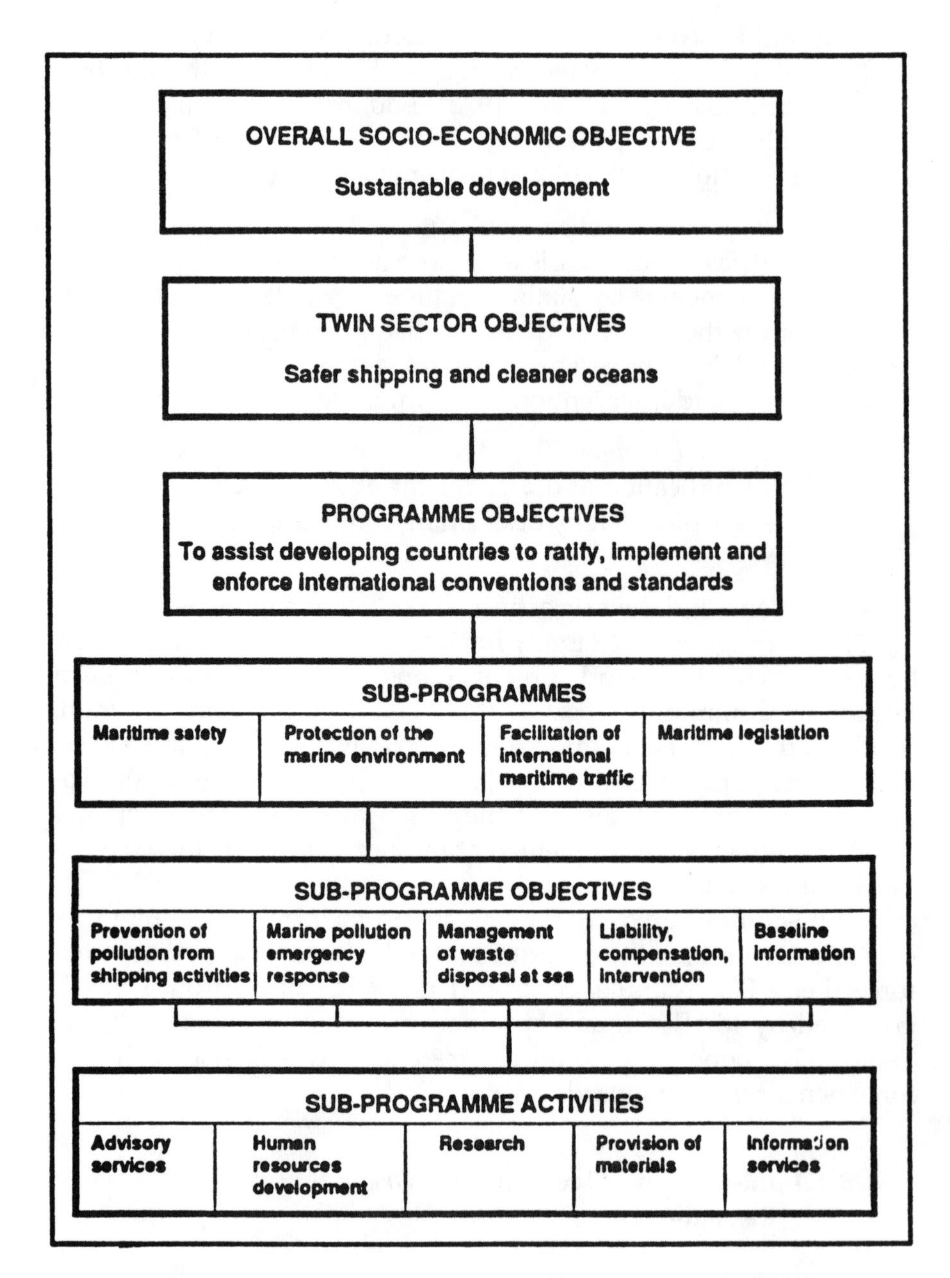

Figure 5–1 IMO Ocean Environmental Protection Programs. From: IMO Report of the Secretary General, June 1993.

TABLE 5–1 Control of Discharge of Oil from Ships

From cargo tanks of oil tankers	
< 12 n mi	No discharge except clean or segregated ballast
< 50 n mi	No discharge except clean or segregated ballast
> 50 n mi	No discharge except clean or segregated ballast
	Exception: tanker is on route and instant rate of discharge is less than 60 l/n mi, and the total quantity discharged is smaller than 1/15,000 (existing tankers) or 1/30,000 (new tankers) of the total quantity of cargo carried on just-completed voyage tanker has oil discharge monitoring and control system as per MARPOL 78.
From machinery	
Oil tankers and other ships ≥ 400 gross registered tons (GRT) < 12 n mi no discharge except proceeding on route and discharge smaller than 15 parts per million (ppm) (without dilution)	

1. faecal coliforms 250/100 ml;
2. suspended solids 50 mg/l;
3. five-day biological oxygen demand (BOD_5) must be less than 50 mg/l; and
4. use of disinfectants other than chlorine (such as ozone or ultra-violet light irradiation) is to be discouraged and residual (also of chlorine) in the effluent is to be minimized.

The principal onboard treatment methods in use today are mechanical sewage processing, biological plants, and chemical treatment methods.

1. Mechanical Sewage Processing

In mechanical sewage processing, the particle size in the sewage is first reduced by use of a macerator pump, followed by screening and sedimentation, with or without adding process water to flush the screens and dilute the effluent. Chlorine addition, as both a disinfectant and to support chemical oxidation, is usually required to reduce the BOD. Mechanical process plants are small and simple but may have difficulty in reaching the required effluent values.

2. Biological Plants

The most common of the biological plants use aerobic bacteria to treat the sewage, followed by aeration clarification and disinfection. Sludge production is usually small and few additives are needed. The process is effective but requires a large volume because aeration requires much time, which in turn imposes the need for large process tanks (about 15 m^3 per 100 persons). Biological treatment processes are also sensitive to toxic agents, such as detergents used to clean toilets, because these may kill the bacteria cultures.

3. **Chemical Treatment Methods**

   In chemical treatment, chemical agents are mixed with the sewage, causing impurities to form flocculents that can then be removed mechanically. This type of plant is small and insensitive to most toxic agents, but has a large sludge output and requires a large volume of costly chemicals.

In a typical marine sewage treatment plant, sewage goes through a sequence of rotary screen, aeration tank, stirring vessel, floatator, and disinfection tank from where it is discharged. Sludge is removed from the rotary screen and the floatator while some of the effluent is returned to the floatator from the disinfection tank via a dispersion vessel. Flocculent is added to the stirring vessel and polymers to the effluent from the stirring vessel before the effluent enters the floatator and disinfectant is added to the disinfection tank.

The reduction results are usually quite good. Typically suspended solids are reduced from 2,000 mg/l to about 20 mg/l, or by a factor of 1/100. Similarly, the BOD_5 is reduced from about 700 mg/l to about 20 mg/l.

The major problem is usually disposal of the sludge. Sludge can be discharged in ports or burned in an incinerator after drying. Another problem of increasing concern is the discharge of chlorine.

5.1.2 Port State Control

Under the so-called Paris Memorandum of 1982, ports in various jurisdictions assume state authority to inspect for, check, and enforce state safety and environmental requirements. In fact, ports represent and act on behalf of both the flag state and their own jurisdiction. The agreements on port state control were the result of increasing concern with the safety of ships sailing between foreign or nonflag ports called cross trading ships that seldom, if ever, called at flag ports. In fact, many had never called at a flag port. With over 50% of the world tonnage under flags of convenience or international registries, the issue of inspection had become a serious concern.

Port state control is also a way to ensure greater uniformity of inspection quality. Although primarily concerned with ship safety, port state control also addresses issues of ship compliance with requirements of international environmental conventions, such as MARPOL and the London Dumping Convention. Attempts are now under way to organize more regional systems of port state control worldwide and to establish uniform standards of inspection.

The experience from Western Europe, the first region to introduce and enforce port state control in all its ports, shows that such a system cannot effectively eradicate the existence of substandard ships despite regional efforts because owners can divert such vessels to other trades. Worldwide port state control regions are required if the system is to ensure the elimination of vessels that do not comply with international safety and environmental standards. Under port state control, vessels can be detained until defects are corrected. As shown in Table 5–2, most vessels with detention percentages exceeding a 3-year rolling average, which are targeted as priority cases for inspection in 1993–1994, are registered under flags of convenience. Although deficiencies in general are declining, there appears to be a rising trend in the number of deficiencies concerned with defective MARPOL equipment, as shown in Figure 5–2.

5.1.3 IMO Regulations for the Prevention of Marine Pollution by Tankers

Recently planned implementation by the IMO of the partial amendments to the Annex of the MARPOL Convention, which imposes mandatory requirements for double hull or similar pollution prevention or reduction measures on both existing and new tankers, has far-reaching effects on world shipping and shipbuilding.

To reduce discharge of oil from tankers, MARPOL 1973 amendments required tankers to use specially designed slop tanks for the collection of oily water mixtures resulting from tank washing and carrying ballast in oil cargo tanks. This was to prevent the discharge of oily water mixtures into the sea. Similarly, the capacity of cargo oil tanks was limited to less than 30,000 tons, independent of the size of tanker.

Also in 1973 the mandatory fitting or adoption of segregated ballast tanks, inert gas systems, and crude oil washing systems

TABLE 5–2 Flag States with Detention Percentages Exceeding 3-Year Rolling Average Percentage to be Targeted as Priority Cases for Inspection in 1993–1994

FLAG STATE	NO. OF DETENTION 1990–1992	TOTAL NO. OF SHIPS INVOLVED 1990–1992	DETENTION (%) 1990–1992	AVERAGE DETENTION (%) 1990–1992	EXCESS OVER AVERAGE (%) 1990–1992
Romania	66	352	18.75	5.11	13.64
St. Vincent and Grenadines	91	551	16.52	5.11	11.41
Honduras	64	415	15.42	5.11	10.32
India	31	205	15.12	5.11	10.01
Morocco	17	113	15,04	5.11	9.93
Malta	128	1,086	11.79	5.11	6.68
Egypt	19	168	11.31	5.11	6.20
Iran	8	71	11.27	5.11	6.16
Syrian Arab Republic	6	60	10.00	5.11	4.89
Lebanon	8	82	9.76	5.11	4.65
Panama	176	2,117	8.31	5.11	3.20
Cyprus	174	2,218	7.84	5.11	2.73
Turkey	42	564	7.54	5.11	2.34
Algeria	8	114	7.02	5.11	1.91
Liberia	86	1,551	5.54	5.11	0.43
Bahamas	73	1,329	5.49	5.11	0.38
Antilles, Netherlands	10	189	5.29	5.11	0.18
Antigua and Barbuda	32	625	5.12	5.11	0.01

SOURCE: *Marine Engineers Review,* Journal of the Institute of Marine Engineers, (London: September 1993, p. 19)

(using crude oil instead of sea water for washing) was adopted by MARPOL. In 1978, Protective Location, whereby the spaces for segregated ballast tanks cover at least 30% of the aggregate length of the ship's side and the projected bottom shell area, was also adopted.

Finally, in 1992, mandatory adoption of double-hull construction in new tankers was adopted according to Partial Amendments to the Annex 1 of the MARPOL Convention. The last was largely the result of the outcry from the *Exxon Valdez* oil pollution disaster of 1989. This grounding caused the U.S. Congress unilaterally to introduce the Oil Pollution Act of 1990 (OPA-90), which made double hulls mandatory for new ships using U.S. waters.

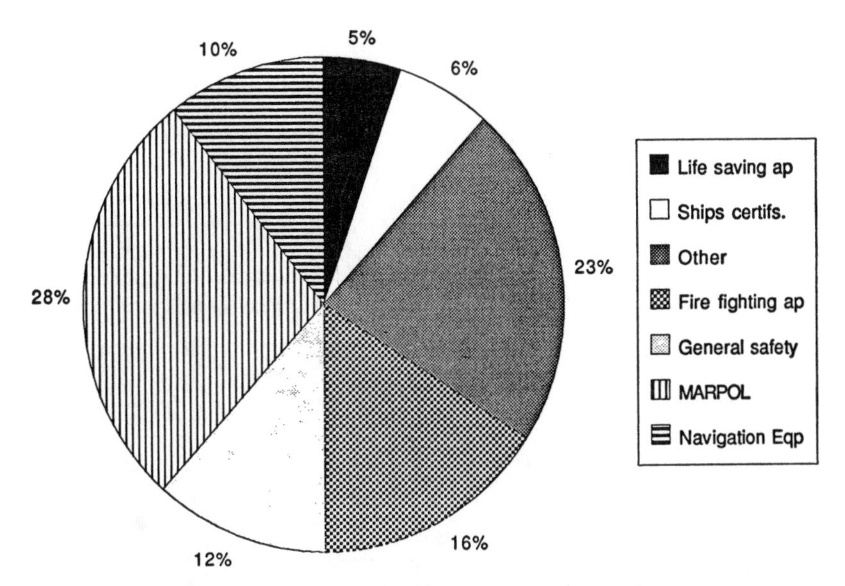

Figure 5–2 Major Categories of Deficiencies as a Percentage of Total Number of Deficiencies. From: *Marine Engineers Review*, The Institute of Marine Engineers (London, Sept. 1993, p. 20).

The new IMO regulations also specify requirements as to the capacity and arrangements of ballast tanks, restrict the installation of suction wells in cargo tanks, address arrangements of cargo and ballast piping, and prohibit carriage of oil in spaces forward of the collision bulkhead.

Double-hull tankers, admitted by the IMO regulations of 1992, are

1. double bottom and sides, and/or
2. double-side hull and midheight deck (Figure 5–3).

Both of these methods reduce, but do not prevent, oil spills from a damaged ship. Details of the Partial Amendments are summarized in Tables 5–3 and 5–4.

5.2 AMERICAN OCEAN ENVIRONMENTAL REGULATION

U.S. ocean environmental regulation has evolved over a very long time and is still being changed and expanded. The most important federal legislation was enacted since 1970; yet the federal govern-

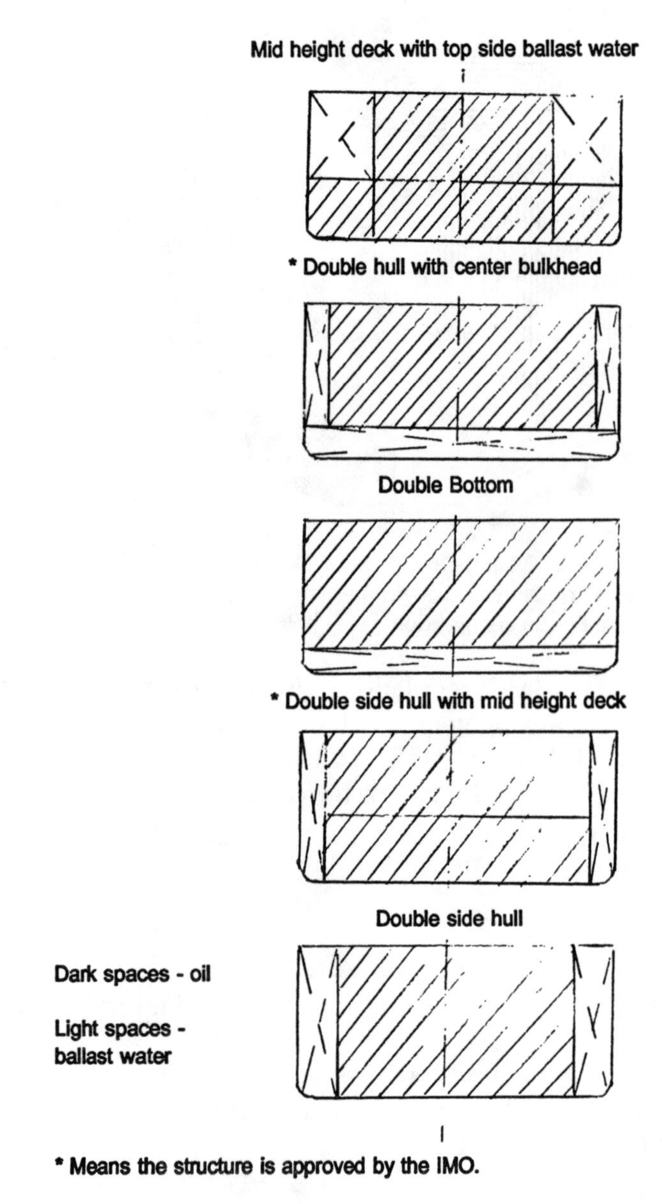

Figure 5–3 Comparison of Structural Designs for the Prevention of Spills from Tankers.

TABLE 5–3 Partial Amendments to the Annex 1 of the MARPOL Convention Relating to Double-Hull Tankers (Summary of the Amendments Relating to New Ships)

<table>
<tr><th>DIVISION</th><th>ITEMS</th><th colspan="2">CONTENTS OF THE REGULATIONS</th></tr>
<tr><td rowspan="5">New ships (Regulation 13F)</td><td>Object ships</td><td colspan="2">(1) Ship type
- Oil tankers engaged in the carriage of crude oil or refined products
- Oil tankers to be newly built or to undergo major conversion
(2) Time limits for compliance
1. A ship for which the building contract is placed on or after July 6, 1993
2. A ship whose new construction or major conversion work is begun on or after Jan. 6, 1994
3. A ship whose delivery is on or after July 6, 1996</td></tr>
<tr><td rowspan="4">Application and structural arrangements</td><td>Object ships</td><td>Hull Structure</td></tr>
<tr><td>Under 600 DWT</td><td>Not applicable</td></tr>
<tr><td>Between 600–5,000 DWT (1 or 2)</td><td>1. DB
a) The height of DB is not less than B/15 m or 0.76 m, whichever is the lesser.
b) The capacity of each tank is less than 700 cubic meters.
2. DS
The width of DS is not less than (0.4 + 2.4 × DWT/20,000) m (but not less than 0.76 m) or the capacity of each tank is less than 700 m^3.</td></tr>
<tr><td>Over 5,000 DWT (1 or 2 or 3)</td><td>1. DH (DB and DS)
a) The height of DB is not less than B/15 m or 2.0 m, whichever is the lesser, but not less than 1.0 m.
b) The width of DS is not less than (0.5 + DWT/20,000) m or 2.0 m, whichever is the lesser, but not less than 1.0 m.
2. MDT
a) The width of DS is same as 1. b) above.
b) The height of MDT is not less than B/6 m or 6.0 m, whichever is the lesser, but not more than 0.6D so as to prevent the outflow of oil from the tank, even if its bottom was broken through while trading with the minimum operating draught.
3. Other alternative structure corresponding to 1. above.</td></tr>
</table>

SOURCE: Resolution and its annex dated March 2, 1992, of Marine Environmental Protection Committee of IMO.

Entry into effect of the new regulations:
The new regulations shall be deemed to have been accepted on July 6, 1993, unless prior to this date the necessary quorum of the contracting countries have communicated to IMO their opposition to the amendments.
Symbols used: DB: double bottom, DS: double-side hull: MDT: double-side hull with mid-height deck; B: the breadth of the ship; D: moulded depth amidships.

TABLE 5–4 Partial Amendments to the Annex 1 of MARPOL Convention Relating to Double-Hull Tankers (Summary of the Amendments Relating to Existing Ships)

DIVISION \ ITEM			CONTENTS OF THE REGULATIONS
Existing ships	Object ships	Ship type and ship size	Crude oil tankers of 20,000 DWT and above Oil product carriers of 30,000 DWT and above
	Scope of application	Pre-MARPOL ship (EE ship: "SBT..YES") (EN ship: "SBT..NO")	1. Compliance with regulation 13F is required not later than 25 years after its date of delivery. 2. In case where the ship's side or bottom shell plating is protected by spaces or compartments which are not used for the carriage of oil, and the total length of which covers at least 30% of the total length of cargo tanks, compliance with regulation 13F is required not later than 30 years after its date of delivery.
		Post-MARPOL ship (NN ship: "SBT..YES")	Compliance with regulation 13F is required unconditionally not later than 30 years after its date of delivery.

SOURCE: Resolution and its annex dated March 2, 1992, of Marine Environmental Protection Committee of IMO.

Entry into effect of the new regulations: As from July 6, 1995.

Symbols used: "SBT..YES" means "The ship is fitted with segregated ballast tanks.
"SBT..NO" means "The ship is not fitted with segregated ballast tanks.

Others: Enhancement of surveys and inspections

1) Programs of surveys and inspections must be enhanced in accordance with IMO's guidelines.
2) Tankers over 5 years of age must have on board, available for inspection, a complete file of the survey reports.

ment still relies on the states, to a large extent, to reduce and control ocean pollution.

Starting with the National Environmental Policy Act of 1968, U.S. ocean environmental policy and regulation has evolved gradually. The Intervention on the High Seas Act and the Oil Pollution Act

Amendments of 1973 were the first serious attempts at putting teeth into the International Convention for the Prevention of the Pollution of the Sea by Oil in 1954 and the original Oil Pollution Act of 1924. These acts have been largely ignored because they lacked both specificity as well as the instruments of enforcement. Furthermore, the impact of oil pollution of the oceans was not fully understood. Most other sources of ocean pollution were either not recognized or their effects were underestimated. In fact, until 1968, the oceans were largely assumed to provide both an economical and safe depository for all kinds of waste, from waste incinerator ship ash to sewage to even most types of industrial waste. While the ill effects of detergents, chemical fertilizers, and other agricultural chemicals were known, emphasis was placed on preventing their intrusion into freshwater, with little effort made to prevent drainage of such agricultural wastes into the oceans.

In more recent years, and particularly since 1970, significant legislation designed to protect the ocean environment has been passed. Most of this legislation was initially imbedded in general environmental policy acts. More and more specific laws have since been passed, and enforcement has been assigned to federal agencies, such as the U.S. Coast Guard and U.S. Army Corps of Engineers, for many ocean environmental impacts.

5.2.1 Early Developments in U.S. Ocean Environmental Regulation

Major federal legislation designed to protect the environment from further degradation has been enacted largely since 1970. Although much of this legislation recognizes that it is the duty of the states to reduce and control pollution, the federal government "stick" is in provisions requiring that if states do not meet federal standards in their enforcement, the federal government will take over.

The National Environmental Policy Act of 1969 (NEPA) mandated concern for the environment in federal agency decision making. Section 102(C), the backbone of this mandate, requires that recommendations for

> major federal actions significantly affecting the quality of the human environment [shall include] a detailed statement by the responsible official on—

(i) the environmental impact of the proposed action,
(ii) any adverse environmental effects which cannot be avoided should the proposal be implemented,
(iii) alternatives to the proposed action,
(iv) the relationship between local short-term uses of man's environment and the maintenance and enhancement of long-term productivity, and
(v) any irreversible and irretrievable commitments of resources which would be involved in the proposed action should it be implemented.

Prior to making any detailed statement, the responsible federal official shall consult with and obtain the comments of any federal agency which has jurisdiction by law or special expertise with respect to any environmental impact involved.

The act also established the Council on Environmental Quality (CEQ) in the president's executive office. The CEQ advises the president on environmental affairs and legislation. The CEQ has also developed guidelines for agency compliance with NEPA. It does not directly regulate any activities outside the government.

Pursuant to CEQ guidelines, each agency has developed procedures for including environmental concerns in its decision-making process. If more than one agency is involved in a decision, only one need prepare an environmental impact statement (EIS).

Frequently, the person promoting a major federal action will hire a contractor specializing in preparing EISs to gather the data and prepare an EIS to go along with the application. The agency, however, is responsible for the content of any EIS prepared for action that agency takes.

The review of EISs by the courts is a study in itself. It may be generally stated that courts will only investigate whether an EIS has been adequately prepared with respect to environmental impacts considered and agencies consulted. In general, an EIS

1. should be understandable and nonconclusory,
2. should refer to the full range of knowledge, and
3. must discuss certain impacts that are typical of some types of action.

If an EIS is held to be inadequately prepared, further agency action may be enjoined until an adequate statement has been prepared. The courts may be vigilant in seeing that all views on environmental effect are considered by the agency (the EIS "procedure"), but may refuse to assess the merits of the contentions included in the EIS or the balance struck between negative effects on the environment and other benefits unless the balance struck is arbitrary, capricious, or an abuse of discretion.

The extent of the effects to be considered in an adequate EIS is also a study in itself. NEPA has been interpreted to be a "full disclosure" law, assuring that decision makers and the public are alerted to possible environmental consequences of proposed actions. Generally, an EIS must consider the direct effect of the action with reference to the five factors in Section 102(C) of NEPA, including whether the action will lead to violation of other laws to protect the environment, whether or not such other laws are policed by the agency preparing it; an EIS must consider alternatives to the proposed action that must be discussed; an EIS must consider the cumulative effect of this action with other known or proposed government actions affecting the same area; and an EIS must also consider secondary effects.

The operation of a port must be in conformity with the requirements of laws regulating water pollution. There are two complementary approaches to water pollution control: definition of acceptable water quality for a body of water, and elimination of discharges of pollutants into the water. These two approaches are exemplified by the two statutory goals (although achievement of the goals is not required): "swimmable" water by 1983 (water quality) and no discharge by 1985 (effluent limitation).

These goals were pursued by a somewhat novel federal-state partnership. Rather than dividing the responsibility on a federal waters versus state waters basis, the Federal Water Pollution Control Act (FWPCA) permits each state to enforce standards that meet federal guidelines over all waters within the state's boundaries (including the sea out 3 mi). The federal guidelines ensure some uniformity and protect the national interest with respect to interstate waters.

The states set water quality standards for each body of water. An example is a requirement of no more than 1,000 fecal coliform bacteria per 100 milliliters. Once these standards are approved by the EPA, they are to be reviewed and revised by the states through public hearings at least every 3 years. Meanwhile, the EPA is required to publish national water quality criteria to be used in establishing and reviewing state water quality standards.

To achieve water quality standards, the discharge of pollutants into a body of water must be controlled. Two types of discharges are identified: point sources and nonpoint sources. Point sources are any discrete sources of discharge identifiable by virtue of some conduit of discharge to the waterway; examples include vessels, manufacturing plants, and sewage treatment plans. Nonpoint sources reflect pollution caused by runoff, such as from agricultural land (water containing pesticides, for example) or construction sites. The two types of sources are subject to different regulations.

Point sources are not permitted to discharge pollutants except in accordance with a permit issued by the EPA or by the state under an EPA-approved plan. The EPA will approve a state plan that ensures that the permit will comply with the FWPCA. After the EPA approves the state plan, the state becomes the permit-granting authority and the EPA only monitors state performance with two devices: the ability to overrule the state on a case-by-case basis and the ability to rescind approval of the state program after a hearing. The EPA may waive its right to object to a particular application unless the application involves discharge in the territorial sea.

A permit under the FWPCA and the National Pollution Discharge Elimination System (NPDES) authorizing the discharge of pollutants will specify effluent limits. These limits might be in terms of pollutants per time period (such as $\frac{1}{10}$ pound of mercury per day), in terms of concentration of pollutant (such as no more than 0.01 ppm of copper), or in terms of maximum discharge per unit of production (such as no more than 5 lb of suspended solids per ton of paper produced).

Discharges of toxic pollutants in toxic amounts are prohibited. In addition, any permit for discharge from a vessel is subject to regulations issued by the secretary of the department in which the Coast Guard is operating that establish "specifications for safe transportation, handling, carriage, storage, and stowage of pollutants."

What this meant to the existing point source was the use of "best practicable" pollution control technology by July 1977, achievement of effluent limitations on toxic pollutants by the same time, and use of the "best available technology economically achievable" by July 1983. In addition, the EPA is required to establish effluent limitations for 27 specific industries (none of which is related to ports) and for such other industries as selected by the EPA. These limitations are to apply to "new" point sources (those on which construction is begun after the regulations were issued), and the regulations must require "the greatest degree of effluent reduction . . . achievable through the application of the best available demonstrated control technology, processes, operating methods, or other alternatives, including, where practicable, a standard permitting no discharge of pollutants." Thus if an existing port is a point source, it is subject to the requirements in its permit but not to special EPA standards. At this point, no regulations have been issued by the EPA concerning discharge standards to be met by new ports.

It is not enough to know the effluent limitations for a particular activity, however. If water quality goals cannot be met through existing effluent limitations, direct dischargers will have to conform to limitations designed to meet those goals. Similarly, even if the water quality goal would be met at a higher level of effluent discharge, dischargers must comply with a more stringent effluent limitation level. Furthermore, under prior law covering water quality, the federal government adopted a "non-degradation" policy, that is, waters (or better-than-required water quality) were to be maintained at their high quality. The 1972 amendments say nothing specific about this problem, and as a practical matter, such a provision may not add anything of substance to the rest of the regulatory scheme. Nevertheless, as a general matter it may be safe to assume that difficulties will be encountered in introducing a new source of pollution into waters that exceed established water quality standards.

If the port is not a point source but discharges into a publicly owned treatment system, the port is not required to obtain a permit under the FWPCA. The treatment works must obtain a permit, however, that provides for notice to the issuer (state or EPA) of a substantial change in the character or volume of pollutants introduced into the treatment works. The permit issuer may restrict or prohibit new tie-ins to the works. If the treatment works are federally funded after March 1, 1973, industrial users must pay a portion of the cost of construction as well as a proportionate share of the cost of operation.

Under the FWPCA, state or regional agencies are required to establish regulatory programs to control various types of nonpoint source pollution. Included within the list of nonpoint sources are construction-related sources of pollution. Control of nonpoint sources is likely to be on an ad hoc basis.

Oil pollution prevention and liability have been the subject of legislation and international conventions. Without attempting a thorough history, it can be noted that oil pollution control legislation dates back to the Oil Pollution Act of 1924 as amended in 1966, and repealed in 1970 by the predecessor of the FWPCA Amendments of 1972. Legislation inspired by the International Convention for the Prevention of the Pollution of the Sea by Oil in 1954 led to legislation in 1961; amendments to the convention led to the Intervention on the High Seas Act and the Oil Pollution Act Amendments of 1973. Because the various acts relating to oil pollution are discussed here as a group, it is necessary to discuss their applicability to vessels and to ports.

One section of the FWPCA deals with discharges of oil or hazardous substances in harmful quantities. It deals also with discharges into the navigable waters of the United States (not "navigable waters" as with other provisions of the act, a term that presumably includes the territorial seas) and with discharges into the contiguous zone. Although it deals with discharges from vessels and onshore or offshore facilities, it does not deal with discharges into the ocean seaward from the contiguous zone.

The Ocean Dumping Act applies to discharges of oil "only to the extent such oil is taken on board a vessel or aircraft for the purpose of dumping." This act regulates transportation from the United States or in U.S. flag ships for dumping anywhere in the ocean.

The Oil Pollution Act regulates discharges of oil or an oily mixture by ships and establishes standards for the construction of tankers in the United States after the act's effective date.

The Intervention Act permits the United States to take action on the high seas to prevent damage to the U.S. shoreline resulting from a marine disaster. In addition, liability for the discharge of oil associated with a deep-water port is provided for by the Deepwater Port Act.

In discussing the pertinent section of the FWPCA, it is necessary to establish what constitutes oil and hazardous substances within the meaning of that section.

> [O]il means oil of any kind or in any form, including, but not limited to, petroleum, fuel oil, sludge, oil refuse, and oil mixed with wastes other than dredged spoil.
>
> "[H]azardous substance" means any substance designated pursuant to subsection (b)(2) [section 1321 (b)(2)].

Subsection (b)(2) provides that the EPA shall designate as hazardous substances those substances that, when discharged into the water "in any quantity . . . present an imminent and substantial danger to the public health and welfare."

The president has delegated to the EPA both the authority to determine what constitutes a harmful amount of oil or a hazardous substance and the authority to issue regulations prescribing what discharges are not harmful.

What, then, are hazardous substances, and what discharges of hazardous substances are harmful? Beginning with hazardous substances, neither question has been answered. At the end of 1975, the EPA gave notice of proposed rule making with respect to a list of 370 hazardous substances. At the same time, the EPA proposed regulations concerning harmful quantities for each substance.

The penalties for discharges of hazardous substances are assessed only if the substance is determined to be not removable from the water. If it is not removable, the penalty may be either a single amount of $500 to $5,000 as determined by the EPA or an amount determined under a formula that multiplies the amount discharged by a dollar figure of $100 to $1,000. In the latter case, the maximum penalty is $5 million for discharge from a vessel and $500,000 for discharge from an onshore or offshore facility. In the case of any discharges of a hazardous substance, the person responsible for the discharge is entitled to the defenses applicable to liability for the cleanup costs for an oil discharge (discussed below) in resisting the penalty assessment. For the 370 hazardous substances identified as to be controlled, the EPA has proposed determinations of removability and penalty rates for substances judged not removable. Presumably, the discharge of a hazardous substance judged removable is subject to the other penalty provisions of the FWPCA.

A harmful discharge of oil has been administratively defined to include discharges that (1) violate applicable water quality standards or (2) cause a film or sheen upon, or discoloration of, the surface of the water or adjoining shorelines or cause a sludge or emulsion to the deposits beneath the surface of the water or upon adjoining shorelines.

A variety of penalties and liabilities apply to an oil spill. The person in charge of a vessel or facility that discharges oil or a hazardous substance must immediately notify the "appropriate" U.S. government agency or be subject, on conviction for failure to notify, to a fine of up to $10,000, imprisonment of up to 1 year, or both. The "appropriate" agency is the Coast Guard in Washington, D.C. After a hearing, the owner or operator of the vessel or facility responsible for a discharge is subject to a civil penalty, assessed by the district in which the Coast Guard is operating, of up to $5,000 for each offense. The commandant is entitled to consider several factors, including the gravity of the violation, in determining the appropriate amount of the penalty.

Regulations "establishing procedures, methods and equipment and other requirements for equipment to prevent discharge of oil and hazardous substances from . . . [non–transportation-related] onshore facilities and offshore facilities, and to contain such discharges" are established by the EPA. Similar regulations for vessels and transportation-related facilities, as well as regulations for inspecting vessels carrying such cargoes and the cargoes themselves "in order to reduce the likelihood of discharges of oil," are established by the Coast Guard. Violation of these regulations can result, after a hearing, in assessment of a penalty of up to $5,000 by the EPA or Coast Guard, as appropriate.

The philosophy of the act and regulations seems to be that a discharger should attempt to remove the oil from the water. If those efforts are improper or if the identity of the discharger is unknown, the government may take over the cleanup effort including, if necessary, the destruction of a discharging vessel. The government effort is coordinated under the National Contingency Plan. The discharger is liable for the removal costs.

A discharger is not liable if it is proved that the discharge was caused solely by an act of God, an act of war, the negligence of the U.S. government, an act of a third party, or some combination of such causes. If the discharge is caused by a third party, that person is liable. Similarly, if a discharge, caused by one of the above causes, is removed by a person, that person can be reimbursed by the government.

Because a vessel may be the cause of a discharge and be subjected to liability for cleanup and consequential costs, the owner or operator of a vessel must establish financial responsibility. If two or more vessels are owned, financial responsibilities must be established only to the maximum liability applicable to the largest of the vessels owned. The Federal Maritime Commission carries out this program. In addition, the secretary of the treasury may withhold the clearance necessary before departure for a foreign port from a vessel that has not established its financial responsibility or, if requested to do so by the commandant of the Coast Guard, from a vessel against which a civil penalty for a discharge has been assessed. The Coast

Guard may deny any vessel entry to navigable waters of the United States or detain in port any vessel bound for a point in the United States if the vessel does not furnish evidence of financial responsibility on request. The Coast Guard is also entitled to board and inspect any vessels in enforcing the act or to arrest without warrant anyone violating the act's provisions within the Coast Guard's view.

Despite all that has been said about liability for oil discharges under this federal law, it may be only the tip of the iceberg. The FWPCA clearly provides that

> [n]othing in this section shall be construed as preempting any State or political subdivision thereof from imposing any requirement or liability with respect to the discharge of oil or hazardous substance into any waters within such State.

The Supreme Court has ruled that this waiver of preemption is valid and to so hold is not to conflict with federal admiralty jurisdiction. Thus Florida did not lack the power to impose liability without fault for damage to its property or private property, to claim liability for state-incurred cleanup costs, and to prescribe "containment gear" for vessels and onshore facilities. The validity of the regulations actually enacted, however, was not litigated; the Court suggested that aspects that conflicted with federal law, rather than supplementing or extending it, might later be struck down. For example, the Federal Limited Liability Act would limit vessel liability to the "value of such vessels and freight pending."

The FWPCA and the 1973 amendments apply only to discharges from ships. The amendments continue the present requirement that a tanker keep a record book, in which all activities of a specified nature relating to the cargo are recorded, that remains the property of the government whose flag the tanker flies.

The Intervention of the High Seas Act was adopted after the Senate accepted the 1969 amendments to the Convention for the Prevention of the Pollution of the Sea by Oil in 1954, previously discussed. These amendments were designed to clarify the international acceptability of a coastal state's intervention in the case of a marine disaster in international waters and were precipitated by the 1967 grounding of the *Torrey Canyon*. Whenever a situation creates "a grave and imminent danger to the coastline . . . from pollution . . . of the sea by oil," the United States may coordinate and direct all removal efforts or undertake necessary salvage operations, or remove and destroy the ship causing the danger without liability for damage except "damage caused by measures which exceed those reasonably necessary" to prevent, mitigate, or eliminate that danger. Anyone willfully violating the act, willfully refusing to comply with orders given pursuant to the act, or willfully obstructing compliance with the act may be fined up to $10,000, imprisoned for up to 1 year, or both.

Under the Deepwater Ports Act, liability for oil discharge is treated almost the same as it is under the FWPCA. Discharges must be reported to the Coast Guard, and penalties are provided for failure to report. The maximum liabilities for removal costs and damages are somewhat greater, though; for vessels, the lesser of $150 per gross ton or $20 million; for licensees, $50 million. Liability is imposed without fault except for the defenses of an act of war or the negligence of the government in establishing or maintaining aids to navigation; and there is no liability to a person for damages caused by the discharge if that person's negligence was the sole cause of the discharge. Financial responsibility to meet these liabilities must be demonstrated. A fund of $100 million was created, derived from a loading or unloading fee of 2¢ per barrel, that will be liable for all cleanup costs in excess of the amounts provided for above.

As under the FWPCA, the states are not precluded from "imposing additional requirements or liability for any discharge of oil from a deep water port," although a person may not recover compensation under more than one state or federal law. Presumably in recognition that the various laws relating to liability for oil discharges (including liability for activities on the outer continental shelf) are not uniform, the attorney general was directed to study the feasibility of a uniform law.

Under provisions of the Ports and Waterways Safety Act of 1972, the Coast Guard may establish regulations for the protection of the marine environment relating to the design, construction, and operation of vessels that carry onboard in bulk liquid cargo that is either flammable, oil, or a hazardous substance under the FWPCA.

5.2.2 Recent Developments in U.S. Ocean Environmental Regulation

Increasing public concern with pollution of the oceans during the 1980s has resulted in new U.S. legislation and regulation of activities in the oceans and those affecting the ocean environment.

Incineration at sea and disposal of incineration ash, toxins, medical and low-level radioactive wastes, dredge spoils, and ship solid and liquid wastes, and most importantly, pollution of the oceans by voluntary and involuntary discharge of oil into the seas have become issues of new and increasingly more stringent regulations.

The most important legislation was introduced after the *Exxon Valdez* grounding in Alaska's Prince William Sound in 1989. This grounding caused significant oil discharge and pollution. A massive billion-dollar cleanup was undertaken and Exxon was fined an even larger amount. To prevent a recurrence of this type of disaster, Congress passed new oil pollution prevention regulations and the FWPCA was amended by the Oil Pollution Act of 1990 (OPA-90). Under this latter act, tankers trading in U.S. waters are required to be equipped with double hulls in the future. In addition, after February 1993 all owners of tankers operating in U.S. waters must have filed vessel response plans (VRPs) that identify personnel, equipment, and procedures sufficient to deal with different levels of spills as discussed in Chapter 4. This requirement can be shown by demonstrating an effective capability to contain, remove, and store recovered spilled oil. This also includes training marine environmental protection experts who can plan and manage response plans.

5.2.2.1 Oil Pollution Act of 1990. The Oil Pollution Act of 1990 (OPA-90) was passed in response to the grounding of the *Exxon Valdez* on Bligh Reef in Prince William Sound, Alaska, in which 10 million gal of North Slope crude oil was spilled, causing the largest oil spill in U.S. history. Although OPA-90 provides legislation for the prevention of future spills, combining technical and operation requirements on one hand and severe economic or financial penalties on the other, it only partially solves the problem of spill prevention and response. Clearly, the response to the *Exxon Valdez* oil spill was inadequate and preparations to deal with this type of disaster were, mildly speaking, primitive. This resulted in long delays, consequential damages, and a large outcry for action.

The Clean Water Act requires the president to develop a national contingency plan to provide efficient, coordinated, and effective action for minimizing damage from oil spills and addresses the requirements for such discharges into the navigable waters of the United States and adjoining shorelines. Yet under the national contingency plan, the response system organization, as currently constituted, is composed of representatives of 14 federal agencies. The

Coast Guard is to provide on-scene coordinators for the coastal zone. This plan was found to be clearly inadequate and unable to respond effectively to a large spill.

The Oil Pollution Act of 1990, passed unanimously by Congress and signed into law on August 18, 1990 (Public Law No. 101–380, 104 Stat. 484, 1990), covers changes in structural design in tankers, addresses financial responsibility, and imposes various other requirements. The primary objectives of the act are not accident prevention but reduction or stoppage of spillage resulting from ship groundings and collisions.

OPA-90 only admits double-hulled construction and has come under attack for not considering other potentially less expensive and equally effective alternatives. The act is designed to reduce pollution by tankers, to introduce effective spill response, and to impose meaningful liability and compensation by perpetrators of vessel or facility caused oil pollution. The involvement of the federal government in oversight of all transportation is substantially increased. OPA sets requirements for tanker design, construction, and operation, crew licensing, and personnel levels, and increases penalties.

OPA-90 also sets liability standards and requires response planning. It similarly broadens the government's enforcement authority and response capability. Further, it created a research and development program designed to improve tanker safety. A trust fund of $1 billion, financed by a 5¢ per barrel fee on oil, to cover cleanup costs and other damage not compensated or covered by those responsible for a spill is also set up under OPA. Also, as described in Subsection 5.2.2.2, the financial responsibility requirements on tanker operators or owners are substantially increased.

The act advocates U.S. participation in an international oil pollution liability and compensation scheme, given that it is at least as tough and comprehensive as the federal or applicable state laws in preventing pollution accidents and is providing full compensation for damage caused. OPA allows states to impose their own liabilities and other requirements concerning the discharge of oil into the oceans, including the imposition of additional liability.

Under the act, the Oil Spill Liability Trust Fund can be used for payment of

1. cleanup and spill removal costs consistent with the National Contingency Plan,

2. costs incurred by trustees in assessing damage and for implementing corrective actions,
3. economic damages to those affected by a spill,
4. immediate removal funds for the states of up to $250,000 per spill, and
5. administrative, operational, and personnel costs associated with the act.

Also, the act makes $50 million available to the president annually for oil pollution removal and damage assessment.

OPA requires double-hull construction of all new oil tankers operating on the waters subject to the jurisdiction of the United States. Existing vessels are phased out over a period of years. To assist U.S. owners, a financing provision is included for double-hull tankers (construction or reconstruction) that permits the secretary of transportation to issue new loan guarantees if certain economic and security requirements are met.

The act also gives the federal government specific authority to direct removal of spills if they pose a substantial threat to the public health or welfare. It also requires the preparation of contingency plans by ship as well as terminal owners and operators.

A new National Response System is mandated that lists all removal resources and is designed to provide technical assistance, equipment, and other resources as well as coordination of public and private removal efforts. Similarly, area contingency plans are to be prepared.

The unilateral introduction of the act has come under criticism, notwithstanding that it recommends compliance with "International Conventions and Regulations" if and when these are more comprehensive or stringent than those imposed by the act. The criticism is not only that the act was introduced to counter public pressure resulting from the worst oil pollution accident in the United States, the *Exxon Valdez* grounding in 1989, but that it put more emphasis on accident impact reduction and cleanup than on accident prevention. In fact, nothing in the act itself addresses accident prevention per se.

Similarly, direct or indirect imposition of unlimited liability is designed to open the door to unjust as well as real claims for indemnity. It also opens the door for exorbitant legal costs of pollution liability cases because of the form and clauses of the act. It is noted that the language of the act admits many loose ends and charges the U.S.

Coast Guard with the interpretation of many clauses, a process that is still under way and that may not be resolved in the near future.

Double-Hull Standards under OPA-90. The Coast Guard is adopting standards for double hulls on vessels carrying oil in bulk as cargo or cargo residue that are constructed or undergo major conversions under contracts awarded on June 30, 1990, or later. The Coast Guard is also introducing standards for double hulls on vessels carrying oil in bulk as cargo or cargo residue that were constructed or underwent major conversions under earlier contracts. It provides the shipping and shipbuilding industries with interim standards to meet the double-hull requirement as follows:

1. Double-hull construction is mandated by law and will occur with associated economic impacts and environmental benefits.
2. Once the tanker fleet is fully double hulled, the standards will prevent the discharge of an estimated 1.5–2.5 million gal (5–8,000 tons) per year of oil into U.S. waters.
3. Environmental benefits of this rule will be negligible until a substantial portion of the tanker fleet has been converted from single hull to double hull.
4. Inasmuch as single-hull vessels will be phased out over a period commencing in 1995 and continuing until 2015, it will take approximately 20 years for the estimated double-hull environmental benefits to come into full effect.
5. Double-hull construction will prevent or mitigate oil outflow in most groundings and collisions. Additional OPA-90 rules that are under development will reduce the number of such casualties, thereby reducing the actual long-term beneficial impacts of double-hull construction on the environment.

The IMO's Marine Environment Protection Committee (MEPC) recently adopted double-hull requirements to the Annex 1 of the 1973 International Convention for the Prevention of Pollution from Ships, as modified by the Protocol of 1978 (MARPOL 73/78). The United States, represented by the Coast Guard, reserved its position during the adoption of these new regulations to the Annex 1 of MARPOL 73/78 due to differences from OPA-90.

According to claims under the Oil Pollution Act of 1990:

The U.S. Coast Guard (CG), U.S. Department of Transportation, promulgated an interim rule (33 CFR Parts 135, 136, and 137) which implements the provisions of the Oil Pollution Act of 1990 (OPA-90; P. L. 101–380) concerning the filing of claims for uncompensated removal costs or damages resulting from the discharge of oil, the designation of the source of the discharge, and the advertisement of where the claims are to be filed. This action is an interim measure needed primarily to explain how eligible claimants may file a claim against the Oil Spill Liability Trust Fund.

OPA-90 preserves the concept that those responsible for pollution incidents have the primary duty to respond to claims arising out of the pollution incidents that they cause. In addition to requiring the responsible party to advertise the procedures by which claims can be presented, OPA-90 provides that, with certain exceptions, a claim cannot be presented to the Fund until it has been presented to the responsible party (or the guarantor) of the vessel, facility, or other source designated as the source of the pollution and has been denied or remains unpaid for 90 days. Like the incentives provided to ensure that polluters take proper cleanup actions, OPA-90 provides methods to ensure that it will not be profitable for polluters to default on the obligation to accept and pay valid damage claims.

5.2.2.2 Certificates of financial responsibility. Under the requirements of the Oil Pollution Act of 1990 (OPA-90), there are provisions concerning evidence of financial responsibility. These could potentially expose vessel owners and their insurers to unlimited liability under a direct action clause for (1) costs of removal and cleanup, (2) environmental damage costs, (3) civil and criminal actions, and (4) separate costs imposed by the state.

Under the U.S. Clean Water Act of 1972, the protection and indemnity clubs (P&I clubs), which usually provide insurance coverage to tanker owners who are members of the club, have provided evidence of financial responsibility of up to $700 million (U.S. dollars). The P&I clubs, however, have refused to issue such certificates under the provisions of OPA-90 because of the possibility of unlimited liability both under federal and state law. This is particularly relevant as, under the OPA-90, third parties may proceed directly against an insurer.

Because 70% of the U.S. imported oil supply by sea is carried by independently owned tankers flying foreign flags, there is a real danger that if the provisions as stated now are finalized and provide for unlimited liability, P&I clubs will refuse to provide guarantees and oil pollution insurance covers. This will result in preventing independent tanker owners from obtaining certificates of financial responsibility, theoretically preventing them from operating in U.S. waters. The U.S. Coast Guard is studying the issue now.

Should P&I clubs, which currently provide 90% of the world's independent tanker owners with oil pollution insurance coverage up to the limits set by the Clean Water Act, refuse to agree to coverage under the OPA provisions, then the Coast Guard would have to forbid these tankers from operating in U.S. waters. At issue is the unlimited liability exposure. P&I clubs currently provide insurance cover to member tanker owners under the Clean Water Act (CWA) of up to $70 million, but have refused to issue certificates of financial responsibility. Issuing such certificates would make the clubs the guarantors of the owners and thereby directly liable for all costs assessed against them. With maximum liability not defined, this makes P&I clubs infinitely liable, a responsibility no commercial organization can assume.

Although Section 2704(a) of the act implies that the total liability, including removal and consequential costs, should not exceed certain limits, these limits are subject to broad exceptions. This means that should the accident fall under any of the so-called exceptions, the limits on liability do not apply and the government and all other "injured" parties could recover all the costs incurred, including consequential costs and even punitive damages, if the courts so decide. The exceptions appear to be so broad that few tanker accidents, if any, could escape the terms of these exceptions.

In fact, the act barely recognizes limitations, and any substantial spill would, as a result, make owners and others responsible and, most importantly, their insurers subject to unlimited liability. As noted in the act,

> [T]he limits of liability are removed if
>
> 1. the proximate cause of the spill was the result of either gross negligence or willful misconduct of the responsible party,
> 2. the incident was proximately caused by violation of an applicable federal safety, construction, or operating regulation by the responsible party,
> 3. the result of failure or refusal of the responsible party to report the incident as required by the Act,
> 4. the responsible party fails or refuses to provide all reasonable co-

operation and assistance requested by a responsible official in connection with removal activities, and

5. the responsible party fails or refuses, without sufficient cause, to comply with an order issued under §311 of the FWPCA or under the Intervention on the High Seas Act.

The act puts all the liability for pollution costs on the owner or operator and that person's insurers or guarantors and exempts the owners of the oil cargo from responsibility for spill costs.

Many argue that the act encourages the use of low-quality tankers whose exposure is limited to the low value of the vessels. (Tankers are often incorporated as separate corporate entities, whereby liability is limited to the value of the ships.) The act, and particularly its liability provisions, have opened a Pandora's box that may have far-reaching effects on the cost and quality of tanker service in the U.S. trade and, as a result, the cost of oil imports and the safety of tanker operations in U.S. waters. As it stands, the liability provisions may become a major impediment to the renewal of the U.S. flag domestic (cabotage) tanker fleet, which had an average age in excess of 22 years in 1993, and encourage use of substandard tankers in the U.S. oil import trade at least for some years.

5.2.3 Local Authority and State Controls

Most ocean environmental regulations are introduced by international conventions such as those pertaining to ships' safety and environmental protection, but are enforced by countries that assume responsibility for maintaining the standards under these conventions in their waters. Although adherence to ship safety standards is basically the responsibility of the country of registry, port states in other countries are increasingly exercising their rights under IMO conventions to inspect and enforce international conventions as well as national standards. This move—termed port state control (PSC)—is due in part to the difference in the level of enforcement used by different countries.

Regional PSC systems have now been introduced in Western Europe, the Caribbean, and other parts of the world. Western European countries have enforced port state control since 1982, when the Paris Memorandum on port state control was enacted. Similarly, the IMO Assembly adopted a resolution in 1991 calling on member governments to conclude similar regional agreements to ensure a uniform, high level of enforcement of international safety and environmental protection conventions.

Under port state control, the inspecting country can not only impose regulations of the flag states, but also international (IMO) conventions and regulations. It can arrest, fine, or otherwise impose restrictions on the vessel, its crew, and its owners or operators who contravene these laws or regulations.

An increasing number of states impose PSC to improve the safety and environmental protection in their territorial waters. Enforcement, as discussed in Section 5.3, however, varies widely even among nations that have adopted or are part of a PSC system such as used in Western Europe, the Caribbean, and elsewhere.

5.2.4 Sewage Disposal Regulations

Sewage is disposed of into the oceans by cities, urban and other residential concentrations, ships, offshore activities, and recreational vessels. The quantities of sewage disposed of in the oceans is huge and growing. Under the laws of most nations, land-generated sewage must be treated before disposal, but less than 10% of all sewage draining into the seas is actually or effectively treated.

Sewage disposal into the oceans is usually regulated at the national and local levels and involves requirements for maximum chemical and toxin levels, biological oxygen demand, solids in suspension, and dilution levels. The requirements differ widely and are also affected by littoral current and tidal conditions, locations, and other physical and geographical factors.

5.2.5 Dredging and Dredge Spoil Disposal Regulations

Although dredging used to be performed and dredge materials disposed of without any regulation, increasing concern with the environmental impact of these activities has led to the introduction of restrictions on and regulation of such activities, on the international level (IMO, London Dumping Convention, and so forth) and on national or local levels in many parts of the world. These regulations often limit or eliminate the possibility of dredging and reclamation that may have major economic impacts on a region.

Dredge material is often found to be contaminated. Similarly, dredging operations put large volumes of clean and polluted sediment into suspension, which affects both sea life and the ocean bottom when the material resettles, often covering or polluting important breeding or otherwise biologically active grounds. Also, reclamation or accretion by dredging may result in potential impact to the ocean bottom. Sediment depositions often contain fine-grained sediments with high concentrations of organic materials, such as PCBs, metals, and other objectionable materials.

Dredging involves both capital (improvement) and maintenance dredging and is usually performed in urban areas, coastal zones, bays, and river estuaries to improve navigation, reclaim land, improve current and tidal domains, and so forth. The principal international convention regulating dredging is the London Dumping Convention (Appendix C), which entered into force in 1975. It adopted the basic principles of the Oslo Convention, which entered into force and was ratified by 13 European countries in 1974. These regulations of dredging and dredged materials are concerned with trace contaminants, toxic components, bioaccumulation, and similar effects. They recommend sampling, measurement of contaminants, turbidity, suspended solids, biological testing, and accumulation of sediments. They are similarly concerned with the choice of dredging equipment, timing of dredging, location and method of spoil disposal, and, obviously, quality of spoils. Effective containment of dredge spoils by dikes or capping is usually required to eliminate potential environmental damage.

5.2.6 Air Pollution Regulation in the Oceans

Air pollution regulation is mainly promulgated by national environmental protection agencies and various international agencies dealing with conditions of the atmosphere. They set standards of air emissions from ships and offshore activities, and in general establish requirements to control air pollution from inshore, coastal, and outer continental sources. The purpose is to maintain air quality standards.

Marine vapor emission from oil cargo, bunker tanks, and various chemical operations are also being regulated now, as are organic air emissions. Although air pollution on the oceans has received less attention than liquid or solid waste and oil pollution, the problem is being addressed aggressively now, with standards as well as antipollution incentives following those set on land.

Emphasis is given to improvements in combustion technology,

low-emission technology, and emission standard setting and monitoring. To reduce emissions, combustion controls, alternative fuels, and exhaust gas treatments are considered. A 25% to 30% reduction of NO_x is the preliminary goal, and this can now be achieved by a combination of combustion controls and alternative fuels.

Many authorities (the IMO, for example) are now preparing standards under conventions such as MARPOL 73/78 to reduce NO_x, vapor emissions, hydrocarbons, and particulate emissions by 30% by 1996, with additional reductions planned 4 years later.

5.2.7 Solid Waste Disposal

The Annex V of the MARPOL 73/78 Convention regulates the disposal of pollution by garbage—such as food, plastics, operational, and other wastes—from ships. Various methods for treating organic, biodegradable wastes exist that, when used, make such disposal acceptable as defined. Even then, such disposal is only permitted if it is done farther than 12 n mi from the nearest land and has passed through a grinder, screen, or other acceptable treatment. Similarly, wastes must have a density of more than seawater to ensure sinkage and may not include plastics, metals, glass, and other nonbiodegradable materials.

5.3 ENFORCEMENT OF OCEAN ENVIRONMENTAL REGULATIONS

Enforcement of ocean environmental regulations has, in the past, been very lax. Even today, when the impact of ocean pollution on the environment and the economy is well established and known, enforcement is still difficult. Not only are there major differences in the approach to enforcement, but many countries and jurisdictions feel that the cost of enforcement is too great or that they have a right to first contribute their share to ocean pollution. The idea is that enforcement not only entails direct enforcement but also indirect economic costs.

This has become a difficult issue because it is nearly impossible to control operations in remote ocean locations. The problem has been reduced with satellite ocean imaging and control systems that now permit identification of ocean pollution by oil, solids, or other major emissions. Most importantly, though, is the agreement by all maritime and coastal nations to enforce environmental standards uniformly and without preference.

5.4 OPERATIONAL ISSUES AND POLICIES

Although operations on the oceans and ocean resource exploitation contribute only a fraction of ocean pollution, these are the types of pollution that are usually in the limelight. The great majority of such accidents are the result of human error, lack of effective training, and ineffective management. At the same time, there is increasing pressure to reduce personnel, training, and associated costs (such as for relocation). The combination of these factors has made a major contribution towards accidents at sea.

5.4.1 The Role of Human Error in Ship Accidents

Considering pollution of the oceans by ships, recent history shows not only that accidental pollution of the oceans by tankers has declined to less than 12% of the total world ocean oil pollution (as of 1991), but also that pollution caused by nonaccidental tanker operations has declined to just under 22%. Therefore, more than two-thirds of the oil discharged into the world's oceans is not caused by tankers. This is largely the result of the success of MARPOL, the international IMO agreement on Maritime Pollution Prevention. But even though IMO and national governments have been quite successful in improving the standards of ship design, construction, equipment, and maintenance of ships, it is increasingly evident that the major cause of maritime accidents is human error, as shown in Table 5–5.

About 60% of all maritime, and particularly tanker, accidents are caused by human error. This percentage appears to increase as ships become more complex, are driven and utilized more, and have crews drawn from more and more diverse and often not reliable sources. Although the IMO and national governments set crew proficiency and training standards, these are often circumvented.

The quality of crew, crew training, and crew discipline is now becoming the major safety issue in shipping, particularly in tanker shipping. Crew quality management not only involves crew proficiency but also crew work management and affects ship operation,

TABLE 5–5 Causes of Maritime Accidents

A. Causes of Major Maritime Accident Claims (U.K.—P&I Club, 1992 coverage)	
Human error	60%
Structural failure	12%
Mechanical failure	7%
Equipment failure	11%
Under investigation	5%
Other	5%
	100%
B. Causes of Human Error Claims (U.K.—P&I Club, 1992 coverage)	
Ship failure	40%
Deck officer error	25%
Engineer officer error	2%
Crew error	16%
Shore crew error	10%
Pilot error	7%
	100%

SOURCE: "Analysis of Major Claims," U.K.—P&I Club, Summary, (London, 1993).

condition, and maintenance management. In the future, staffing ships will require much more attention, and the approach to hiring may have to be changed from casual hires or subcontracting of ship management to full-time, permanent hires, as used by airlines.

Although airlines have a much better safety record than ships, nearly two-thirds of all accidents are caused by pilot error, not lack of skill.[2] It is increasingly important not only to provide skill training and periodic skill upgrading, but also to ensure that crews

1. are disciplined, yet collegial;
2. have a positive attitude and cooperative personality;
3. understand and believe in teamwork;
4. are willing to learn from each other and from their mistakes; and
5. have good communication skills.

An inordinate number of accidents are a result of inadequate communication. Like other technologies, ships and tankers can never be

[2]Federal Aviation Administration (FAA) "Report on Aviation Safety," Office of Aviation Safety, (Washington, DC, 1992).

made perfectly accident proof, but the quality of ship management and crews can certainly be improved, thereby eliminating the bulk of ship and tanker accidents and the resulting ocean pollution.

Environmental incentives are best provided by the marketplace, not by traditional regulatory controls. One possible approach is that polluters should pay, but more may be achieved by positive reinforcements, such as environmental credits, than by penalties. Environmental economists, such as R. N. Stavins of Harvard, have shown that market-based regulations are more effective than simple regulatory controls because they provide a motive to reduce pollution by selling credits to less-efficient polluters.

5.4.2 Environmental Response Planning and Prevention Training

Notwithstanding all the regulations establishing environmental standards and methods of prevention of ocean pollution, effective response planning and prevention training appear to be the best protection against ocean pollution accidents. Yet because such programs in government and industry require large budgets, ocean pollution response planning and prevention training has not received adequate attention and was only seriously introduced after the *Exxon Valdez* disaster. Response planning goes well beyond accidental contingency planning, which addresses the practical aspects of oil spill preparedness and response.

Contingency plans must be realistic and effective and should include periodic tests as well as regular and rigorous exercise, training, and trials. Deficiencies in time, response, and capability must be removed, and plans, equipment, and other resources must be continuously updated.

Effective coordination must be developed to ensure that organizations pool their resources in an effective and timely manner in case of an accident. Worst-case scenarios must be developed and redeveloped to provide effective examples of possible situations. Plans designed to address catastrophic spills must include effective plans for rapid relocation of personnel, equipment, and other resources. Most importantly, effective management procedures to deal with any location, type, and size of spill that make clear beyond any doubt how the cleanup, prevention, or other spill response strategy is to be handled must be readily available. Response plans include the following:

1. information on stockpile, condition, operation, and location of oil spill response equipment;
2. rapid mobilization and relocation facilities, support personnel, and equipment;
3. consistent coordination among government agencies and industry with oil spill response capabilities;
4. effective coordination of oil spill contingency plans;
5. knowledge and proof of private and industry oil spill capabilities;
6. regular and coordinated training;
7. development of newer cleanup and containment technologies, such as bioremediation, chemical cleanup, and mechanical oil recovery equipment; and
8. improvements in prevention.

Response planning includes contingency planning, training, cooperative arrangements, technology evaluation and updating, and periodic reevaluation of existing and potential threats.

Effective training programs have been developed at institutions such as the Massachusetts Maritime Academy (Buzzards Bay, Massachusetts). This institution not only offers one of the most effective training programs in existence for spill response and contingency planning, including spill containment and cleanup, but it also has developed a very realistic and effective oil spill accident simulation that permits participants to test their response and contingency plan effectiveness. The simulation also allows the evaluation of alternative containment and cleanup strategies. Similar programs are now being planned or introduced in a number of places in the United States and worldwide.

5.5 ENVIRONMENTAL AWARENESS, POLITICAL WILL, AND ECONOMIC COSTS

Although the maintenance of the ocean environment has become an important issue and both public and political awareness of the importance of maintaining the ocean environment abound, talk is often not followed by effective action.

Most importantly, emphasis is increasingly put on the reduction of environmental damage and not on its prevention. In comparison to the vast efforts under way to reduce oil spills from damaged tankers, comparatively little is done to improve navigational safety. The reason appears to be largely that emphasis is given to the cost of environmental action and not to the benefits derived. Preventing tanker accidents introduces a benefit, but oil spill reduction reduces the cost of the oil spill.

Environmentalists are largely to blame for this situation, as they usually object to the increase of environmental costs, however marginal, even if the environmental benefits far outweigh those costs. For example, inshore oil terminals in a bay caused long-term and persistent oil pollution of the bay and presented a potential tanker grounding disaster in the shallow waters of the bay. Yet a proposal to relocate the terminals on an artificial, reclaimed island offshore was turned down because it entailed reclaiming about 40 acres of land, in fairly deep water, even though the ocean bottom at that location did not serve as a breeding ground nor was otherwise biologically valuable. The resulting deep-water terminal would have eliminated tanker grounding potentials and the continued pollution of the bay, with ultimate cleansing of the whole area. Although it was readily shown that the environmental benefits far outweighed the environmental costs, the project was turned down.

Few environmental improvements are costless and future regulations designed to encourage effective environmental cost-benefit trade-offs and not just reductions in environmental costs should be promoted.

6

Economics of Ocean Environmental Management

Since the early 1960s, environmental progress has mainly been made through legislation and regulation, not as a direct result of economic or social pressures. The economic implications of environmental improvements have, as a result, usually been overlooked or lost. In fact, because social and not economic factors were often primarily used to push for environmental legislation, business by and large assumed that environmentally beneficial action in response to regulations were automatically uneconomic and contrabusiness.

In the past, regulations have usually been economically inefficient and environmental standards often too rigid to permit effective economic solutions to environmental problems. As a result, adversarial relationships have grown between business and environmentalists as well as environmental regulators.

New approaches now encourage the marketplace to reflect true environmental costs and benefits as well as to establish a marketplace in rights to pollute, environmental credits, user fees, congestion charges, and so forth.

So far, comparatively little work has been done to develop a meaningful understanding of the economic impact of environmental regulations, conventions, and agreements, the cost of enforcement, and the cost of compliance, particularly as they relate to the ocean environment. Similarly, the market for environmental credits, rights, or options is in its infancy, and the impacts of such a market on the environment and on the cost of environmental improvements are not yet understood. On the other hand, people must learn how to deal with these issues in a fair and unbiased manner, particularly now when environmental inequities among industrialized and poor developing countries are being highlighted. This is partially the result of criticism of developing countries that sell "rights" to dump waste (or pollute) in their countries and argue that they have the economic justification of catching up with the level of pollution that benefited or at least advanced the industrialization and economic growth of "rich" countries in the twentieth century.

Many industrialized countries and international organizations are responding with offers of payment (or delete swaps) for retention of the environment. Although this approach has been in the limelight regarding the protection of the rain forest in the Amazon River area of Brazil, many similar efforts are under way elsewhere to reduce the sustained pollution of the oceans.

Ocean environmental regulations and their economic costs and benefits are even less understood than other types of regulations, largely because the oceans are usually remote and appear to be immense. In addition, the oceans' role in the support of economic development and humankind is not really evident to most people, including politicians and lawmakers. To many, the oceans still constitute a huge infinite sink that can absorb anything with impunity. Therefore, money for ocean environmental management is difficult to obtain and expenditures difficult to justify.

6.1 OCEAN ENVIRONMENTAL ACCOUNTING

Effective regulation and management of the ocean environment can often be efficiently encouraged by the use of economic incentives and instruments. As a result, these have become major elements of environmental policy and are usually designed to make it more efficient, cost-effective, and acceptable. Although initially controversial, the use of financial aid, penalties, and credits to encourage pollution control has now become increasingly accepted. In fact, most agree now that economic instruments provide powerful complements to direct environmental regulation.

Economic instruments are designed to affect costs and benefits of alternative approaches to the management of the ocean environment. Economic instruments may consist of payments by polluters to the public through taxes, fines, and charges or financial aid, user charges, or duties. Innovative new instruments consist of marketable permits or pollution credits that can be traded among polluters.

The objective of economic instruments is to set a price on pollution and ensure effective economic valuation of ocean environmental resources. This is particularly important in ocean environmental management, where the economic use of ocean resources and the economic cost of pollution on their value can often be directly linked.

Although environmental pricing is difficult, in the oceans it is possible to establish a relation between marginal costs of pollution reduction and marginal environmental damage costs. Pricing methods using hedonic pricing or contingent valuation have been developed, but they can often be employed only with difficulty because of the lack of information about correct environmental pricing.

An attempt is often made to make environmental prices economic incentives for pollution reduction. It is very difficult to set charges at appropriate levels and furthermore to ensure that such charges are borne by, and therefore provide an incentive to, the polluter and are not simply passed on to the public as a cost of providing the service or producing a resource for public use or consumption. As a result, the application of economic instruments in ocean environmental regulation and management has not been effective in the past.

Another issue is the use of the revenues obtained from economic instruments. In theory, these funds should be used for pollution prevention, abatement, cleanup, and containment. In practice, they are usually lost in the labyrinth of revenue streams and are used for general government expenses.

Environmental charges are usually designed to provide an incentive for pollution abatement by inducing economically efficient investment for pollution control. On the other hand, earmarking revenue may lead to inefficient allocation of antipollution investment.

Pollution credits, if marketable, can provide both revenues to the public and incentives to polluters. If environmental charges produce revenues that offset other taxes, then environmental taxes may permit budget neutrality and provide both environmental incentives and tax relief.

The combination of direct regulation and the use of environmental charges or other economic instruments can serve to reinforce regulation while providing additional funds. Economic environmental instruments serve to provide the freedom to polluters to work at the most efficient level possible to meet regulatory standards. This is done by equating the marginal cost of environmental control to the cost of pollution charges across the whole range of compliance levels with environmental standards. These instruments provide incentives to reduce pollution below given standards, assist in paying for new abatement technology, and assure flexibility.

Environmental accounting is usually difficult. Not only are costs and benefits difficult to determine, but often sufficient data are not available. Similarly, to be useful, information should be site and pollution-type related. There is very little data on the cost of pollution. Costs are unique to each accident or pollution event and depend on the type of event and a large number of physical, meteorological, chemical, and environmental factors.

Furthermore, the required data are seldom collected in a timely manner, if at all, and with rapid dissipation of pollutants cannot be reconstituted. Similarly, the inputs and outputs or cause-and-effect relationships are often different because various chemical pollutants cause different reactions and therefore different impacts under various conditions. As a result, the information must be related to the particular sites and the pollutants emitted.

Usually the environmental impact costs from pollution damage include:

1. intermediate costs incurred for containment, cleanup, and prevention;
2. consequential costs;
3. indirect costs such as medical services connected with pollution-linked diseases;
4. loss of income or revenue;
5. quality of life and related social costs; and
6. investment in pollution prevention or reduction.

To establish an effective set of environmental standards useful in environmental accounting, information concerning the environment may be organized hierarchically:

- Level I: Gathering diverse data from environmental field and related socioeconomic data.
- Level II: Forming a data bank for monitoring water, atmosphere, land noise, industrial risk, marine pollution, regional flora and fauna, and cost and efficiency of nonpolluting technologies.
- Level III: Evaluating studies (using data from previous levels) on national—and more recently, regional—levels on how pollution affects the state of the environment and the indicators of progress in meeting the national economic plan.
- Level IV: Accounting on environmental issues, considering national environmental expenditure, funding, and beneficiaries.
- Level V: Accounting for forecasting and simulations on how pollution, prices, and foreign trade of various environmental policies as well as pollution levels are linked to various development strategies.
- Level VI: Extracting quality-of-life indicators.

The question of who should pay to restore the damaged environment to the set standards, as well as the cost of environmental compliance by industry and the public, is still wide open, although experience with the regulation of air emissions from electric power plants in North America may provide meaningful precedents.

To establish environmental accounting procedures, standards for environmental interactions that ensure public health and maintenance of the environment, while permitting sustained economic development, should be established. Such standards would involve not only methods and uses of materials, products, and processes, but would also include disposal. This would define permissible sources of materials and methods or conditions of their exploitation.

6.1.1 Environmental Auditing

Effective environmental management requires good environmental accounting and auditing. Environmental auditing is a systematic, documented, periodic objective review of conditions and operations as they affect or may affect the environment. Environmental auditing is proactive and is done not to account for something but to determine that everything is as it should be. It is a check of the conditions under which operations take place. It provides a record that the conditions have not changed beyond reasonable deviations and are still within acceptable environmental performance bounds.

During an audit usually all the equipment and monitors that may influence or emit pollutants or otherwise contribute detrimentally to the environment will be tested. In a typical audit, a process, plant, or activity will be checked under various operating conditions that represent the spectrum of possible conditions. These will usually not only cover the operating range but also the various external conditions (weather, motion, impact, temperature, and so forth) in which the process, plant, or activity may operate.

The findings will then be compared with known standards, if available, and any deviation from such standards will be noted. Similarly, the potential seriousness of the deviation will be determined, and the owner or operator will be directed to correct the deviation to reduce the environmental risk.

6.1.2 Ocean Environmental Economic Charges

The enforcement of ocean environmental regulation by economic charges, could be organized into a number of useful categories:

1. direct environmental taxes;
2. environmental penalties or fines;
3. added cost of reestablishing public acceptance;
4. permits and credits, both of which are usually marketable;
5. refunds; and
6. subsidies.

In general, subsidies are considered inefficient economic instruments and are not in line with the concept of the "guilt of the polluter." In ocean environmental management, there are no good guys; there are simply small and large polluters, some who try to minimize their impact and often others who do not care. In fact, subsidies may distort environmental pollution by encouraging excessive use of polluting materials and services. As examples, subsidies for transport fuels may encourage CO_2 emissions, and subsidizing coal production may encourage sulfuric oxide emissions. Environmental charges can be levied on pollution, on products that produce pollution, or on polluting services.

Emission charges are levied on discharges into the air, water, or soil. In some cases, they may also include charges for the emission of sound (noise charges). Product charges are levied on those who produce emissions above standards, are inefficient in the use of polluting materials, or cause environmental problems because of the composition, form, or toxicity of their emissions.

Service or user charges are levied on the basis of volume or amount of pollution emitted. They are often used to recover public costs. These charges are often used interchangeably, and the efficacy of using them depends on the following:

1. measurability of emission,
2. enforcibility of environmental standards,
3. costs of enforcement and collection,
4. product life, and
5. personality of the service provider and user.

Rates are often arbitrary because it is difficult to measure emission in absolute terms and because the purpose of the charges may be undefined. In most cases, charges are used as general revenue and not to cover specific environmental costs.

Contrary to popular belief, states with stronger environmental policies did not experience lower rates of economic growth than states with lower effective environmental regulations. Stephen M. Meyer of MIT used five indicators of economic growth to reach this conclusion:

1. gross state product,
2. total nonfarm employment,
3. construction employment,
4. manufacturing labor productivity, and
5. total labor productivity.

In general, environmentally concerned states outperformed those with low environmental concern. Meyer concluded that although it is not proven that environmental concern stimulates economic growth, it can be stated that, based on his U.S. data, environmental involvement certainly does not impede economic growth.

Many contentious issues in ocean environmental management are less a debate about scientific factors than about economic impacts, particularly how environmental restrictions affect the use of the oceans and the cost of using the oceans and exploiting their resources. Because developed nations have greater ability to use oceans, ocean environment management also involves compensation of less developed countries for their abstinence from ocean pollution.

6.1.2.1 Environmental pollution rights. Because pollution prevention equipment is very expensive and because owners of ships and offshore platforms, as well as industrial and residential investors who use the oceans as depositories for waste materials, infrequently make investments in equipment, there will always be large discrepancies in the environmental quality of equipment in use. The most important may be between old and new ships or older and newer coastal industrial plants.

Notwithstanding extensive new regulations and international agreements on ocean pollution, enforcement is by and large lax and rules are often delayed because of the investors' inability to change equipment rapidly.

Furthermore, all these regulations are based solely on deterent incentives, an approach commonly found less effective than regulations that offer economic or other incentives. A commonly used incentive now used in the electric power generating industry in the United States and Germany is that of air emission rights. These give plants that exceed required emission rights bankable credits that can be sold or traded. In fact, the Chicago Board of Trade is starting an active market in air emission rights, and specialized brokers have emerged. These brokers will match owners of rights with potential purchasers, usually power plant operators who cannot or will not afford the expenditure of meeting environmental standards of an existing (often older) power plant.

There are many opportunities for similar economic incentives to be provided for ocean activities. For example, credits for safe tankers that exceed requirements could be used to permit retention of an older tanker without conversion. This could be modeled after the air emission rights promulgated by the U.S. Clean Air Act of 1991. Although initially designed to address sulfur dioxide allowances for electricity generation in the United States, this act is expected to be applied to nonutility generating projects as well. Purchasing rights to emit by-products of combustion will, under this act, become fundamental to power generation of all sorts. It is designed to introduce competition by forcing power producers to engage in the market for emission "allowances" and emission reduction credits, or ERCs. This therefore represents the stock in the emission offset program that allows an effective trade and, hence, the use of credits and allowances.

6.1.3 Ocean Environmental Market Accounting

In most societies and regions, national, local, and economic accounting systems designed to standardize accounting procedures and facilitate the evaluation and comparison of economic performance within the nation or region and across nations exist. Such systems can also be designed to ensure the collection and use of data on economic activities to support policy making.

In recent years, proposals for expanding national and regional income and product accounts to include environmental costs and benefits have been made. Using the approach advocated by Wassily W. Leontief,[1] all flows of costs and benefits can be traced in an input-output framework, independent of the valuation in market prices. The advantage of such an approach in environmental accounting is that all interactions are considered and thus there is little chance of ignoring important relationships.

All potential sources of pollution as shown in Figure 6.1 must be considered because each has a substantial propensity for pollution. Therefore, most types of pollution cannot be traced to a single source and general, often overlapping, pollution cause analyses must be performed.

A cause-and-effect analysis or tree framework, which links each effect to a cause that in turn is often the effect of another cause, is therefore required. Such hierarchical analysis often highlights the sequence of developments that lead to environmental impacts and serves to identify the most effective remedy or correction needed to eliminate or reduce the damage at the least cost. It also permits effective design of required regulations and incentives towards that end.

[1]Leontief, W. W., *Input-Output Economics* (New York: Oxford University Press, 1966).

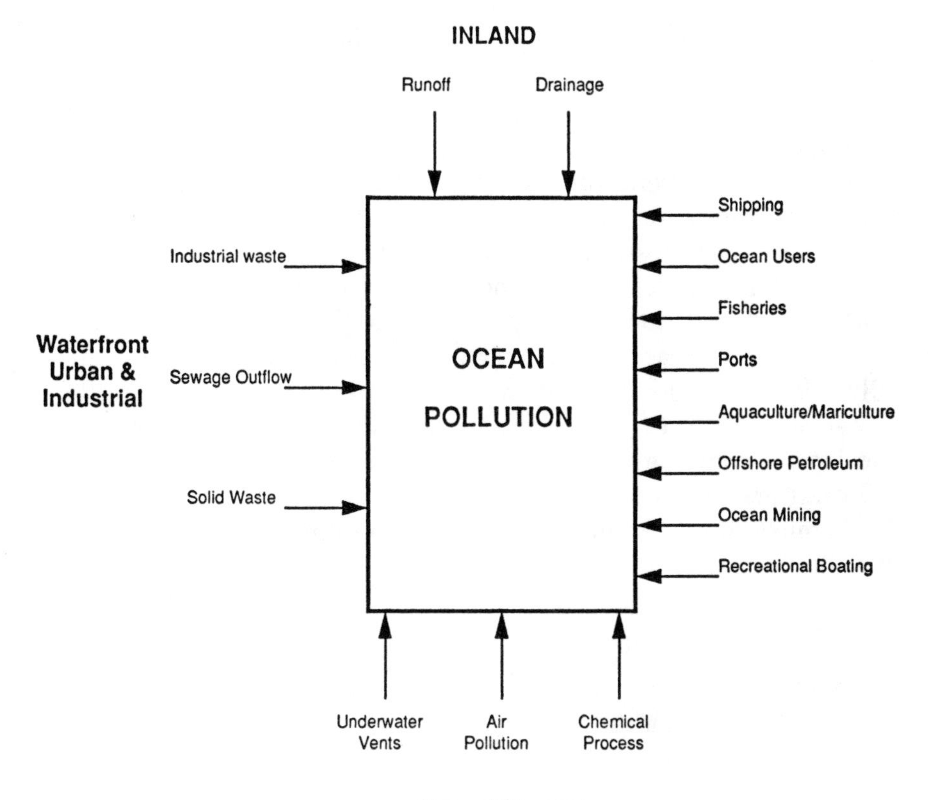

Figure 6–1 Major Sources of Ocean Pollution.

6.1.4 Methods of Environmental Accounting

All accounting requires disclosure of the effects of losses, liabilities, and gains or benefits, unless their occurrence is very remote.

Only now are methods for disclosure and standards of accounting for environmental costs, liabilities, and benefits on the national as well as corporate or company levels beginning to be developed. Although environmental policies abound and agreements or conventions continue to multiply (and as a result, standards are set on international, national, local, and industry levels), no uniform methods for accounting have been adopted or associated with the environmental standards.

Only Norway, for example, requires companies to disclose annually the impact a company's operations have on the environment and what measures are planned to eliminate or counter environmental impact. In other countries, accounting is more reactive and emphasizes costs and liabilities arising from past environmental damage. Such accounting, however, does not attempt to account for environmental expenditure required in the future, with the exception of insurance and other risk-covering costs. Methods of accounting for contingent losses are in their infancy.

Capital costs for environmentally related investments that are made to reduce future liability or because they are required by law must be properly accounted for because they must be environmentally related operating expenses. To permit environmental audits to be performed and to investigate and possibly reveal risks, exposures, and lack of compliance with existing laws that in turn permit financial auditors to assess the cost of potential liabilities, proper standards must be set for environmental accounting. Environmental audits should therefore consist of

1. compliance audits,
2. cost audits,
3. liability risk audits, and
4. environmental effects audit (effects with or without liability impacts).

Environmental accounting seldom involves assignment of all the environmental costs associated with the manufacture of a product or the production of a service to the costs for that product or service. As a result, production costs are often underestimated. Similarly, the relative cost of products or services with little environmental impact may be overestimated.

There are several schools of environmental accounting. One advocates an input-output type analysis in which a material balance approach is used. Here all inflows and outflows are accounted for, independent of their positive or negative contribution to the ocean environment.

Another environmental accounting scheme attempts to account for the positive and negative effects of pollution, ocean uses, ocean resource exploitation, and natural inflows directly. The difficulty with this approach is in developing an effective measure of the environmental damage done by these activities. Such a metric must value the damage done by pollution and other types of environmental degradation.

On the other hand, material input-output flows by themselves or a flow balance, although easier in measurement terms, is not sufficient to determine or even estimate environmental impact. Both methods offer advantages even though the first does not assign economic value or cost to the pollution and other environmental activities in the oceans.

Ultimately, any environmental accounting scheme, be it to control a local or regional ocean environment or one designed to measure the health of whole oceans or oceans at large, must consider not only the effects on the physical, chemical, and biological composition of the oceans but must reflect economic welfare.

There are various schools of approach to national and world income accounting, such as the treatment of recreation, subsistence production, nonmarket transactions, and different types of services. Similarly, the accounting for various environmental protection and resource use or depletion issues is often not effectively done. The problems are usually with the effective accounting of

1. environmental depletion,
2. environmental protection,
3. resource access and use, and
4. environmental asset degradation.

The economic concept of "sustainable income or consumption" is the maximum resources that can be consumed or depleted without reducing the amount of possible, required, or desired consumption in the future. This concept, however, is flawed; future consumption cannot be effectively predicted because little is known of future lifestyles, population densities, or consumption requirements.

As a result, it is usually assumed that future demand will be the same as current demand and that maintaining the level of available resources at their present level will satisfy sustainable development. Ideally then, people should only consume replaceable resources. On the other hand, lifestyles change under pressure of

1. technology,
2. societal preferences,
3. changes in demographic conditions, and
4. environmental opportunities.

For example, fossil fuels, particularly oil, were of little importance to humans until the late eighteen century, and their demand grew largely as a result of the introduction of the internal combustion engine. In recent years, pressure has been exerted on governments to ensure prudent economic management, which was interpreted as effective maintenance of the environment for posterity.

6.1.5 Port Environmental Audits

Audits are investigations designed to determine conditions prevailing or being maintained at a port. Audits include determining the environmental requirements imposed on or required to be maintained by the port and involve review of the environmental permits, licenses, approval, and so forth that apply to the port and its operations. These permits usually include environmental standards to be complied with. Wherever regulatory standards are missing, self-imposed or generally accepted standards would be identified.

An audit is concerned with the port's compliance with these policies, regulations, or standards. It will therefore involve evaluation of methods used to attain compliance and the degree or level of compliance achieved. Although environmental audits are more commonly employed in private industry in developed countries than under any other situation, ports—whether private or public—increasingly find a need for accurate environmental measurement and accounting for both internal operational and external reporting reasons. Ports do not control all the operations within a port, and port users are largely independent operators using port assets or facilities. Similarly, relations between ports and port users are usually defined by the degree of responsibility or control each assumes in the ports' operation. Many ports, for example, delegate various port operations to port users or their agents. This obviously makes it much harder for a port to manage the port's environmental impact.

Yet a port remains responsible for dealing with environmental emergencies, such as oil spills, fires, waste disposal, and toxic and hazardous material discharge. Therefore, even if a port does not control port facilities, operations, and services, it should ensure that leases and operating agreements contain terms to ensure that users do not endanger the environment and do perform regular and accurate environmental audits, followed by correction of all deficiencies.

Similarly, a port must demand that users provide it and its delegates with all relevant environmental, operational, and compliance data. An audit must be planned. Such plans should be port specific and include consideration of age, site, construction, and operational methods used.

The documents and data usually inspected by an audit team include the following:

- legal and regulatory documents defining the standards required of the port;
- environmental policy employed by the national and local government;
- copies of permits, licenses, compliance reports, and so forth;
- previous audit reports;
- data of ongoing environmental monitoring or testing;
- amounts of toxic and hazardous cargo handled and stored and conditions and methods of storage, including protection; and
- plans of the physical facilities and equipment.

Environmental audits are usually performed and audit plans submitted for adoption once a year. Port environmental audits consist of

1. site visits and inspections,
2. compliance review, and
3. audit documentation.

During the actual audit, physical and data inspection will usually deal with these issues:

- chemical handled (methods and storage);
- presence and handling of hazardous materials and wastes;
- treatment and disposal of water and wastewater;
- air quality, noise, and odor;
- soil and sediment; and
- protected natural resources and land use.

The goal is not only to gain access to data, but to identify what additional data are required for effective environmental audit and control.

During the compliance review, physical findings are compared with those recorded and required by permits, licenses, or other documents. Similarly, expiration dates of permits and licenses are checked. Other compliance issues of interest are

- cargo declarations and manifests;
- port and port user personnel training records and licenses; and
- maintenance and repair records, particularly of pollution prevention, containment, and cleanup equipment.

Audit reports will identify deficiencies in standards, compliances, training, and so forth, will document such facts, and will make recommendations. The reports will often include suggestions for long-term improvements also.

6.1.6 Debt for Nature Swaps in the Oceans

Although debt for nature swaps were begun by private, non-government environmental groups to encourage the preservation of tropical rain forests in Latin America, many swaps were later negotiated between governments or governments and financial institutions.

The idea is to compensate a country, usually a poor, developing country, from the loss of revenue from environmentally objectionable activities—such as deforestation of the rain forest, dredging of estuaries, or dumping of waste—by canceling debt. In these swaps, an indebted country is effectively forgiven parts of its debt in return for stopping or reducing dumping, deforestation, and similar activities.

Although debt for nature swaps are not extensively used to reduce ocean environmental damage, some proposals to that effect have been made and are under serious consideration.

6.2 COSTS AND BENEFITS OF OCEAN ENVIRONMENTAL MANAGEMENT

The costs and benefits of ocean environmental pollution and its management are difficult to determine. The first issue is control and ownership of the oceans and ocean resources, vested historically in territorial (3–5 mi) coastal zones extended to more limited rights by the coastal jurisdiction in the 200-mi (or 200 m deep continental shelf) line, comprising the economic zone of a country. In territorial waters, a jurisdiction has the same rights as on the adjacent land and controls not only resources in the waters, but also passage of any sort. Control in the economic zone is usually restricted to resource exploitation, such as fish, oil, or minerals.

The rest of the oceans and the resources therein are, according to various U.N. protocols, the property (heritage) of humankind. Minerals and other seabed exploitation in these waters are legally controlled by the International Seabed Authority, an agency of the United Nations.

The costs of ocean environmental pollution are usually expressed in terms of the expected damage caused and the cost of cleaning up or remedying the damage. This, for example, is commonly the approach taken in oil pollution cases. On the other hand, most ocean pollution causes a cause-and-effect chain reaction, and pollution-caused damage often becomes the cause for secondary and other effects. This is not only a phenomenon in the ocean food chain where pollutants ingested by low-level creatures affect higher- and higher-level marine life—and ultimately humans, if they consume fish or shellfish—but it also happens in purely physical or social interactions affected by ocean pollution.

In some cases, cause-and-effect reactions may be feedback phenomena. For example, a successful resort on a pristine shore equipped with effective pollution prevention may cause the growth of a nearby village, with a resulting increase in untreated human sludge and other waste that is discharged into the sea and pollutes the beaches. As a result, this causes a decline and ultimate closure of the resort which, in turn causes the village to die.

The cost of ocean pollution is therefore not just the direct cost of damage caused by it. It must be estimated carefully to include consequential costs. Similarly, benefits from the management of ocean pollution may be direct and indirect and may include consequential benefits. Sometimes, as the cost of pollution to one becomes the benefit of pollution to another, costs and benefits are mixed. For example, controlled treated waste or sludge along a coast may be a benefit to coastal fish farms or fisheries but a cost to coastal resorts and recreational activities.

6.2.1 Cost of Oil Spills in the Ocean

The economic or environmental cost of an oil spill at sea is a function of

- properties of the oil spilled,
- location of the spill,

- amount of oil spilled,
- environmental conditions at the location of the spill, and
- the rate of discharge or time taken for the spill.

Marine oil pollution causes direct and indirect costs. Conversely, the effective management of the ocean environment may cause direct and indirect benefits. Oil pollution caused by a tanker accident, for example, has the following direct and indirect benefits.

DIRECT COSTS	INDIRECT COSTS
Loss of oil	Damage to marine life
Loss of vessel	Loss of revenue from fishing
Loss of use of vessel	Damage to mariculture and aquaculture farms
Loss of life	Loss of tourism
Transfer of oil	Damage to the beaches
Salvage operations	Loss of use of coastal or estuarial waters
Containment	Income
Cost of emergency response	Cost of cleanup
	Health damage costs

Similarly, a list could be compiled for direct and indirect benefits of effective ocean environmental management for preventing or reducing the impacts of tanker accidents. The indirect costs often constitute causes for secondary indirect costs. The same type of hierarchy can be developed for benefits, although it is sometimes preferable to combine the cost and benefit hierarchies into a single cost hierarchy in which benefits are simply negative costs.

It is important to note that the costs of marine, and particularly oil, pollution are not necessarily proportionate to the amount of oil spilled or the size of the spilling or damaged vessel. These costs are a function of the following factors:

- type of oil spilled and its chemical and physical specifications;
- quantity of oil spilled,
- location of oil spilled: coastal, offshore, deep ocean, and so forth;
- rate at which oil spilled;

- local environmental conditions, such as wind, waves, currents, and so forth;
- containment of oil spill achieved;
- method of oil cleanup, if any;
- economic activity at location or potentially affected locations of oil spill;
- public concern with and awareness of oil spills and their effects; and
- actual property damage.

As a result, the costs of oil spills may differ widely, independent of the amount spilled. The differences may vary by as much as a factor of 100. In other words, the costs of an oil spill of 30,000 tons may be $20 million or $2 billion, as in the *Exxon Valdez*. Another example is the *Tanio* accident in which the 28,000 DWT tanker broke in half off the French coast in 1986 and discharged 13,000 tons of heavy fuel oil. Costs of oil transfer from the sunken section of the ship were over $60 million.

There is a serious question, though, on how to compute the cost of oil spills because of several levels of consequential and often delayed costs. The indirect costs are usually easy to estimate. Similarly, it is quite simple to identify the individuals, parties, or communities who bear the direct costs. The difficult parts are estimating first and higher levels of indirect costs and designating those affected.

Because many effects are delayed, their costs cannot be immediately determined. Yet financial settlements are often arranged in short order and long before potential claims are filed and proven. As a result, many legitimate claimants are never compensated because the effect of the pollution was only recognized long after the accident. Thus the claim could not be satisfied because a deadline for claims was missed, compensation funds were exhausted, direct cause and effect was difficult to establish, or, as is often the case, the company owning the tanker at fault no longer exists, has no assets, or both. In fact, it is common for owners now to incorporate each tanker as a separate corporation or entity so that other assets cannot be claimed. As a result, only the insurance coverage of the tanker, the tanker itself, and whatever other asset the "single" tanker company has can be attached to satisfy such claims.

For example, considering a typical oil spill by a 90,000 DWT tanker that grounds and discharges 50,000 tons of oil with the rest recovered by salvage, typical costs are estimated as follows:

DIRECT COSTS	
1. Loss of oil	$ 4.5 million
2. Loss of vessel (replacement cost insured)	$ 62.0 million
3. Loss of use of vessel (charter party, opportunity cost)	$ 3.2 million
4. Loss of use of oil (additional oil replacement costs)	$ 1.2 million
5. Transfer of oil	$ 0.8 million
6. Salvage costs (typical)	$ 7.2 million
7. Emergency response and containment	$ 2.8 million
8. Loss of life, life-saving accommodation, repatriation	$ 1.0 million
9. Contingency costs	$ 3.0 million
Total direct costs	$ 85.7 million
of which $62.0 million is normally covered by insurance	

INDIRECT COSTS	
1. Damage to marine life	$ 50–100 million
2. Loss of revenue from fishing	$ 50–100 million
3. Damage to mariculture and aquaculture farms	$ 0–100 million
4. Damage to beaches	$ 80–250 million
5. Loss of tourism income	$ 60–200 million
6. Cost of cleanup	$ 18–500 million
7. Long-term health damage costs	$ 20–300 million
8. Contingency and others costs	$ 50–100 million
Total indirect costs	$328–1,650 million

Indirect costs tend to be significantly higher, but are often not collected in full.

6.2.1.1 Economic impact of ocean oil pollution. Transport of oil by sea, production of oil at offshore sites, and various land-based activities with potential for oil spills or discharge that could drain into the seas are all essential economic activities that cannot simply be eliminated to prevent ecological problems in the oceans and reduce external diseconomies to the world at large. The question of oil pollution's cost to society, which some claim should result in making the polluter pay the full social costs, is not that simple.

The problem is not only that the social cost of the pollution cannot really be compensated, but there is great difficulty in determining the loss to society incurred in removing or outlawing these activities. Another issue is that if such activities are just made to pay, those added costs would likely be passed on to society, which would then be the ultimate payer. In many cases, it is possible to compare environmental benefits and costs and social benefits and costs in determining a proper socioenvironmental balance sheet.

6.2.2 Costs and Benefits of Oil Pollution by Tankers

As a result of a number of spectacular tanker accidents, ocean pollution resulting from tanker accidents has been in the limelight in recent years. Although these accidents contributed only a small fraction of the oil discharged into the oceans by tankers, a worldwide effort to improve the safety of tanker navigation, led by the United States, has been under way in the last few years.

As shown in Table 6–1, the International Maritime Organization (IMO), as well as other international organizations responsible for marine safety and the marine environment, had advocated or imposed a whole slew of rules and regulations to improve tanker safety and to reduce voluntary and accidental oil pollution by tankers.

The new rules introduced by the Oil Spill Prevention Act of 1990, passed by the U.S. Congress and imposed on tankers trading in U.S. waters, and subsequently developed IMO regulations, which also emphasize tanker design for outflow tanker damage reduction and reduced outflow from damaged tankers, have resulted in a large number of new tanker orders for double-hull tankers.

Other methods, such as middeck center and side tank design systems that maintain a vacuum or ullage under pressure on top of the oil in cargo tanks, were also studied. Yet double-hull designs are generally preferred, not because they are inherently safer or less expensive to build and operate than other designs but because they are recommended by OPA-90. At the same time, little attention has been given to preventing tanker accidents by use of improved navigation,

TABLE 6–1 Marine Conventions

Year	Convention
General Conventions	
1958	Geneva Convention on the Territorial Sea and Contiguous Zone
1958	Geneva Convention on the High Seas
1958	Geneva Convention on Fishing and Conservation of the Living Resources of the High Seas
1958	Geneva Convention on the Continental Shelf
1972	Stockholm Declaration and Action Plan on the Human Environment
1982	The U.N. Convention on the Law of the Sea
Marine Pollution Conventions: Global	
1954 (1962) (1969)	International Convention for the Prevention of Pollution of the Sea by Oil
1969	International Convention Relating to Intervention on the High Seas in Case of Oil Pollution
1972	International Convention on the Dumping of Wastes at Sea
1973	International Convention for the Prevention of Pollution from Ships (MARPOL 73)
Marine Pollution Conventions: Various Regional Conventions	
1982	Memorandum of Understanding on Port State Control
Liability and Compensation Schemes: Intergovernmental	
1957	International Convention Relating to the Limitation of the Liability of Owners of Sea-going Ships
1969	International Convention on Civil Liability for Oil Pollution Damage
1971	International Convention on the Establishment of an International Fund for Compensation for Oil Pollution Damage (FUND)
1971	Convention Relating to Civil Liability in the Field of Maritime Carriage of Nuclear Material
1976	Liability for Maritime Claims
1984	Protocol of 1984 to Amend Civil Liability for Oil Pollution Damage, 1969
Liability and Compensation Schemes: Industry	
1969 (1978)	Tanker Owners "Voluntary" Agreement Concerning Liability for Oil Pollution (TOVALOP)
1971 (1978)	Contract Regarding an Interim Supplement to Tanker Liability for Oil Pollution (CRISTAL)
1985	Pollution Liability Agreement among Tanker Owners (PLATO)
General Maritime Safety	
1960 (1966–1969) (1971–1973)	International Convention for the Safety of Life at Sea (SOLAS)
1966 (1971, 1975, 1979)	International Convention on Load Lines
1972	Convention on International Regulations for Preventing Collision at Sea
1978	International Convention on Standards of Training, Certification, and Watchkeeping for Seafarers

ship management, crew training, vessel control and vessel traffic control, collision or grounding avoidance, and related systems.

Considering that less than 11% of all oil spilled by tankers is the result of tanker groundings or collisions and that there are many such accidents when double-hull construction may have done little to prevent or reduce resulting oil outflow, the question of the economic and operational costs of OPA-90 must be addressed in relation to other options for the improvement of tanker safety. It is now admitted that several major tanker accidents since the *Exxon Valdez* would have benefited little from double-hull construction. In both the La Coruna (Spain) and the Shetland Island cases, double-hulled tankers would probably have broken up just as readily as the single-hull design. There is the additional problem of maintaining outer-hull spaces gas as well as corrosion free.

The added cost of constructing double-hull tankers is already known now that over 100 such tankers have been delivered, but the difference in operating costs and relative cargo transport costs are still unknown.

Another issue is that most single-hull tankers will not be replaced by double-hull tankers anytime soon, if at all, because they are not used in U.S. or European trades, are exempted under a historic clause or for political reasons, or simply do not operate under any jurisdiction that imposes or enforces these new rules. This applies to many cabotage fleets, including that of the United States, that simply cannot afford fleet replacement.

At the same time, in 1992 the average age of the world tanker fleet was 16 years and that of the cabotage tanker fleets, such as that of the United States, even older, averaging over 24 years. Under these circumstances, the risk is often not oil pollution resulting from grounding or collision, but leakage resulting from tanker breakup, structural leaks, and other causes. Furthermore structurally weakened old tankers are much more prone to experience large or catastrophic structural damage on impact than are newer vessels.

This situation is particularly disturbing because port approaches and other navigational channels, where more than 88% of tanker accidents occur, are increasingly congested. This condition will become worse. By 2004, world seaborne trade is expected to grow by a compound 4% while ship sizes will generally remain constant. This will double channel traffic by about 2010.

Yet the management of navigational channels has remained traditional, and navigational controls in channels in most parts of the world still rely largely on visual, audible, or radar (reflecting) devices. The vast majority (over 90%) of tanker accidents are, in fact, the result of human, usually navigational, error.

Today's technology permits a radical change of this condition, with a steep increase in the safety of navigation and a large decrease in the pollution of coastal waters and navigational channels. All this would be a fraction of the costs of building safer tankers and oil spill response management systems.

This approach would not only prevent a significant number of ship accidents and resulting spills but also improve the traffic capacity, safety, and movement effectiveness in the channels. Channel delays would be reduced and channel capacity radically increased.

A large number of technological developments are available today that could not only improve tanker safety passively after damage. These developments would actively reduce the probability of tanker damage by improving its maneuverability, stopping distance, and impact resistance or by reducing the likelihood of tanker damage through improvements in navigational control, collision avoidance, and active or passive vessel traffic control systems and through the use of accurate global positioning systems, electronic charting, and electronic or acoustic channel guidance control systems.

Various approaches are being taken to prevent or reduce the outflow of oil from tankers. Passive systems attempt to reduce the outflow after an accident, while active systems are designed to reduce the probability of an accident.

6.2.2.1 Cost of passive outflow reducing systems. With an average age of the world tanker fleet (as of 1992) at 16 years and with the average age increasing annually at the rate of 0.4 years, by the year 2000 about 227 aged tankers will have to be converted to or replaced by double-hull vessels annually, in compliance with OPA-90 and IMO regulations (crude oil tankers of 20,000 DWT or over and product carriers of 30,000 DWT or over). This is a most difficult prospect and will severely strain world shipbuilding capacity.

Between 1986 and 1993, 34 double-hull tankers were delivered in sizes of 30,000 to 180,000 DWT, with most (27) delivered in 1991. Another 76 double-hull tankers, including 6 Very Large Crude Carriers (VLCCs), were delivered in 1992 and 1993.

Some of existing single hull tankers would normally continue to serve as single-hull tankers at least until an average age of

18 to 20 years. Therefore, the investment costs of OPA-90/IMO passive outflow system requirements can be assumed to be the difference of the cost of replacing average tankers by double- instead of single-hull tankers plus the cost of replacing younger tankers by double-hull tankers. Using the construction costs of Table 6–2, the differential cost of replacing the above-mentioned tonnage will grow from $1.820 billion in 1995 to $2.724 billion in 2000 to $3.487 billion in 2005 (in 1993 dollars).

In other words, the differential costs of replacing a single-hull with a double-hull tanker during the period from of 1995 to 2000 will amount to the equivalent 1993 cost of $20.614 billion, a sum roughly 50 times the amount expected to be spent on improvements in active ship accident preventative systems.

At a small fraction of this expected cost of converting about 46% of the world tanker fleet of 6,086 oceangoing tankers to double-hull vessels, navigational and other systems to eliminate most all the causes of ship accidents could be improved. In addition, the fleet of double-hull tankers, which will roughly comprise 49% of the world's tonnage capacity by 2005, will have increased fuel and maintenance costs of about 6% and 16%, respectively, when compared with an all–single-hull fleet. The differential cost of operating a typical 90,000 DWT double-hull tanker is estimated at $100,000 and $92,000 per year, respectively. The total additional operating costs of the world's double-hull tanker fleet will therefore be about half a billion dollars per year by 2005 (in 1993 dollars). Thusly, added operational costs increase by another $6.9 billion, for a total conversion cost of more than $26.9 billion (again in 1993 dollars).

The incremental repair costs were determined after accounting for the savings in repair costs by the use of newer vessels and additional costs of maintaining inner hull voids and compartments. Savings in insurance costs were not considered because as yet there is no stable insurance market and because cost savings of double-hull tankers are difficult to identify in the aggregate. Similarly, the effects of dumping an inordinately large number of older tankers on the scrap market, which will probably depress that market, were not considered.

Overall, therefore, the cost of replacing about 50% of the world tanker fleet with double-hull tankers with a ten-year differential 1993 cost of $26.9 billion will add an average of about 12.8% to the total cost of tanker operations over the period, which will eventually

TABLE 6–2 Tanker Construction Cost Factors

	SINGLE HULL	DOUBLE HULL	DOUBLE SIDE WITH MIDHEIGHT	MIDHEIGHT DECK
Weight of Steel	100	115–130	115–130	108–116
Personnel hours	100	110–135	110–135	105–120
Area requiring special coating	100	250	150	140
Construction time	100	117–125	117–125	110–118
Ship price	100	120–130	120–130	112–120
Ship size, gross tons	10,000–80,000	10,000–80,000	10,000–80,000	10,000–80,000

Note: Comparative numbers based on gross tons.

SOURCE: Japanese Ministry of Transport and Japan Maritime Research Institute, Report ISSN 0913–5480, no. 45, February 1993.

be reflected in tanker rates and oil prices at the delivery end. The question is how much this investment buys in terms of spill reduction.

6.2.2.2 Benefits of a passive outflow reducing system. Recent statistics indicate that on average, 28% of tanker accidents resulting in spills is caused by grounding and 22% by collision contact.[2] Similarly, 30% and 25% of all oil spilled by tanker accidents is caused by groundings and collisions, respectively. Analysis of casualty reports indicates that had all the tankers involved in these accidents been equipped with double bottoms, the spilled volume could have been reduced by 30 to 50%.

Over the same period, collisions and groundings accounted for just over 50% of the oil spilled accidentally by tankers but only 24% of the total amount of oil spilled by tankers (including spills during loading and discharging, tank cleaning, ballasting, bilge cleaning, and so forth). The total accidental spills by tankers during this period averaged just under 400,000 tons per year. In other words, the oil spilled by tanker accidents could have been reduced by 120,000–200,000 tons per year, had all tankers been equipped with

[2] *Lloyd's Casualty Reports 1970–1989* and S. Kristiansen and E. Rensvik, "Human Factors in Safe Operation and Pollution Prevention," International Maritime Conference, Cyprus, 1992.

double hulls and by about half that amount had half the tankers been so equipped.

Therefore, an investment of $26.9 billion (in 1993 dollars) could have reduced the amount of oil spilled by about 60,000–100,000 tons/year. Crudely speaking, therefore, the cost of reducing oil spillage by double-hull construction is $269,000 per ton of spill reduction per year. Similarly, translating the total differential construction costs into an annual (amortized) cost, the total cost of reducing spills by 1 ton would be about $50,000. Clearly, this is a very high cost-to-benefit ratio, and one wonders if money could not be spent more effectively in fighting oil pollution by tankers.

In a way, passive outflow reduction at such cost is only justified if tanker spill accidents are unavoidable. Yet there is clear evidence that the probability of tanker accidents can be greatly reduced. Most (88%) of these accidents occur in navigational channels and confined waters where both the movement and management of ships can be more effectively controlled. There is also ample evidence that better training, ship management, and navigational control, particularly in confined waters, can go a long way toward reducing the probability of ship collisions and groundings.

6.2.2.3 Reactive spill response. One of the major requirements of OPA-90 is that tanker owners or operators trading or planning to trade in U.S. waters must submit an approved vessel response plan (VRP) that demonstrates the steps that will be taken to contain and clean up any spill. It also requires agreements with oil cleanup contractors, including listing of their equipment, capabilities, and organization or method of response. However laudable the requirements for a VRP may be, individual states in the United States and now also various countries have or are drawing up their own, often quite different, spill response plan requirements.

On top of this, the IMO has the requirements that vessels delivered after April 4, 1993, and all existing vessels after April 4, 1995, shall carry shipboard oil pollution emergency plans (SOPEP), which unfortunately cannot be used to replace VRPs. To draw up VRPs and improve local response capability costs hundreds or thousands of dollars and numerous new "oil response contractors" have sprung up and offered their services. The uncertainties and costs involved in this are now affecting responsible owners' willingness to trade in U.S. waters.

6.2.2.4 Managing ship movements. Notwithstanding the availability, though not necessarily the effective use, of modern navigation and collision avoidance systems, traffic separation schemes, vessel traffic systems, and electronic charts, ship accidents occur at the same rate year after year. Roughly 0.5% of all the world ships are involved in major accidents every year, of which about one-half are tankers.

As mentioned, an average of 217 accidents per year occur in navigational channels (88% of the total). Considering collisions, only 22% happen in open waters, while nearly all groundings occur in channels and coastal waters. Similarly, the vast majority of collisions are caused by crossing, overtaking, end on, or hitting static (anchored or moored) vessels.

Very disturbing is the finding that the major causes of ship collisions or groundings in descending order are

- navigational aids,
- ship movement mistakes,
- ship management and management mistakes, and
- misreading traffic information.[2]

These four causes account for well over 72% of all such accidents. In other words, the majority of accidents are caused by human error and ineffective ship management. Although the IMO has introduced improved crew training requirements, there are really few mandatory ship management requirements that apply worldwide, such as used in air traffic where pilot-aircraft navigation and approach management is performed under strict rules.

6.2.2.5 Tanker accident risk prediction. Various studies of tanker accident risk and consequential spills have been performed. Accident rates have been statistically determined as accidents (collision, grounding, and so forth) per movement in particular navigational channels, for major ship types and sizes, as a function of channel characteristics.

For tankers, the mean number of accidents varies from about 1 to 3.8 in 10,000 movements in navigational channels with traditional navigational aids. Similarly, the magnitude of the accidents and re-

[2]B. Jacques, "Collision Course," *Seatrade Review* (Gollchester, U.K.: July 1993).

sulting spill sizes have been analyzed. The probability of a spill resulting from a channel accident is 12% to 20%. Spill size probability, given an accidental spill occurs, is shown in Figure 6–2, which also shows the range of costs of cleaning up for various sizes of spills.

As a result, for example, in the Strait of Malacca, with traffic of about 132,000 ships or ship movements per year, the expected number of accidents would be 13.2 to 50.16, of which 12% to 20% would

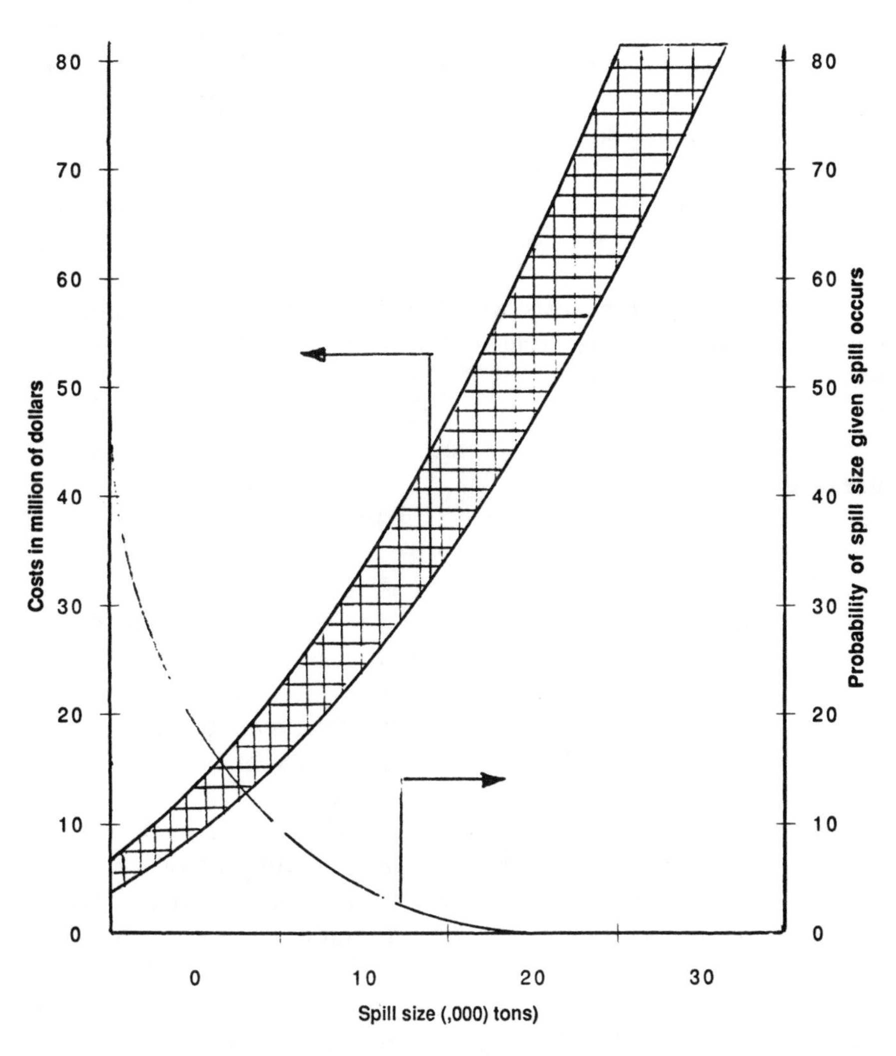

Figure 6–2 Spill Cleanup Costs.

result in a spill. This is consistent with Lloyd's casualty data cited previously.

Without improvements in position and vessel traffic control, this accident ratio will continue to increase, even if all tankers are equipped with double hulls. Oil spill outflow and cleanup costs may be reduced, but total damage costs would remain or even increase.

The effectiveness of VTS and traffic separation schemes in reducing accidents in confined waters with complex traffic patterns was estimated to be about 70%. The risk of accidents could be further reduced by the use of integrated GPS, electronic charting, radar, and expert systems control, which are mandatory for all but small fishing and recreational vessels that in turn are confined to areas outside navigational channels (very much as in air traffic control). Under such conditions, it is estimated that more than 85% of accidents could be prevented. These estimates are extrapolated from results obtained for various types of VTS, VTS with radar, and VTS with radar and traffic separation systems.[3]

6.2.2.6 Economic costs and benefits of integrated mandatory global positioning systems/vessel traffic management systems/radar electronic chart system GPS/VTMs radar/electronic chart systems. Considering that 78% of all tanker accidents occur in fewer than 30 navigational channels and that effective introduction and mandatory use of such an integrated GPS/VTM system is expected to reduce accidents by more than 85%, the total number of tanker accidents could be reduced by 66% with the introduction of 30 such systems.

Assuming a proportional decrease in spills, or 66% of 400,000 tons per year (the average spills per year in recent years by tanker accidents), although these 30 channels accounted for most of the accidents in the past, the reduction in oil spills would be 264,000 tons per year. The cost of installing such systems is estimated at $1.4 billion, with operating costs of about $120 million per year (including satellite transmission, GPS, and so forth).

In rough terms, therefore, the introduction of such systems would cost about $368 million per year, including amortization, finance costs, and operating costs (ten-year amortization or payback period). This implies a cost of $1,400 per ton of reduced oil spills, or

[3]T. K. S. Quon, G. E. Bushell, and J. A. Laube, "Risk Analysis of Vessel Traffic Systems," Maritime Policy and Management (Basingstoke, U.K., Taylor & Francis Ltd-1992, Vol. 19, p. 319–336)

about 2.8% of the cost of reducing oil spills by outflow reduction methods, such as the use of double hulls.

Even if less sophisticated mandatory VTMs with radar integration systems were used (with GPS and electronic charts), a technology currently available at a cost of about 5% to 8% of the added cost of double-hull use by tankers, the expected reduction in oil spills greatly exceeds that achievable by use of double hulls as now regulated.

Study of collisions and groundings in confined waters with complex traffic patterns, which account for the bulk of all tanker and ship accidents, indicates that effective mandatory use of sophisticated vessel traffic and separation systems, combined with GPS and electronic chart use, would eliminate most such accidents. Such systems could cover most confined waters and operate under mandatory conditions similar to those imposed on air traffic worldwide.

The expected savings in terms of the expected reduction in accident-induced oil spills, loss of property, cleanup costs, channel capital and maintenance costs, and ship transit time are so great that they defy the logic in delaying the introduction of modern sophisticated VTMS/GPS.

Traditional concepts of freedom of navigation would still apply in open waters, but the financial, economic, and environmental costs imposed by lack of regulation and control of shipping in confined waters with complex traffic patterns can no longer be afforded.

6.3 ECONOMIC IMPACT OF OCEAN POLLUTION

Humans' dependence on the oceans for food, raw materials, transportation, and recreation has increased greatly in recent years. In economic terms, it has doubled every 20 years since World War II and the value of the use of the oceans now accounts readily for over 12% of the world's total product.

Ocean environmental management imposed many costs and benefits, although people have become increasingly conscious of the environmental costs of various human activities and have introduced many environmental guidelines, regulations, international agreements, and so forth. Improvements are spotty and many people are as yet not aware of the damage caused by them, nor familiar with what they could and should do to reduce the costs of their actions to the ocean environment and ultimately to themselves.

Environmental management education, for example, is seldom available and even when offered deals more with an exposition of the laws or regulations than with methods of improvements in lifestyle, work style, and ocean environmental management.

At the same time, ocean environmental degradation is becoming more widespread because the costs of environmental damage are lower for polluters than for society as a whole, according to Visvanathan Rajagopalan, World Bank Vice President for Sector and Operations Policy.[5] There are insufficient incentives to stop polluters from harming the ocean environment.

Typically, the increased yields of increased fertilizer and pesticide use make the use of these materials an attractive agricultural strategy, particularly if farmers are not charged for polluting rivers and coastal zones. Today there are no market forces that recognize that ecological costs and markets fail to demand payment from polluters, particularly when the environment costs are deferred. For example, subsidizing coal or oil consumption by allowing prices below those of the world market to be maintained causes not only severe greenhouse effects but ill health, ill land and ocean pollution.

The costs of pollution are usually many times the price of the polluter's benefits. Similarly, the costs of cleanup and other remedial action are nearly always substantially higher than the cost of preventative action or alternative measures that satisfy the polluter's needs.

It is not by chance that both the most populous and industrialized countries depend on the oceans for resources, food, transport, recreation, and defense, as shown in Table 6–3. The impact of the oceans on the economies of these countries is pronounced, and damage to the ocean environment may cause them major economic hardships.[6]

Although the costs of claims resulting from oil pollution caused by ship accidents were small in the past (Table 6–4), this will change radically now that most jurisdictions abide by internationally agreed punitive and corrective liabilities. Yet regulations such as MARPOL and, in the United States, OPA-90 refer to only a small section of new tankers and an even smaller percentage of all tankers. This makes

[5]*Ocean Yearbook 9,* Editors Borgese E. Mann, N. Ginsburg, and J. R. Morgan (Chicago: The University of Chicago Press, 1991).

[6]Personal Communication with H. Peter World Bank, and H. Peteos, "A Framework for Environmental Assessments in the Maritime Industries (Washington, D.C., World Bank, 1991).

the retention of old tonnage more attractive now that replacement costs have skyrocketed.

Since MARPOL, however, large tankers such as VLCCs have undergone a change from a large tank, low tanker depth/draft ratio to a small tank and larger tanker depth/draft ratio. This affects hydrostatic balance outflow positively.

The claims paid bear very little relationship to the actual costs caused by the pollution. Although this is particularly evident in ship accidents, it is even more distorted in other cases of pollution, many of which cause no costs to the polluter. As noted before, costs are imposed mainly on the spectacular accidental polluters and much less frequently on the habitual, voluntary polluter.

6.3.1 Costs of Pollution

At this time, the direct costs of pollution are mounting, without greatly affecting the indirect costs of pollution. In 1990, for example, $90 billion was spent on pollution control in the United States (14% of the GNP). Yet pollution of the earth, water, and air continued nearly unabated.

In most cases, money is only spent on directly objectionable and often discernable pollution, such as visible, smelly, noxious, or otherwise objectionable pollution. Although much of this cost is spent on pollution prevention, the controls are usually reactional controls. In other words, most pollution controls are designed to clean part of the pollution caused by the primary action, such as trying to control emission pollution without attempting controls of the fuel or the combustion process used.

Environmentalists do not readily admit that the cost of environmental damage can be determined by just adding all the direct and indirect cost of pollution. Economists, on the other hand, require such cost analysis, as do politicians and other decision makers who have to weigh alternatives. The condition of the environment affects the value and its use. A waterfront plot along a polluted beach has less value than one along a pristine beach. Costs and benefits of environmental action and resulting conditions are implicitly judged. Although it may be unfair to put a value on nature, humans make their decisions based on value judgments, where value usually involves value to people affected by or users of the particular environment.

Environmental policy and the resulting regulation always entail

TABLE 6–3 Rankings of Comparative Maritime Interests (For Top 20 Countries)

LENGTH OF COASTLINE	EEZ AREA[a]	OFF-SHORE OIL/GAS PRODUCTION	FISH CATCH LANDED	MERCHANT SHIPPING TONNAGE[b]	EXPORTS[c]	NAVAL TONNAGE[d]
Canada	United States	United States	Japan	Japan	Malaysia	United States
Indonesia	France	United Kingdom	USSR	USSR	Belgium	USSR
Denmark	Australia	Norway	United States	Greece	Ireland	China
USSR	Indonesia	Mexico	Chile	United States	Libya	United Kingdom
Australia	New Zealand	Venezuela	China	China	Netherlands	France
Philippines	United Kingdom				Kuwait	Japan
		Australia	Peru	Philippines	Korea, Rep.	India
United States	Canada	Netherlands	Norway	United Kingdom	Chile	Taiwan
Norway	USSR	USSR	Korea, Rep.	Italy	Ivory Coast	Italy
United Kingdom	Japan	Malaysia	Denmark	Korea, Rep.	Sweden	Turkey
New Zealand	Brazil	Indonesia	Thailand	India		

China	Mexico	Saudi Arabia	India	Norway	Portugal	Peru
Greece	Denmark	India	Indonesia	Brazil	Trinidad and Tobago	Spain
Japan	Papua New Guinea	Nigeria	Korea, Dem. P. Rep.	France	Saudi Arabia	Brazil
France	Chile	Brazil	Iceland	Spain	Germany, Fed. Rep.	Canada
Mexico		Denmark	Guatemala	Denmark	Denmark	Pakistan
Brazil		Thailand	Philippines	Taiwan	Tunisia	Netherlands
Turkey		Iran	Canada	Germany, Fed. Rep.	Indonesia	Greece
India		New Zealand	Spain	Iran	Canada	Australia
Chile		Ghana	Mexico	Netherlands	Israel	Argentina
Colombia		Italy	Ecuador	Poland	Ecuador	Germany, Fed. Rep.

SOURCE: These rankings are based on data extracted from a wide range of sources, particularly the International Institute for Strategic Studies. *The Military Balance 1989–1990* (London: HSS. 1989). Elisabeth Mann Borgese, Norton Gunsburg, and Joseph R. Morgan (eds.), *Ocean Yearbook 7* (Chicago: University of Chicago Press, 1988): Lloyd's *Register of Shipping 1987;* and *The Times Atlas* and *Encyclopedia of the Sea*, 1990 edition.

[a]Taken from Clyde Sanger, *Ordering the Oceans* (Toronto: University of Toronto Press, 1987), p. 65. Only the largest 14 states were listed; the remaining order is controversial.

[b]Flags of convenience omitted. If they were to be added, Liberia, Panama Cypreus, Bahamas, and Singpore would be in the top 10 states.

[c]Exports are ranked by percentage of GNP and are essentially a potential vulnerability rather than a measure of strength.

[d]Tonnages of major warships Principal Surface Carriers (PSC) only.

TABLE 6–4 Claims Paid for Oil Pollution Caused by Operational Pollution

	NUMBER OF CASES	PAYMENT (IN THOUSANDS OF DOLLARS)
1971	200	3,825
1972	251	3,079
1973	254	3,123
1974	220	7,532
1975	168	4,855
1976	312	4,975
1977	232	10,094
1978	190	4,990
1979	289	49,763
1980	245	40,747
1981	200	8,087
1982	197	48,620
1983	147	7,100
1984	188	6,437
1985	68	39,400

SOURCE: E. Gold, *Handbook on Marine Pollution* (Oslo: Assurance Foreningen, GARD, 1985, p. 264), and E. Gold "Changing Marine Pollution Damage Regions: A New Role for Marine Arbitration" (Washington: Proceedings of the Eighth International Congress of Marine Arbitrations 1987, p. 73).

costs that must ultimately be justified by the value created or maintained. Although some pollution is very detrimental and must be prevented or eliminated at all cost (toxic, nuclear, and so forth), some pollution must be tolerated because, in fact, human life would be impossible without it. Humans themselves emit pollutants by just their being. Similarly, getting rid of all pollution at whatever costs would not only be very expensive but would actually bring civilization as it is now known to a standstill.

Two basic approaches are used to set values on environmental assets or the cost of pollution. The direct approach tries to discover the value people place on it, while in the indirect approach the market value of environmental assets is evaluated.

The direct approach assumes that it is possible to get a consensus on value by determining the willingness to pay value for an environmental asset. Others maintain that the willingness to accept, which includes the possibility of exchange for other value, should be determined. It is interesting to note that both valuing methods are affected by exogenous factors such as local economic conditions and prospects.

The indirect market valuation approach is less affected by local factors but may be affected by broader market conditions. In other words, the market value of the pollution of local fishing grounds is affected by the prevailing availability and price of fish similar to that usually caught in those grounds.

In addition, there is the value of pollution's long-term impact, including consequential costs. Therefore, the cost may not only be weighed against the benefit of correcting the environmental damage now but also in preventing future environmental damage. It is important always to weigh costs against benefits and to use the same or a consistent time horizon for both. Often initial costs may be significantly higher than initial benefits, but if they are lower in net present value terms when considering the whole time period affected, then the action is obviously justified.

Governments often fail in making effective or fair benefit and cost evaluations of environmental policies. The double-hull requirements for tankers plying U.S. waters are a typical example where costs will probably exceed benefits. Many such decisions are made in response to political pressure.

6.3.2 The Economic Effectiveness of Environmental Regulation

Environmental regulation is more often punitive than other regulation and not compensatory. In other words, it tries to punish only, not repair the damage caused by pollution or compensate society or individuals affected by pollution or other environmental impact. Environmental regulation is often introduced reactively and in response to public or political pressure caused by a polluting event, such as a ship grounding, a power plant accident, or some health emergency resulting from a hazardous emission. As a result, environmental regulation is usually largely designed to reduce the type of damage or accident and the resulting pollution, independent of the probability of this type of accident recurring. Most environmental regulators only cover a narrow range of environmental problems.

The reason for government intervention in environmental pollution is that, unlike other transactions, market forces usually fail to intervene. Markets do not generally consider the interests of the individual or corporation polluter and those of society at large in the same terms. The costs of pollution to society nearly always exceed those of the individual or corporation. Government must therefore intervene to establish a balance. This has resulted in the general principle of "making polluters pay," which underlies most environmental regulation.

Governments have usually tried to adjust social and market costs by setting standards, but in ocean pollution, governments often introduce large penalties over and above social or market costs. The idea is that such an approach will create incentives to polluters to clean up their act. This is contrary to a market-based approach or even one that determines both the market and the social costs. Although it is in society's interest to ensure that polluters pay the full cost of the direct and indirect damage caused, and thereby eliminate the potential that costs are dumped on society or the environment, standards set by government are sometimes discriminatory and deliberately protect, for example, the old decrepit U.S. flag cabotage tanker fleet rather than encourage the introduction of newer safer tankers.

Standards are also sometimes set without regard to their effect on consumer prices, such as the landed cost of petroleum. Governments often prefer to set rigid standards for large polluters and more flexible ones for small operational polluters. Similarly, such standards are often designed to make the cost a parabolic function of the pollution damage caused. Yet such strategies often backfire because more stringent environmental standards and costs cause diminishing environmental returns.

Increasingly, market-based costs are introduced into environmental protection, and market-based instruments are used to impose on polluters the total costs to the environment, such as cleanup and damage replacement, including loss of opportunity costs. Such instruments create incentives for polluters and can be designed around fair economic standards and for effective trading or trade-offs. Here polluters can trade off excess of standards against measures below standards. Such instruments can also be designed to encourage continuous improvements in environmental standards.

Trade in pollution permits, which is now restricted to the United States, could be extended internationally in the future. This is of particular interest to ocean environmental management because national ocean boundaries are less defined than land boundaries and most of the oceans constitute international waters.

Marketable permits are usually environmental quotas, allowances, or limits on pollution levels that can be traded subject to some prescribed rules. The quotas are allocated by a local, national, or international authority and are set up to ensure achievement of environmental objectives. Marketable permits are expected to reduce the cost of compliance and may make it more palatable for developing nations to abide by environmental standards. In a way, such permits—if traded internationally—would legitimize the argument made by many poor developing nations that they should be allowed to use up their "share" of pollution in furthering their economic and industrial growth, as was done by industrialized nations.

Marketable air emission permits are now actively traded on the Chicago Board of Trade, but the method may provide a rational and fair approach to the enforcement of international standards in ocean environmental pollution. Trades of such permits could be between governments, between enterprises, or even internally within an enterprise or country. Another instrument is a deposit-refund scheme where a deposit is paid by potential polluters. If pollution is avoided, a refund is made.

The most efficient approach appears to be a combination of ocean environmental regulation and the use of economic instruments designed to reinforce and complement each other. For this to work, though, nations must take and enforce the standards they ratify seriously. Only then can uniform and successful ocean environmental management be achieved.

Unfortunately, this is not the case today, and a majority of nations do not abide by or enforce the very regulations or conventions they negotiated and ultimately ratified. Although in some cases this is the result of a lack of enforcement capability, there are many instances where nations make little effort to enforce standards or where enforcement is corrupted or simply lax.

It appears that not only are incentives needed for polluters but also for nations and their enforcement agencies. Today's technology permits early discovery of the location of serious pollution, even in remote waters. Unfortunately, identification of the polluter is a different matter.

Some have suggested that international enforcement should be introduced in international waters by an agency of the United Nations, such as the IMO, but this would burden the overstretched United Nations even further. This does not appear practical at this stage. Extending port state control from territorial water boundaries to a midocean division line where jurisdiction is handed over to another port state control agency is also a possibility. This would, for example, be in line with jurisdiction in international air traffic control.

With air traffic, responsibility is transferred from one jurisdiction to another at a defined point in space. For such a system to work in international waters, the concept of port state control would have to be revised and reorganized to include coastal control and guardianship. Some nations have moved in this direction. For example, the port of Singapore is not only responsible for the traditional port state control functions but also for coastal security and the safety of adjacent waters to the midwater boundaries of neighboring countries such as Indonesia and Malaysia, with which it shares the Strait of Malacca.

The economic effectiveness of ocean environmental regulation is rather poor. The choice of economic instruments in ocean environmental regulation should be made in terms of their economic efficiency, social equity, environmental effectiveness, political acceptability, and implementability.

Economic instruments can be based on the discharge or emission caused and the polluting product or service provided. Sometimes a mixed strategy may be the most effective strategy. It is important to make the instruments easy to understand, easy to apply, easy to measure, and noncontrovertible. The use of such instruments may not reduce compliance costs, but will often increase incentives, raise revenue, and offer a flexible pollution reduction approach.

Arguments are often raised that ocean environmental regulation will not only add major costs but will also reduce productivity or efficiency of economic activities in the oceans. The same arguments were made when pressure was put on manufacturers and service providers to improve their quality. Just as quality did not reduce productivity or increase costs in the long run, so environmental regulation will not reduce ocean activity productivity in fishing, mining, oil production, recreation, and transport. In fact, experience shows that the opposite is usually the case.

The most important issue is the need to back up ocean environmental regulation with political will. For long-term successful protection of the ocean environment, narrow partisan politics and interests by nations, companies, and individuals must be set aside. Only in this way can it be ensured that the oceans will make an increasingly important contribution to human well-being.

6.4 CONTINGENT VALUE AND WORTH OF THE OCEAN

The cost to the public or the value of ocean pollution is hard to determine, and numerous approaches to do so have been offered by economists and others. After the *Exxon Valdez* disaster, the State of Alaska commissioned a study to find out what Americans would be willing to pay to avoid such a disaster over the next decade. The result was $30 per capita or a sum of $2.8 billion, if every American's share was $30. Exxon actually settled for $1 billion, but the question if such a contingent value estimate is valid remains.

Contingent value as a basis for determining the ocean's worth or the cost of ocean pollution is being criticized for a number of reasons. One is that respondents will usually overestimate hypothetical costs or will include costs that they will not be asked to bear. If required to back up their cost estimate with an actual contribution, their cost estimate will often decline precipitously. In fact, several experiments prove this point. For example, when all respondents who agreed that the public should pay to maintain a particular local environment were asked to actually contribute, the percentage dropped to 10% to 20% of the earlier proponents of public contribution.

Similarly, the methods used in surveys designed to establish contingent values of environmental impacts have themselves been a major effect on the outcome. In response to OPA-90, the U.S. National Oceanic and Atmospheric Administration (NOAA) has laid out standards for contingent value surveys in damage assessment for oil spills at sea. These standards conclude that contingent value studies could be used to develop a preliminary estimate of damage caused by ocean pollution. The legality of contingent value damage estimates has not been tested yet, and there is great concern that the very magnitude of such estimates may have severe effects on the commercial use of the oceans. Particular problems arise due to the lack of basis for estimates of the value of lost opportunity, when quite often the opportunity would never have been taken anyway.

The value of the ocean to the world and its economy is hard to determine, but the value of all the resources harvested from the oceans, plus the value of economic ocean activities such as transport, recreation, and coastal developments, is estimated to amount to about $1.35 trillion per year, or about 6.5% of the world's gross product in 1992. Only about half these activities would be seriously affected by severe ocean pollution, and even then the impact on the oceans' worth in economic terms may be hard to determine. The contingent value of the oceans is even harder to estimate as the oceans form an integral part of the earth's ecosystem and their conditions affect the atmosphere, rainfall, freshwater supply, and most other essential physical needs of the earth. In other words, the oceans per se have an infinite contingent value.

The problem is more readily addressed locally, particularly in confined waters such as various basically landlocked seas (for example, the Aral, Caspian, or Mediterranean). The Aral Sea has, for all intents and purposes, become extinct. Its waters were drained, marine life in them killed, and the sea made biologically inert. The area of the sea has been reduced by over 60%, and desolate deserts developed around it. The contingent values lost here are life support and subsistence for millions of people and near economic extinction of a complete region the size of France and Germany combined.

Pollution of the Mediterranean has become so bad in recent years that fishing is possible in only a few parts of that sea. The coast off southern France is so polluted now that most beaches are unsafe. Even more important is the effect of ocean pollution on the ocean atmosphere and climate as well as on intrusion into ground waters. What is the contingent value of the damage pollution of the Mediterranean? It is probably in the tens of billions of dollars per year. The most serious effect, however, is often caused by irreversible developments that cannot be corrected at any cost. Similarly, the Caspian Sea has become highly polluted and much of the nutrient inflows reduced by locks on the rivers flowing into the sea.

Environmentalists increasingly insist on including contingent value on pollution liability, even though such values cannot be determined. As a result, the total liability and resulting damages assessed against Exxon in the *Exxon Valdez* disaster was several billion dollars, of which cleanup costs were only about 50%.

Another issue is who should be awarded contingent damage awards. The most reasonable method would be to make these awards to those directly affected, such as fishers, but in many cases contingency-based awards are collected by government agencies and others not directly or even indirectly affected by the accident. Once the connection between the contingent damage and the beneficiary of the award becomes murky, valuing contingent values and resulting damage claims often becomes more a political than economic exercise. It is then that any reasonable relationship between contingent value and assessed liability becomes meaningless, and liability is perceived to be assessed as a punitive and corrective measure. This approach is counterincentive.

7

Ocean Environmental Management

The ocean environment is under increased pressure. The rate of ocean environmental degradation is becoming greater. The most serious ocean pollution is still largely in coastal waters, estuaries, landlocked seas, or ocean extensions, such as the Baltic and Mediterranean Seas. Even the open ocean now suffers environmental damage. The problem has become more serious with humans' increased dependence on the oceans. Similarly, the earth's physical balance depends on the oceans. The continued ability to use the ocean resources and the oceans as a resource effectively, as well as to maintain the traditional role of the oceans in ensuring a balance in the air and water circulation phenomena that revitalize the earth as a continuously renewing world, requires control of the ocean environment.

Unlike on land, where the impacts of pollution are not only more visible but affect people and human activities in many direct and indirect forms, the oceans are as yet sparsely used and inhabited. As a result, the impacts of ocean pollution are not directly evident and for a long time have simply been ignored. In fact, the oceans have been considered a depository of infinite capacity that could not be damaged, at least in terms of direct impact on local or parochial interest. For people to recognize the fragility and damageability of the ocean environment, large-scale accidents had to happen. This in turn has led to certain ocean environmental requirements. Yet, as noted in sections 5.3, 5.4, and 5.5, existing regulations, conventions, and laws are often

1. highly fragmented;
2. introduced to address narrow issues or impacts;
3. designed so as to miss important requirements;
4. economically counterincentive;
5. unenforceable; or
6. unfair to sectors of an economy, industry, or the world community.

As a result, little progress has been made to reduce the overall level of ocean pollution.

The annual costs of controlling U. S. environmental pollution in line with existing regulations were estimated by the EPA (1991) to have increased from $25 billion in 1972 to over $118 billion in 1990 and to continue to increase linearly at a rate of about $5 billion per year. About 40% of that accounts for the cost of control of ocean pollution from U. S. land sources. Worldwide, the annual cost of controlling ocean pollution to the level of standards set by existing regulations is estimated to have grown from about $20 billion in 1972 to over $100 billion in 1992.

Only a fraction of that money is actually available and spent, and as a result, the pollution of the oceans continues largely unabated, notwithstanding the introduction (ratification) and partial enforcement of increasingly stricter ocean environmental standards. It appears that many of the standards or their underlying regulations, conventions, or laws are not effective and approach the problem of ocean pollution reactively instead of proactively. Only a few of the new laws are oriented toward prevention and even often consider not the prevention of the basic causes of the pollution but the subsequent events leading to the pollution. For example, a law may legislate tanker design to prevent or reduce outflow of oil from grounded tankers, but many not legislate the various operational events leading to tanker grounding. In other words, much more effective ship traffic control and guidance, which may be much cheaper, may be needed to achieve similar, if not larger, reductions in oil pollution by tankers while also reducing loss of life and property at sea at the same time.

In fact, preventing ship accidents from happening may be a much more effective strategy than the one popular now, which concentrates on reducing the damage caused by and the impact of tanker accidents.

The current approach could be compared to equipping commercial aircraft with giant parachutes that allow aircraft damaged in the sky to float safely to land in one or more pieces as a replacement for air traffic control. It is unfortunate in a way, but probably understandable, that major legislation concerning ocean pollution always follows disasters that cause major environmental damage. Most of this legislation is reactive and not proactive. It tries to reduce, not prevent, damage.

Questions that have not been satisfactorily answered are who the custodian of the oceans is and who should legislate or set rules or laws and enforce them. The role could be done by various interested parties such as the following:

- international organizations;
- governments;
- intergovernmental organizations;
- government agencies;
- learned societies;
- international technical organizations;
- commercial organizations;
- businesses;
- experts and consultants;
- communications agencies, publicity organizations, press, TV, and so forth;
- public interest groups, or
- advocates.

Ocean environmental management in terms of legislation is usually a government function on the national level and a function of the International Maritime Organization (IMO) and other U.N. environmental organizations on the international level. Ocean environmental legislation has been fraught with problems of discord. On the national as well as international levels, reaching a consensus (or compromise) among hundreds of stakeholders, interests, and nations is not only difficult but often requires painful and scientifically damaging compromises.

Most importantly, notwithstanding prodigious inputs of teams of experts, conflicts of local and national opinions and vested interests have, in most cases, produced environmental standards that combine the lowest level of standards for the ocean environment.

Although most of the international standards adopted have been widely accepted by the family of nations, the most significant weakness is the lack of enforcement powers by international organizations. One problem is that the IMO, for example, assumes tacit acceptance of standards if no more than one-third of the nations object to them. This is because the time taken by nations to legislate such agreements formally is inordinately long. Even more important is the often real or perceived differences in international and national standards as enforced by national authorities. Enforcement of environmental regulations has been deficient. About half of the IMO's members are not signatories of the MARPOL covenants, and compliance has been limited to some of the most important countries, largely in response to commercial pressures from oil companies and shipping lines that desire to maintain their good names with respect to the environment. Some countries have public interest groups that have succeeded in raising consciousness regarding ocean pollution, and some have established environmental protection agencies.

Enforcement, however, is sporadic, even where environmental protection agencies exist. At the operational level, enforcement may depend on the courts, police, or armed forces, which become involved in such issues only if the matter is significant and evidence of transgression exists. Port authorities could perform enforcement functions, even where there are private ports and commercial arrangements for operation, by making concessions subject to compliance with environmental norms.

National environmental enforcement may also be coordinated by a dedicated agency such as the Environmental Protection Agency of the United States.

International standards will have to be enforced by national agencies, and therefore some consistency in standards will be essential.

7.1 ENVIRONMENTAL MANAGEMENT FUNCTIONS

International, national, and local environmental agencies and organizations can perform diverse roles, from identifying environmental impact and conducting engineering, scientific, and economic research to studying environmental impact problems and potential solutions to developing guidelines, writing regulations, and setting statutes designed to implement solutions and prevent the occurrence of environmental problems. All such agencies and organizations share the difficult problem of setting priorities for implementing statutes, regulations, and standards in an imperfect world, subject to conflicting objectives, diverse interests, and the resulting political, social, and economic pressures.

Over the years, these agencies have accumulated large amounts of data and have performed numerous surveys, tests, and studies that acquired information for improvement in the regulatory requirements. Information is generated on potential sources of pollution, ameliorating approaches designed to prevent pollution, and various methods for the cleanup of pollution and, once it has occurred, its effects.

Most agencies, particularly those responsible for ocean environmental management, have concentrated on reducing environmental damage and on cleanup. Less effort or attention has been devoted to prevention and to policy analysis, which may ensure more effective ocean environmental management under conditions of limited resources and competing financial, economic, social, and strategic interests. Most attention is currently given to pollution control and cleanup, not to prevention. The reasons for this are in part that

1. control is reactive and can be justified by or imposed on real developments that have been experienced, while prevention is politically more risky and the expected effects can often be challenged, and
2. prevention may have undesirable economic and social side effects few policy makers are willing to face. Reducing the real or potential effect of pollution, on the other hand, is always creditworthy.

By and large, environmental policy making has not benefited from substantive analysis and is based mainly on assessment of environmental impacts and risks. Few factors considered in environmental policy making can be accurately determined with respect to both cause and effect. As in human health, more credit is given for a cure or even partial healing than for prevention of the illness. Reducing outflow from a damaged vessel is therefore a much more understandable contribution than preventing damage to the vessel in the first place. Thus it is the preferred policy of the United States, even though it is probably much less effective and more costly than preventative measures.

7.2 MONITORING OCEAN ENVIRONMENTAL EFFECTS

A major deficiency in ocean environmental management today is the lack of effective instrumentation such as measuring and recording devices designed to monitor the existence and effects of ocean pollution and various ocean processes. Although great progress in sensory equipment and related electronic or magnetic storage and data communication technology has been made, the ability to monitor pollutant levels and their causal effects is still rather primitive.

There is an urgent need for improvements in the following areas:

1. monitoring pollution loading, pollution transport, and pollution dispersal in the oceans;
2. measuring pollution absorption, chemical interaction, dispersal, and deposition in the oceans;
3. identifying and measuring the origins of pollution and the method of transport and dilution of pollutants from the source;
4. monitoring the direct and indirect causal effects of pollution in the oceans, and
5. measuring the effects of containment and cleanup of pollution.

To permit a discussion of measuring, monitoring, transmittal technology availability, capability, and identification of the needs for new technology, the various coastal and deep ocean processes involved must be identified and the measuring, monitoring, and data storage and transmittal requirements must be specified. It is similarly necessary to develop a specific worldwide plan and design a system for real-time ocean environmental monitoring. Only then will standards be able to be enforced.

7.3 CULTURAL FACTORS IN OCEAN ENVIRONMENTAL MANAGEMENT

In the early 1960s, Japan suffered severe health problems caused by mercury ingestion through consumption of contaminated seafood. Today, many people are still disabled as a result of that accident. This shocked the country to such an extent that industry, government, and the people at large banded together to ensure that such an accident would not recur. The Japanese Federation of Economic Organizations (Keidanran) used its extensive influence to convince companies to reduce environmental pollution voluntarily. Since then, Keidanran has issued a Charter for Environmental Protection. Similarly, the government provided technical and financial assistance for industrial pollution control and environmental protection using the Japan Environmental Corporation as an instrument for offering soft medium-term loans to small and medium-sized companies to install pollution abatement equipment. It also offered help to ensure soil pollution control in urban areas and coordinated site and shared waste-treatment facility development. In addition, it helped relocate and consolidate small-scale, pollution-prone industries.

It similarly provided help in the development of buffer zones to abate air, noise, and aesthetic pollution impact. It is important to note that the principle is to work with all the parties concerned, sharing and disclosing information and gradually moving towards consensus among government, industry, and the affected population.

Cultural and social pressures in Japan ensure effective cooperation toward reaching a consensus. Few industrial firms would dare to contravene the consensus reached or to bypass the consensus-seeking process. The resulting loss of face would ruin a company in the long run.

Local communities, media, government, and industry meet together to resolve the interlinked environmental and economic problems and usually agree to abide by controls that are stricter than national or international standards. These agreements usually do not provide for any penalty, yet Japanese firms consider it a matter of honor to not only meet but to exceed the agreed-upon requirements.

In many cases, this approach has led industries in communities to move their pollution facilities onto new consolidated sites or even newly reclaimed artificial islands and to develop joint waste-treatment and disposal facilities. The result is not only a vast reduction in pollution control and waste-treatment and disposal costs, but also an identification of opportunities that use polluting waste from one industry as a raw material in another.

There are other examples of the important role cultural factors play in the management of the ocean environment. Nations with a long historic dependence on the seas—such as Iceland, Japan, Norway, and many other island and coastal nations—take great pains to ensure the maintenance of the ocean environment. On the other hand, nations with little, if any, historic dependence on the seas, even if they are ratifiers of international conventions that strictly limit pollution, often fail to recognize the importance of the ocean environment and permit or ignore blatant ocean pollution.

7.4 PERFORMANCE OF OCEAN ENVIRONMENTAL MANAGEMENT

Ocean environmental management is recognized as important, yet it is more often than not performed in a diffused manner. The many parties involved in it often appear to engage more in a tangle than in a coordinated, cooperative process designed to prevent or reduce the effects of ocean pollution. This may be due in part to a lack of leadership. In many instances, the real question is not performance of ocean environmental management. Instead it is, who is in charge and what are the cooperating roles to be played by all concerned? There is general agreement on the value of the ocean environment and the importance of maintaining it, but few will agree on the relative weight of different ocean environmental management goals and objectives and the alternative implementation methods to be used toward their achievement.

Ocean pollution response and contingency plans are attempts to develop some prepared coordination and joint use of resources in fighting ocean pollution, but they are seldom subscribed by all the concerned parties or agencies. A major problem is often a lack of agreement about who is to pay for the effective response. This in turn causes serious delays and a less-than-effective use of resources, which often results in greater environmental damage than necessary had timely action been taken.

7.4.1 Planning Environmental Management

Although planning can be defined as formally identifying activities, their sequence, and the requirements necessary to accomplish a management goal, U.S. citizens are not comfortable with the process. Planning is associated with vision and can be defined as a documented thought through vision or the determination of all the requirements needed to make something happen. In a democracy like the United States, planning, particularly by the federal government, is perceived as interference with free choice, a control of individual actions, and in general an infringement of the rights and freedoms of citizens and society. This is so even though people usually recognize that to achieve a clean environment, certain standards of behavior must be introduced, advocated, or even mandated.

Planning environmental management and the related regulation of various processes and activities are also often charged as introducing anticompetitive barriers by imposing additional costs not seen by those subject to these environmental plans, standards, or regulations.

In recent years, a move towards worldwide standards and regulations, an attempt to reconcile diverse requirements, and equally important, the use of different approaches to enforcement used by different countries and jurisdictions have been started. The problem is magnified by the various approaches taken, where some countries plan and emphasize prevention while others concentrate on containment and cleanup.

Environmental management planning usually consists of the following major steps:

- identifying and monitoring sources of pollution;
- analyzing sources of pollution;
- mapping the pollution domain;
- modeling the pollution process where possible;
- formulating a strategy for effective ocean environmental management and pollution prevention;

- developing containment strategies, cleanup strategies, and correction of impacts caused;
- developing pollution prevention management;
- setting standard and evaluation regulation and control pertaining to pollution prevention management;
- formulating the enforcement, response, and planning;
- managing environmental quality; and
- analyzing economic environmental issues and pollution management.

Not all these steps necessarily need to be taken; each, however, is important in designing, planning, and implementing ocean environmental management.

Ocean environmental management usually involves many parties, each with a distinct and often different focus, objective, and management style. It involves perpetrators, regulators, public interest groups, public agencies, insurers, governmental agencies, and various commercial and service organizations.

Planning environmental management goes beyond response planning. Response planning deals largely with reactive requirements to a spill or other environmental preventative action planning, with coordination of parties involved or affected by ocean environmental pollution, with integration of response activities, with control of regulatory and standard requirements, and with other factors. It also involves government and other agencies at the international, national, and local levels. Similarly, international, national, and local private or public interest groups may play a role.

Effective environmental management is necessary because it not only affects an essential global resource but because it involves local, national, and international politics and policy making.

7.4.2 The Ocean Environmental Management Process

Ocean environmental management, as mentioned, involves many parties with different concerns, interests, agendas, and even objectives. This makes the ocean environmental management process difficult to control, and full coordination as well as cooperation is seldom achieved. Although the overall objective—maintenance of the ocean environment—is generally accepted, perpetrators are often interested in covering it up or, if caught, in minimizing the cost and liability or in passing on responsibility to others. In many cases, regulators may also have an agenda to pass on responsibility or liability to others.

Public agencies are also interested in minimizing their costs and maximizing their political capital, particularly their reputation as guardians of the public's interest. Others involved may be concerned with maximizing their financial benefits from ocean environmental accidents (Figure 7–1). In most cases, ocean pollution is either not discovered or, if it is, results in drawn-out litigation that often assumes greater importance and sometimes greater costs than the

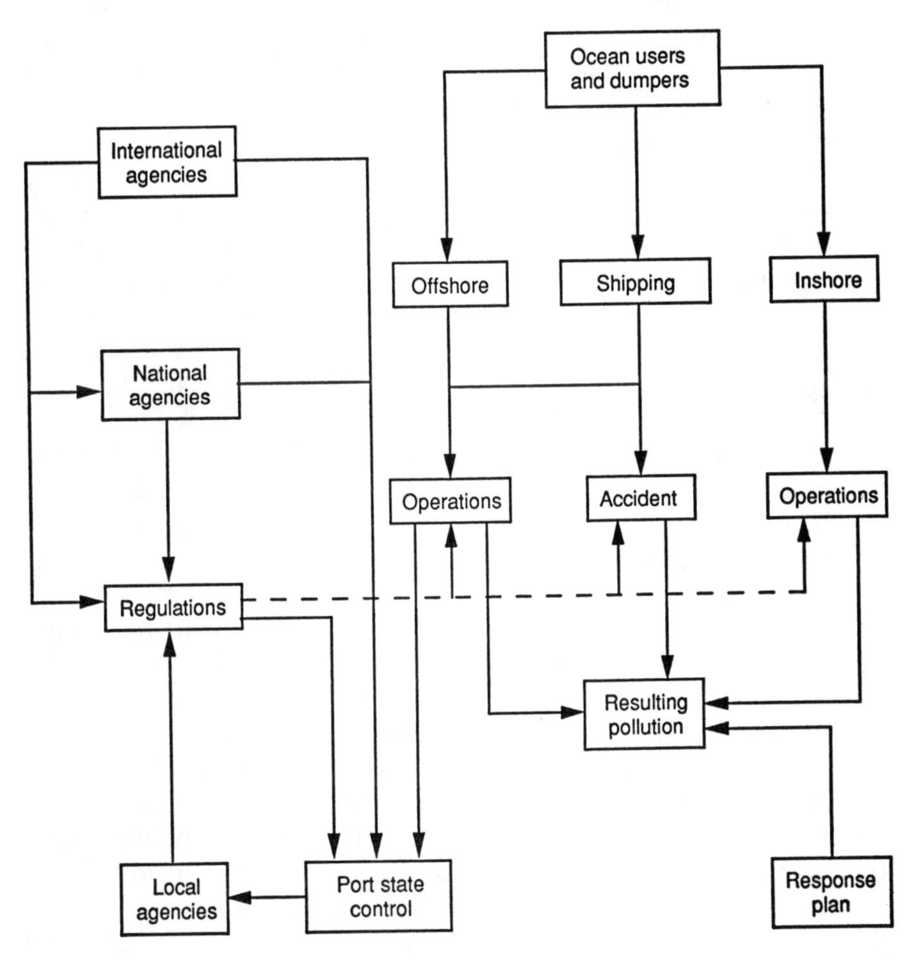

Figure 7–1 Major Parties Involved in Ocean Environmental Management.

cleanup itself. In some cases, cleanup and other corrective action may actually be delayed or faulted because of legal maneuvering, bickering about jurisdiction or other control, and conflicting goals.

Although much effort has been devoted to the development of oil spill and other ocean environmental accident response and contingency plans, the management of ocean environmental maintenance is still far from being effective. The major cause is the lack of definition of the process. Although the roles of the different parties involved are usually defined, the process by which their roles are implemented and how the ocean environment is managed are often not. As a result, most ocean environmental accidental and longer-term pollution takes a long time to resolve and correct.

In part, this may be due to the large number of parties involved, the difficulty in determining cause and assigning liability, and most importantly, the problem of identifying all costs and benefits. As a result, huge amounts of money are often wasted in attempting to manage ocean environmental pollution.

There is an urgent need to define the process more explicitly and regulate the limits of the roles of the different parties involved. If this is not done, ocean environmental management will continue to be performed in a haphazard or impromptu manner at greater than necessary expense, with large losses in time and greater than necessary damage to the environment. The ocean environmental management process consists of a number of major functions, as shown in Figure 7–2.

One major problem is that response and contingency plans are designed to act when an unforeseen accident happens. They are not designed to respond to a buildup of pollution from ongoing inshore or offshore polluting activities, even if such pollution increases precipitously, unless it is a result of an accident. This implies always knowing that an accident has happened. Although evident when a ship runs aground or an offshore oil well blows out, it is not at all evident when a waste-treatment plant malfunctions, a flood removes a lot of agricultural chemicals, or similar developments.

Response and contingency plans are similarly not designed to prevent or respond to nonaccidental, willful pollution, unless detected or reported. Spill response and contingency planning assumes that a spill or other polluting accident is discovered and the plan is implemented. Its major defect is the lack of integration of preventative and reactive ocean environmental management processes. Port state control functions, for example, are not linked to spill response

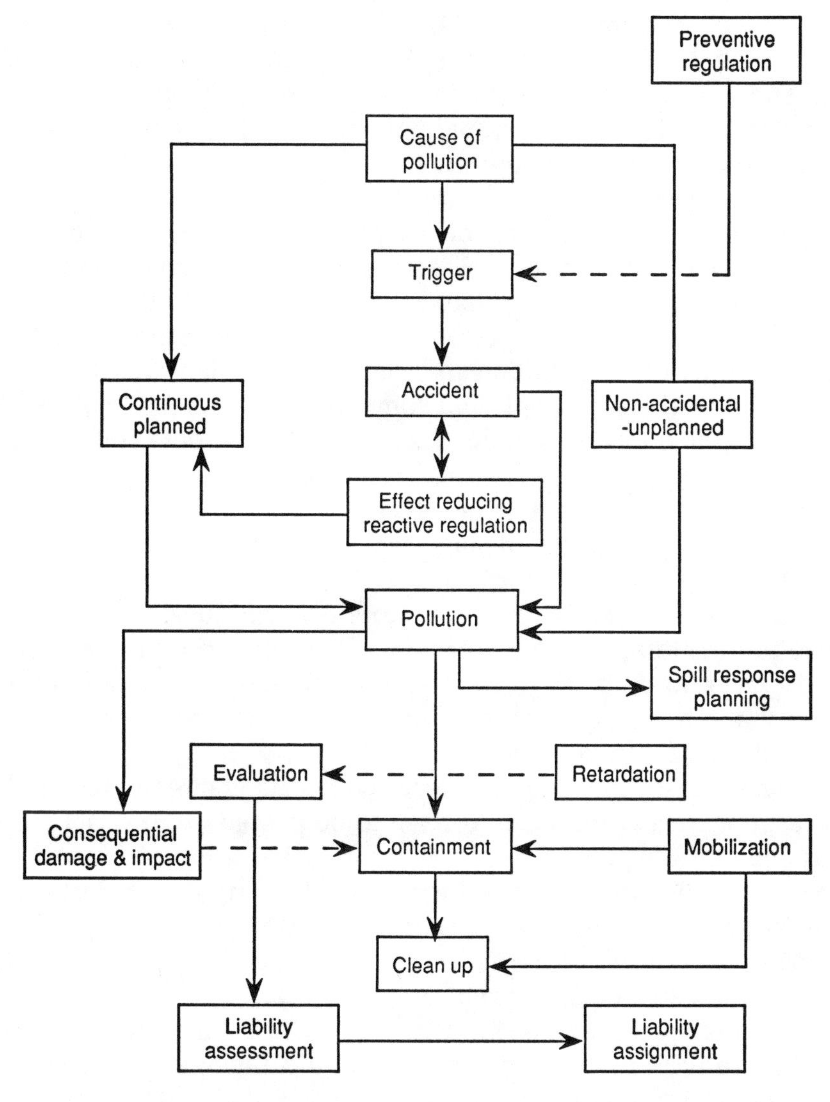

Figure 7–2 Ocean Environmental Management Process.

and contingency planning and management. As a result, there is little feedback toward more effective enforcement.

The problem is that effective management of the ocean environment needs advanced methods of management to manage the complexity not only of pollution's causes and effects, but also of the relationships of the parties involved and their approaches and interests.

Environmental management needs organization and integration as well as control with feedback and learning. Effective ocean environmental management must be designed to deal effectively and simultaneously with different parties and stakeholders, not just either the perpetrating or injured parties. In fact, quite often other related parties, some of whom may not have a direct involvement in the incident or even its effects, are affected.

Because the oceans are mainly international domains, national concerns, and national responsibilities, loyalty to a community, one of the driving forces of environmental management on land and in coastal waters, is often superseded by the lack of concern for both the consequences of pollution and for being held liable for the effects caused. In fact, many people and companies still feel that their pollution is incremental and that they have a "right" to some pollution.

7.4.3 Economic Factors in Ocean Environmental Management

In a free market world, operators and producers try to maximize profits, minimize costs, or both. They often do this by passing environmental costs on to society. These external costs are not audited without government regulation, and even if such exists, strict accounting rarely takes place.

The market's failure to accept such costs is often defended by the argument that they would have to be passed on to society anyway, but this argument is fallacious. It makes a lot of difference if such costs are part of the production function input costs instead of externalized social costs. In fact, it negates the very principle of free market economics and reduces effects to deal with environmental impact more efficiently or even competitively.

People are increasingly aware that ocean environmental impact not only affects the physical, chemical, and biological processes of the oceans, and as a result, life on Earth itself. It also affects the users of the oceans and those who allow wastes to be dumped into the ocean. In other words, there is not only an economic cost to society but also to ocean users themselves. Markets in general, both in developed and developing countries, do not recognize that this cost usually distorts the effects of ocean pollution. Indirectly it does affect the quality of ocean use and the operation of the ocean user. Using an internalized market-based approach would force businesses to use their comparative advantage in lowering their environmental impact prevention costs. In many cases, this would also improve overall operations and, most importantly, customer and society valuation.

Environmental regulation fines and taxes are always internalized because they are based on the "polluter pays" principle. Unfortunately the polluter only pays when caught and held liable. Only then does pollution affect the polluter's costs and may ultimately affect the prices. Long-term investment in pollution abatement or prevention technology and various antipollution operations management approaches are encouraged if pollution charges are recognized as permanent, strictly and uniformly applied, and effective. In the highly competitive ocean user environment, where operations are often far from the enforcement arms of national government, incentives remain for users to lower operating costs unless they can be convinced that it is not in their economic interest.

Portnoy defined "the economic cost of pollution as the opportunity cost of pollution control measured by the general welfare loss from diverting resources from alternative productive uses."[1] Generally, internalized costs by government are lower in economic terms than when the costs are externalized and borne by society directly.

A particularly difficult issue is that the effects of ocean environmental pollution are, in all but accidental spills, slow, cumulative processes that are only recognized after a long period as physical, chemical, or biological deterioration. The impact of the degradation and the resulting costs are usually nearly impossible to determine or even estimate.

7.4.4 Ocean Environmental Management

The management of ocean environmental pollution implies the following:

1. continuous evaluation or audit of the situation;
2. setting regulations and standards for rates, volumes, concentration, and types of discharges;
3. defining the policy and control measures applied;
4. putting in place legal, jurisdictional, or institutional arrangements for enforcement of regulations and standards;

[1]P. R. Portney, ed., *Natural Resources and the Environment* (Washington, DC: Urban Institute, 1984), p. 12.

5. providing resources in terms of capital, labor, equipment, and monitors to measure compliance and monitor enforcement of the regulations and standards;
6. information and communication systems in place to transmit status and need information,
7. a formal and informal cooperative network of direct and indirect pollution-fighting agencies;
8. a management system to coordinate response activities in a timely and effective manner;
9. mobilization and transport equipment to locate and transport pollution-fighting equipment and personnel to site;
10. local control and jurisdictional arrangement that provides response teams with full authority to act as necessary;
11. waste collection and removal capability;
12. diving, testing, and aerial surveillance capability;
13. liaison with government at different levels to facilitate transfer of authority to act as necessary;
14. monitoring and reporting systems;
15. enforcement agencies and systems;
16. efficient judicial systems able to deal quickly with pollution liability cases;
17. large condition data banks and real-time monitoring and measuring systems; and
18. feedback and learning systems that ensure comparisons of conditions, trend determination, and learning to improve both the understanding of cause-and-effect relationships and the trend in environmental conditions.

There is an urgent need to establish not only national ocean environmental management systems but also national and international ocean environmental management coordination.

The systems and programs now in place are often uncoordinated and exist more to satisfy regulatory requirements than actually to provide effective pollution prevention, containment, and cleanup. In most cases, they are set up as reactive systems designed to respond to accidents. Without central coordination of all the resources and response agencies, the systems do not usually react as quickly and effectively as they could or should.

Also, the roles of government and private industry in ocean environmental management must be more clearly defined. Government agencies are currently supposed to provide guidance and issue rules, regulations, and standards for preventative and corrective measures that comprise the guidelines for ocean environmental management by operators and various response firms.

The emphasis is not on prevention but on reduction, containment, and cleanup. Long ago, industry recognized that correcting the defects or faults of a product is the most expensive in direct cost, market, and liability terms when left until after delivery and the least expensive if corrected before delivery. The same holds true for ocean environmental defects. Much more costly and less effective than the prevention of accidents is to build ships, platforms, or other structures for use in the oceans that, if damaged, will leak less or otherwise reduce environmental impacts. Reducing the potential outflow from a damaged ship does not make for a safer ship. Only methods that first reduce the likelihood of a ship accident do so.

To be effective, ocean environmental management must combine preventative and corrective ocean environmental management. These activities must be integrated, and lessons learned from accidents must be used to improve the prevention of such accidents and not just the cleanup after the accident. At this time, prevention and correction are in most cases handled as distinct and separate issues.

Few accidents are subjected to a formal cause-and-effect analysis, and even when this is done, it is usually performed only to show and impose liability, not to identify methods or techniques that could have prevented the accident in the first place. For example, in a case where a ship went aground in an unmarked ship berth basin, the cause was identified, but because such accidents had occurred before, marking of the ship berth basin was not an imposed requirement. There are many similar examples where a lack of integration of preventative and corrective ocean environmental management perpetuates accidents and reduce the effectiveness of response. As a result, the management of ocean environmental pollution also requires, in addition to the above-listed functions, preventative ocean environmental management, such as the following:

1. Effective vessel and ocean user guidance and control systems such as vastly improved navigational aids, ship or vessel traffic management, up-to-date (real-time) charting, and mandatory position fixing and assignment that ensure that ocean users' location can be readily determined at all times, must be used.

2. Control of the use of the oceans must be improved, without affecting their unimpeded use. In other words, ocean users should be required to report not only their location but also their activity, particularly when operating in international waters.
3. Ship and other ocean users should file and get approval of their routing, very much like aircraft are required to now.
4. Ocean environmental management policy and rules should be drafted by the international community and not by different governments, local government agencies, and even commercial companies. These parties should participate in their developments and implement and/or enforce the policies and rules. It is surprising that this has been fairly effectively done in aviation, while it seems out of reach in shipping and offshore ocean activities.
5. Satellite systems should be used more effectively to identify and manage ocean pollution. Although this capability is possible, there is no effective feedback of the information. This could also lead to a worldwide ocean pollution monitoring and auditing system that in turn would help in setting up preventative measures everywhere.

Ocean environmental management requires intra- and international cooperation. Not only can response capability be greatly enhanced by pooling equipment and other resources, but coordination of preventative measures is essential if they are to be effective.

7.5 ROLE OF INTERNATIONAL AGENCIES, NATIONAL GOVERNMENTS, AND LOCAL AUTHORITIES

International agencies and various levels of government have assumed increasingly important roles in ocean environmental management, not only in setting standards and introduction as well as enforcement of regulations but also in the actual management of pollution prevention, containment, or cleanup operations. They are also increasingly involved in training, public education, and inspection activities related to ocean environmental management.

The most important international organization charged with responsibility of maintaining standards and conditions of ocean environmental protection is the International Maritime Organization, a technical agency of the United Nations. Other international organizations, such as the World Health Organization, the U.N. Conference on Trade and Development (UNCTAD), the U.N. Environmental Program (UNEP), the Organization of Economic Cooperation and Development (OECD), the World Bank, and regional international development banks all play a role in regulating, managing, or promoting ocean environmental management.

Although all these organizations exist or are currently chartered and responsible for various aspects of ocean environmental management and protection, no regional or international mechanism exists for enforcing environmental protection measures, nor do most countries have a national enforcement mechanism. As a result, there is an increasing concern that these organizations draft agreements, rules, and conventions that have little, if any, teeth and that serve largely as loose standards by which few abide.

7.5.1 International Maritime Organization (IMO)

As noted in Chapter 5, the principal functions of the IMO are the promotion of maritime safety and the protection of the marine environment. To this effect, the IMO has concluded about 30 international conventions. Most of these have been ratified by the required number of nations. In addition, the IMO has reached many resolutions and amendments designed to explain and clarify the convention. It has a competent technical staff that provides technical as well as training and management assistance to member countries.

The IMO is not a regulatory agency, and it must rely on member states to give effect to the various conventions and regulations agreed on or ratified. By its constitution, it undertakes

> to provide a machinery for cooperation among governments in the field of governmental regulations and practices relating to technical matters of all kinds affecting shipping engaged in international trade, to encourage and facilitate the general adoption of the highest practical standards in matters concerning maritime safety, efficiency of navigation, and prevention and control of marine pollution for ships.

The IMO serves and advises governments in their efforts to ensure maritime safety and environmental protection.

The IMO does not serve owners, operators, ship crews, charterers, and other individuals. It neither assigns nor controls seaways and performs mainly an advisory and technical assistance function even to nongovernmental bodies (with the consent or request of their respective governments). The IMO also acts on issues of controls of port and flag states and in fact helps organize groups of cooperating port flag states.

The rights and enforcement powers of port states are often more limited than those of the flag state. As a result, IMO conventions were introduced to facilitate port state control and inspections. Similarly, unlike the flag state, port state control can only be imposed on working vessels. Port states' prime responsibilities are the checking of all papers and licenses and then the vessels' actual conditions. Port states do not inspect the ship's hull or machinery.

The IMO provides a forum and administrative structure for the convening of government representatives to define standards, rules, and regulations to be imposed to safeguard the ocean environment. Some of the most important IMO conventions are described in the appendices and in Table 7–1.

Many people would like the IMO to assume a role in enforcement, as certain other technical agencies of the United Nations do. Others feel that the traditional concept of the freedom of the seas and interference in sovereign rights may be impacted if the IMO assumed a role of enforcer instead of being a standard and rule setter that leaves enforcement to the ratifying members who drafted them in the first place.

7.5.2 The Environmental Protection Agency, (EPA), U.S. Army Corps of Engineers, and U.S. Coast Guard (USCG)

The principal responsibility for environmental protection, including environmental standard setting and rule making, is assigned to the U.S. Environmental Protection Agency (EPA). Other federal agencies assume more limited or specialized roles. For example, the U.S. Army Corps of Engineers is responsible for setting standards and reviewing and licensing of dredging and reclamation in the oceans and U.S. coastal waters, including river estuaries and inland water. The corps authorizes such projects and enforces its own and EPA standards. It reviews and approves applications for dredging spoil disposal as well as coastal area construction.

TABLE 7–1 Organization of the International Maritime Organization (IMO)

COMMITTEE	FUNCTION
Maritime Safety	Safety of navigation Communications Standards of training and watchkeeping Carriage of dangerous goods Ship design and equipment Fire protection Stability and load lines Containers and cargoes Bulk and chemicals
Marine Environmental Protection	Pollution prevention
Technical Cooperation	Program to help member countries implement technical measures adopted by the IMO
Facilitation	Measures to simplify documentation and formalities required in international shipping
	Secretariat consisting of 300 civil servants

Other U.N. bodies: U.N. Environmental Program (UNEP)

Intergovernmental organizations: International Oil Pollution Compensation Fund (IDPC Fund)

Nongovernmental organizations: International Tanker Owners Pollution Federation Ltd. (ITOPF)

Latest instrument: International Convention on Oil Pollution Preparedness, Response, and Cooperation

1990 major Resolutions:

- Establish oil pollution combating equipment stockpiles
- Promote technical assistance
- Cooperation between states and insurers
- Ensure oil pollution preparedness, response, and cooperation
- Improve salvage services
- Develop training programs
- Oil pollution reporting procedures

The corps approves and in some cases performs dredging and maintenance dredging of navigational channels. On the other hand, the U.S. Coast Guard (USCG) is responsible for navigational aids and controls, for the management of vessel and offshore operations, and for the latter's impact on the ocean environment.

The USCG enforces both U.S. ocean pollution standards as well as those of IMO conventions ratified by the U.S. It manages OPA-90 and continues to define and refine various aspects of these laws. It oversees training requirements of onboard staff as well as the maintenance of oil pollution response plans.

7.5.3 Oil Pollution Liability and Compensation

The *Torrey Canyon* disaster in the English Channel led to the 1969 Civil Liability Convention to assign strict liability, without the need to establish fault, on ship owners whose vessels cause pollution damage through accidents or by other discharge from a ship carrying oil in bulk. The liability was limited to 14 million Special Drawing Rights (SDR) (about $20 million) and was based on a ship's tonnage. Under the convention, owners must carry compulsory insurance and may direct the liability to their insurer or Protection and Indemnity Club (P&I Club). The 1971 Fund Convention assesses a supplemental liability to the 1969 convention if the pollution damage exceeds the above amount, but it limits the added liability to 900 million gold francs (about $90 million). The 1969 convention includes pure economic loss, which may include cleanup and consequential costs of damage caused.

The 1971 convention also provided a second level of compensation, the International Oil Pollution Compensation (IOPC) Fund, which actually only started operation in 1979. It is funded by contributions from the tanker industry.

Even though compensation for economic losses is generally accepted, there is great controversy about compensation for noneconomic environmental damage that is often claimed by states, their subordinate jurisdictions, and social or community organizations. One purpose in setting up the IOPC Fund was to ensure prompt settlement of claims and effective pursuit of ship owners or others responsible for the pollution.

One of the issues to be settled by the 1969 Civil Liability Convention and the 1971 Fund Convention was the just allocation of liability to the ship owner, the cargo owner, and the insurers. These two conventions were amended by the 1984 Protocols, which have objectives of specifying higher limits of compensation and inducing participation by the United States in this intergovernmental system.

Only major European countries, such as the United Kingdom, Germany, and France, had ratified the 1984 Protocols by 1989. Under the 1984 Protocols, the limit of compensation was increased to 135 million SDR (about $200 million), with a potential future increase to 405 million SDR (about $580 million). As a consequence of the *Exxon Valdez* disaster, the U.S. Congress unilaterally passed the Oil Pollution Act of 1990 (OPA-90), which specifically excludes U.S. ratification of the 1984 Protocols.

Under OPA-90, a ship owner is strictly liable for oil pollution with liability only limited to an amount based on the tonnage of a ship. Notwithstanding the mention of limitation of liability, it is generally accepted that the owners face unlimited liability under OPA-90 because it allows not only claims for cleanup and economic damage but also for noneconomic environmental damage, which can be very loosely defined. Insurers are subject to direct action under the act and are therefore reluctant to provide coverage and certificates of financial responsibility as required under OPA-90. When claims exceed owners' limits, a revolving federal fund of about $1 billion financed by taxes on oil imports to the United States can be used.

In 1992 international negotiations under the IOPC Fund and the IMO resulted in the 1992 Protocols, which were supported by many nations that were unwilling to accept the untried provisions and requirements of OPA-90. These protocols retain most of the provisions of the 1984 Protocols, including those on limits of liability.

Successful compliance with ocean environmental regulations and successful ocean environmental management requires the provision of requisite facilities such as waste reception, dredge spoil disposal, oily water separation, and liquid waste treatment facilities. Although provisions of such facilities are mandated by various international conventions and national laws, their use is often inadequate because

1. a lack of funds affects their provision and maintenance;
2. use and access to such facilities is expensive and inefficient;
3. there is concern that use of such facilities reduces operational effectiveness such as the need of additional moves by ships, for example;
4. cargo and other port or offshore activities could be interrupted for cleanup transfer of wastes or for environmental inspections;
5. there is little or no information available on these facilities;
6. the user cost of the facilities is exorbitant; and
7. the facilities, even when available, are badly managed, and there is an inadequate availability of trained personnel.

Some countries are more successful than others. For example, Singapore has developed large oily water waste reception facilities into which ships, and particularly tankers, can discharge oily wastes for recycling. The operation is self-financing and its terms are very attractive to users.

7.5.4 The Global Environment Facility (GEF)

The Global Environmental Facility (GEF) was first suggested in 1989 as a specific means of helping developing countries finance environmental projects with implications that were not just local.

Since then, the GEF has become a strong complement to the World Bank's increasing environmental activities in individual countries. The GEF is not intended to replace those activities, but to reinforce them.

The GEF was set up with a fund of $1.3 billion. Of the 24 member countries in 1991, nine were developing countries. Although most of the GEF funding is intended for investment projects in developing countries with per capita gross national product no greater than $4,000 in 1989, other activities—training, various studies of problems and possible solutions, and gathering scientific information—are eligible for grants from the GEF.

Those grants will enable governments, with the help of international agencies, to gain practical experience in strengthening environmental policies and the institutions that implement them. The U.N. Development Program, U.N. Environmental Program, the World Bank, and the agencies in charge of implementing the GEF play distinct roles in meeting these goals.

The U.N. Development Program works with governments to identify projects and ensures that GEF projects complement other development activities. UNEP provides guidance in selecting projects, and the World Bank administers the GEF trust fund and is responsible for appraising and supervising investment projects.

The three multilateral agencies—the World Bank, UNDP, UNEP—together determine whether a project qualifies for GEF support and then ensures that the project protects the global environment in a cost-effective and technologically sound way.

The goals of the GEF are limiting emissions of greenhouse gases, preserving the earth's biological diversity, protecting international waters, and preventing further depletion of the ozone layer.

7.6 MANAGING OCEAN POLLUTION BY SHIPS

Pollution by ships is not only a result of accidents that generate oil or dry cargo spills, but includes discharge of the following pollutants:

1. exhaust gases,
2. solid waste,
3. liquid waste,
4. cargo and fuel tank gases,
5. cargo spillage,
6. CFCs,
7. hull treatment chemicals, and
8. solid waste of scrap ship.

Although past emphasis has been on reducing the consequences of polluting discharges (accidental, operational, or voluntary), a more effective approach is to try to prevent harmful discharges by preventing accidents, improving operating conditions, and eliminating opportunities for voluntary discharges. This includes more effective vessel traffic control and navigation, improvements in engine operations, cleaning of exhaust gases, replacement of CFCs, measurement and control of gases from fuel and cargo tanks, controlled and safe liquid and solid waste disposal, controlled cargo tank washing and oil ballast, bilge water disposal, and the effective elimination of ocean pollution by paint and antifouling systems.

Since OPA-90 was passed, double-hull tankers have been built in increasing numbers. The act stipulates that any tanker ordered after June 30, 1990, or delivered after January 1, 1994, must be fitted with a double hull to enter U.S. waters.

Unfortunately, this act will delay the replacement of nearly 200 U.S. flag domestic tankers (with an average age of 21 years) that account for 65% of all U.S. port calls by tankers because such replacement ships must be built in U.S. yards and would be prohibitively expensive. Even though only a small percentage of spills resulting from tanker groundings—including the *Exxon Valdez* spill, which triggered the act—would have been reduced or prevented by the use of double hulls, the U.S. Coast Guard concluded that a double hull would have reduced the spill by 25% to 60%. Others contend that it may have caused the vessel to slide off the reef and capsize.

OPA-90 also stipulates that large tankers must have a vessel response plan (VRP), which must be prepared every 5 years. In addition, owners have to certify to the USCG that their plans have been updated annually. VRPs must also be consistent with the U.S. National Contingency Plan and 50 area response plans or one per state, excluding Washington D.C. (most of which remain as yet unpublished).

Antifouling paints on ships have become particular environmental hazards because many of the more effective coatings contain TBT compounds, which are believed to damage marine life. TBT or self-polishing copolymer systems react with seawater to reduce soluble material at the point surface that acts as a biocide. This process occurs with a self-polishing action but causes potentially damaging effects on the marine environment.

The IMO adopted a resolution in 1990 to

- eliminate the use of TBT on nonaluminum vessels of less than 25 m,
- eliminate the use of paints with a release rate of more than 4 micrograms/cm^2 per day,
- develop a code of practice for paints,
- develop alternative systems, and
- monitor control measures.

For ship owners, however, there are costs involved. TBT coatings extend the need for repainting from 2 to 5 years and provide a smoother lower resistance hull than other coatings. TBT-free coating or other conventional coating systems reduce this to 2 to 3 years. In addition, it is argued that outlawing TBT coating would add about $2.7 billion in operating costs ($500 million for fuel, $400 million for drydocking, $800 million for maintenance, and indirect savings of $1 billion).

Ballast water in ships is another pollution source as it often contains microorganisms and larger species of marine life. Sometimes ballast water also carries bacteria such as strains of cholera, which are known to have been transferred to U.S. port waters by ships from Latin America in 1991. As a result, it is now recommended that ships should not take on ballast water in shallow water or during toxic blooms of dinoflagellates and that ballast water should only be discharged into ports at approved areas.

7.6.1 The Solid Waste Service Industry

The U.S. solid waste service industry became a world leader during the 1980s and has become a major industrial sector. There are several multibillion dollar companies, such as Waste Management, Browning-Ferris Industries, and Attwoods PLC. Although competition in the industry was always important at the local level, it has increased nationally now that growth opportunities have been constrained.

The number of public companies in the industry continues to increase, but most are small and face the same problems that the larger, established companies do, such as increased regulation, demand for more complex and costly services, and as a result, larger capital needs. The importance of integrating collection, sorting, recycling, and disposal is increasingly pervasive if solid waste companies are to control their destinies.

Contributing to the large cost increases and recent regulatory issues are the following items:

1. *Subtitle "D":* Enacted September 1991, Subtitle "D" requires wastes to pass stringent landfill regulations. It raises the costs of developing and operating existing and new landfills and should reduce the number of landfills by 30% to 50% and capacity by 10% to 15%, by year 2000.
2. *Interstate transportation:* Final legislation should give local communities the right to decide on accepting out-of-state waste, a solution acceptable to solid waste companies.
3. *Mandatory recycling:* The public continues to demand this service, but the most rapid growth has already taken place. End-market demand must catch up with supply.
4. *Landfill permitting and capacity:* With rising landfill standards at both federal and state levels, regulatory, political, and public opposition have become pervasive and now require (a) economies of scale by use of larger landfills and (b) replacement of smaller fills by larger fills. Other pressures are introduced by greater permitting and host fees.

Companies in this industry face barriers to entry, large capital requirements, and problems with permitting.

Although landfills represent 70% of solid waste disposal and the emphasis has been on source reduction rather than on development of alternative disposal opportunities, land disposal remains the least expensive form of solid waste disposal available today. Disposal in the ocean has always been considered an alternative after or without incineration.

Landfill disposal costs have now reached a national average of $26.60 per ton, a cost that can only be beaten by ocean disposal (after incineration) if performed on a large scale.

7.6.2 Trade and Environment

There is growing concern that increased environmental quality standards may impact international trade and that environmental regulation may be used to restrict free trade. Similarly, environmental costs impose added costs and indirectly provide a subsidy for goods manufacturers in countries with fewer or no environmental requirements.

The absence of environmental regulations reduces costs because less regulated firms have fewer environmental costs than more strictly regulated firms. Countervailing duties and other steps to address competitive impacts of differential environmental standards may be required. Unilateral trade measures are sometimes used to address such imbalances or to protect the environment, which may also be directly affected by trade-induced environmental impacts such as waste generation, biological pollution, or other pollution.

Environmental regulation influences trade competitiveness as well as the environmental impacts of trade.

7.6.3 Spill Contractors and Response Management

The increased concern with oil spills has sprouted a thriving industry of contractors offering spill response services as required under OPA-90. These companies have spill containment and cleanup equipment and expert personnel in various ports and undertake to respond as required by OPA-90 rules. These oil spill contractors offer various services and equipments and have the mobility to respond in a very short time.

This new industry is now developing rapidly and although currently concentrated in the United States, it is expected to provide services in other parts of the world shortly. At the same time, the IMO is developing oil spill response requirements and service specifications.

Another development involves training ship crews and oil spill service personnel in oil spill response requirements. Simulators that produce realistic conditions of an oil spill and effectiveness of various response decisions and actions are now available to train personnel in the decision and action requirements to respond to particular spill conditions.

Spill situations can be considered from different angles such as a ship's bridge or a helicopter. The first sophisticated oil spill simulator was installed at the Massachusetts Maritime Academy, as described in more detail in section 5.4.2.

7.7 ENVIRONMENTAL IMPACT ASSESSMENT OF OCEAN DEVELOPMENT PROJECTS

As people attempt to make better use of the oceans and coastal areas, inshore, coastal, and offshore development projects now abound. Offshore resource exploration and exploitation, such as oil and mineral production from the ocean bottom, has increased significantly, as have coastal shore development, dredging, and reclamation, in addition to the large-scale construction in recent years of artificial islands for industrial, airport, seaport, residential, and recreational use. Other ocean developments are the increased use of aquaculture for the controlled growth and harvesting of food from the oceans.

Ocean development projects often impose environmental impacts that must be identified and evaluated. In most ocean development projects, there are development project alternatives which may have different costs and benefits as well as different environmental impacts.

Figure 7–3 provides a general framework for an ocean environmental impact assessment analysis. For most such projects, a formal step-by-step, cause and effect and resulting impact study is performed. Such a study considers impacts, for example, on the following aspects of ocean environments:

- water quality,
- marine life,
- paleontology,
- soil,

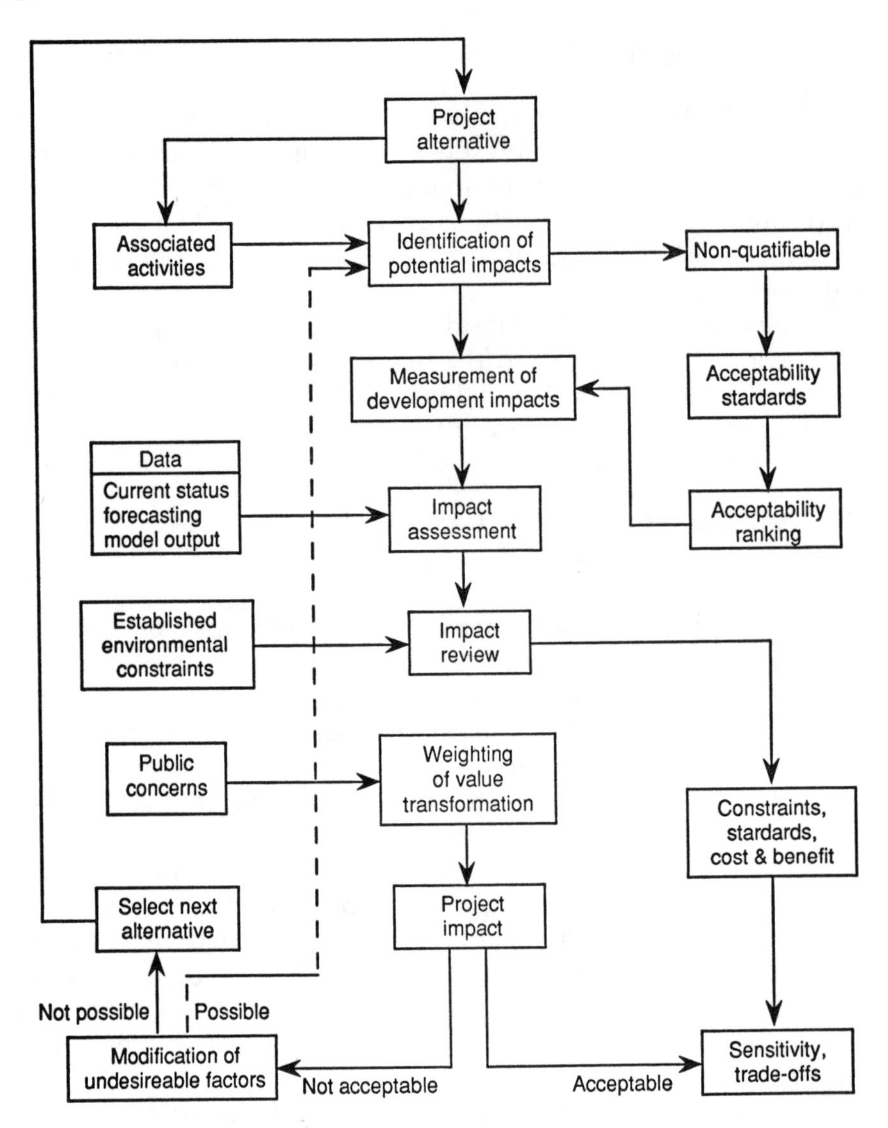

Figure 7–3 Ocean Environmental Impact Assessment Process.

- flora and fauna,
- ocean currents,
- sediment flow and composition,
- erosion and accretion,
- coastal processes, and
- boundary flows.

The costs and benefits of impacts are usually determined in social, economic, and financial terms. A typical step-by-step procedure for impact assessment is shown in Table 7–2.

Considerable variation is encountered between impact statements required by different agencies, although theoretically all are aimed at achieving the same requirements.

An environmental impact assessment for ocean projects is usually a multiobjective analysis in which feasible alternative solutions or actions are objectively traded off, subject to imposed constraints and limits such as standards. An assessment must be performed in a formal, organized, or structured manner that ensures that all independent and dependent impacts are considered and established early enough to eliminate unacceptable actions from consideration without affecting the project's time, economics, and effective implementation.

The development of port facilities, for example, requires explicit consideration of all ecological factors in selecting location and design

TABLE 7–2 Ocean Environmental Project Impact Analysis

1. Development of an exhaustive checklist of all project activities, environmental status, and expected impacts (both temporary during construction or permanent).
2. Cause-and-effect analysis for all the expected impacts and all directly and indirectly impacting activities.
3. Development of a complete cause-and-effect tree and matrix.
4. Determination or estimation of the magnitude and importance of effect (and effect-generating cause). Importance should be specified as a real value and a scale of weighing indices, respectively.
5. Collection of data for impact assessment from data checks, public meetings, reviews, and analysis.
6. Establishment of environmental impact index for type of project under consideration for effective, fair ranking of alternative projects.
7. Development of environmental impact assessment model by formal analysis of the interaction and total effects of project impacts.
8. Determination of environmental impact abatement costs and costs of remaining environmental impacts of projects capable of passing acceptable environmental standards, stated objectives, or both.
9. a. The addition of environmental impact reduction, protection, and impact costs to economic costs of a project.
   b. Additional financial costs of projects of real financial environmental impact reduction and protection.

alternatives, including engineering and operational details. A required formal phased analysis must include the following information:

1. A description of the proposed development for each state of the port system. Such descriptive information will provide some basis for judgment.
2. A determination through cause-and-effect relationships of the amount of change in environmental conditions with and without implementation of the alternatives.
3. An analysis of each element of the proposed port system with reference to the environmental ecological and socioeconomic changes caused by the implementation of the port system (such as air quality, aesthetics, and recreation and residential impacts). The effects could be summarized as discussed before. A group judgment, using an accepted polling technique applied in nonquantifiable decisions, can be accepted. Each element considered to be significant or highly unpredictable should be further evaluated.
4. An environmental impact statement for selected alternatives must be prepared in accordance with the requirements of the National Environment Policy Act, including the following:
   a. A description of the proposed action.
   b. The probable impacts on the environment, including primary and secondary consequences on the ecological system, population patterns, resource use, and the adverse environmental effects that cannot be avoided.
   c. Alternatives to the proposed action.
   d. Relationship between the short- and long-term uses of the environment.
   e. Irreversible and irretrievable effects of the proposed action.

Only by such formal approaches to port development, design, and operation will it be possible to reestablish the dialogue between user operators and environmentalists. Such dialogue is essential if humans are to benefit by the economic advantages offered by modern ports or ocean resource development and use.

7.7.1 Environmental Risk Assessment

Environmental impact is assessed in terms of its

1. occurrence,
2. source,
3. release,
4. dispersion,
5. medium of dispersion (air, water, land),
6. life forms affected,
7. mechanisms of absorption (chemical and so forth),
8. toxicity,
9. rate of deterioration, and
10. ultimate impact.

These factors cannot be established accurately even for the most common environmental impacts. Most measurements or observations dealing with the establishment of environmental impact cause-and-effect relationships experience inherent uncertainty and risks, resulting from a lack of adequate knowledge and innate variability of observation. In many cases, the primary concerns are the short- or long-term effects on human health, although economic, social, and technological effects are also considered.

As noted by F. W. Talcott, "estimated human health effects are usually approximated by a log normal distribution with a geometric standard deviation between 5 and 10, which implies a 5% chance that the real risk may be more than a factor of 25–100 times greater than or less than the median estimate".[2]

Estimating uncertainty in the various factors used in environmental assessment is probably one of the most important issues in ocean environmental management. Much more effective analytical techniques must be developed and used to come up with environmental risk assessment. Similarly, the assumptions made and data used should be clearly identified and their basis or source explained.

[2] F. W. Talcott, "Environment," *OR/MS Today*, Vol. 19, No. 3, June 1992, p. 34.

7.7.2 Economic Impact of Ocean Pollution

The cost of the economic impact of ocean, particularly coastal, pollution must be deducted from the GNP because it, or the cost of antipollution actions, has a negative economic effect. Pollution causes direct economic costs, while antipollution or cleanup costs are negative costs that prevent damage or redress damage done so as to reestablish a prior state; therefore, they similarly constitute economic costs. Health impacts, structural damage, and other causal impacts resulting from either pollution or antipollution measures also constitute economic costs, including indirect costs such as a loss of jobs, opportunities, or value of real immobile assets.

7.7.3 Uncertainty in Environmental Evaluation

There is usually extensive uncertainty in environmental measurement. Fault tree and cause-and-effect diagrams are just two of a larger array of methods available to study the low probability–high consequence events that abound in environmental evaluations.

The usual concern is risks to human health, resources of use to humans, and the ecosystem in general. Environmental risk analysis requires

1. identification of causal factors;
2. assessment of the probability and associated magnitude of release;
3. dispersion, dilution, and diffusion through the ocean waters;
4. affected physical, biological, and other receptors;
5. factors influencing absorption by affected receptors;
6. toxicity, chemical, and physical interaction;
7. conditional probabilities of the cause-and-effect chain; and
8. probability of various environmental outcomes.

To capture the factors above and to compute the low probability–high consequence events, Monte Carlo modeling or other analytical techniques to permit evaluation of the uncertainties have been developed.

7.7.4 Ocean Environmental Impact Assessment Methodologies

Environmental impact assessment, a step in the ocean environmental management process, is an interactive procedure in which requirements for ocean use development and expansion are formulated. These are then expressed, in a manner conducive to review by responsible government agencies and the affected public, in terms of impacts.

The basic steps of requirements definition, plan formulation, impact assessment, and evaluation are repeated until agreement is reached. The requirements definition involves examining the needs and their expression in terms of use demands. It includes ocean ore projections, ocean user technology assessment, capacity demand projections, and all other inputs needed to establish development and expansion requirements in terms of physical facilities and infrastructure to meet the assumed growth. If this growth is accepted as a reasonable need over the planning horizon considered, then alternative plans are formulated to meet this need in an environmentally acceptable manner. Each alternative plan is then studied from the point of view of operational feasibility, economic viability, and environmental impact.

For each alternative plan the impact is forecasted and described in such a manner as to permit effective assessment. The impact analysis and evaluation phases of the planning process can be broken down into a detailed process, as shown earlier in Figure 7.3.

In the ocean project formulation base, alternative ocean development projects designed to meet the objectives and needs identified are investigated and developed. Each alternative project or project alternative is then studied to determine its relative costs, benefits, and environmental impacts. The factors of each project is displayed and a decision is made.

The environmental impact assessment process begins by identifying development and operational activities resulting from the proposed ocean development project. For each activity the probable impacts on the environment, community, economy, and so forth are identified. Whenever possible, interrelationships and combined effects are identified as well. For the impacts that are quantifiable, data are collected and models and forecasts are conducted to describe the current values of the areas impacted and to predict the effects due to the alternative project being examined. Some impacts may be considered nonquantifiable and must therefore be ranked subjectively.

The measurements of the impacts can be considered as a set of impact assessments that describe the beneficial and adverse effects for use in multiobjective planning. The values for each impact assessment are displayed as the output of the impact evaluation. The rest of the methodology consists of determining the acceptability of impacts and providing some rational process for comparing alternative projects.

In the impact review it can be determined if the ocean development project is in compliance with existing standards and regulations.

The impact reviews are then combined via several procedures to produce a numerical value for total environmental impact. A transformation of the reviews or multiple environmental objectives into a single value or a ranking of projects is the final step in the impact assessment. Only projects that meet at least minimum acceptable standards are maintained in the set of alternatives.

Because the preceding steps require the consideration of many subjective judgments and predictions, a sensitivity analysis is often performed to find the critical impacts and activities as well as to provide a confidence interval for the values produced.

If costs have not been combined in the impact value, then some trade-off of cost and environmental impact is performed. This trade-off is not necessarily numeric and may be the result of a subjective decision.

An ocean environmental impact assessment is started by compiling an impact checklist. The use of checklists is a common means of identifying and standardizing various development and operational activities to be included in an environmental impact analysis. Checklists guarantee that all potential environmental issues are considered, independent of the type of plan or the concern of the planners or agencies involved. They also make explicit which activities are considered significant. This is important for both the assessment and the review of the impacts. A checklist must not only be comprehensive; it must also include inputs by all concerned and interested parties and not only the port developers' own inputs.

Checklists are often used as an input to a cause-and-effect matrix to identify the possible impacts of the project activities. The summary of a cause-and-effect matrix for a deep-water port, shown in Figure 7–4), is an example. This checklist is simplified; the entire ma-

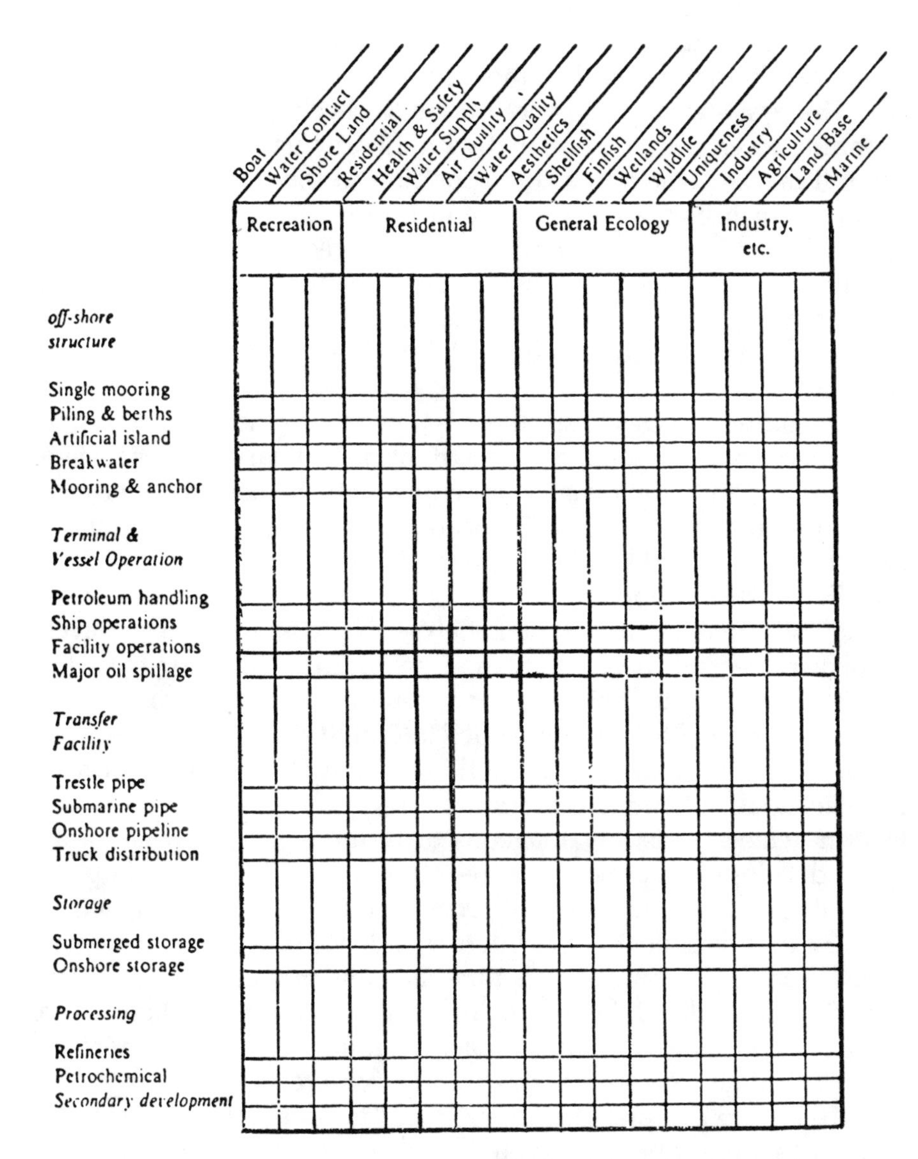

Figure 7–4 Summary of a Cause-and-Effects Matrix for a Deep Water Port. From *U.S. Deep Water Port Study,* vol. 4, (Washington, DC: Robert Nathan Associates, 1973), and Frankel, E. G. "Port Planning and Development" (New York, John Wiley & Sons, 1987 p. 222)

trix consists of many more causal and environmental impact components and characteristics than those shown.

The first step in this procedure is to check each column corresponding to an action associated with a particular project. For each column marked, the boxes corresponding to the impacts are examined. For each box, a magnitude and importance are specified as a real value and a scale of ranking indices, respectively. These two numbers are placed in the boxes and separated by a slash. Each ocean development project alternative usually has a separate matrix that forms the basis for assessing the development and operational activities.

In addition to checklists, there is a need for other input through public meetings, personal contacts, multidisciplinary groups, listening sessions, and opinion surveys, which must be used to determine the whole range of potential concerns. Several gaming techniques have been proposed to ensure group interactions and feedback of cause-and-effect factors.

Most formal environmental analyses begin after an ocean development project of plan formulation has been completed. Thus the analysis concentrates on the comparison of alternative projects and the justification of the recommended alternative. The formal requirements often consider the "do-nothing alternative" as one form of feedback to the planning process.

In general, it is advantageous to formulate the impacts of an ocean development project as a tree structure, with primary impacts branching at the first node and secondary or dependent impacts at the next or subsequent node. Interdependence of impacts or dependence of secondary impacts on more than one primary impact can be explicitly formulated in this manner. The network is therefore a structure that shows multiple impacts resulting from one or more actions, including cross-effects and cumulative effects.

To ensure complete identification of impacts resulting from all possible actions, the tree type of impact formulation is recommended. After impacts and their relationships have been identified, the effects of these impacts—such as how flocculation or how much salinity intrusion will result from the dredging of a channel over time at each potentially affected location—must be forecasted and quantified over time.

Some impacts can be measured or effectively quantified, but most depend largely on judgmental factors or "accepted" practice.

Safety, environmental quality, community acceptance, aesthetics, and other impacts are not readily measurable. In many cases of this sort, subjective (or comparative) measurement may have to be used.

Because of the difficulty of impact measurement and resulting assessment, it is important to introduce probability and conditional probability as implicit factors. Similarly, effects over time should be divided into immediate, short-term, and long-term impacts with their associated probability of occurrence and magnitude.

A major objective in the ocean environmental impact analysis is to analyze policy and design or development alternatives seriously, before actual (often irreversible) decisions are taken relative to potentially adverse environmental effects.

Each port environment impact statement must include:

- a comprehensive technical description of the proposed action and alternatives considered;
- an analysis of the probable impact (both costs and benefits) of the proposed actions on the overall environment, including the impact on ecological systems, land use and development patterns, community and social organization, and relevant quality of life indicators.
- a description of any probable adverse environmental effects that cannot be avoided or that can be reduced in severity to acceptable levels and a statement of the environmental impact limits against which actions and alternatives have been designed;
- analysis, studies, and descriptions of possible alternatives to the recommended course of action and their environmental effects where in each case environmental effects are assessed cumulatively; and
- detailed consideration of any irreversible or irretrievable commitments of scarce environmental resources.

Considerable variation is encountered between impact statements required by different agencies. Theoretically, however, all are aimed at achieving the same requirements, as shown in Figure 7–5.

In summary, the port environmental impact assessment is a multiobjective analysis in which feasible alternative solutions or ac-

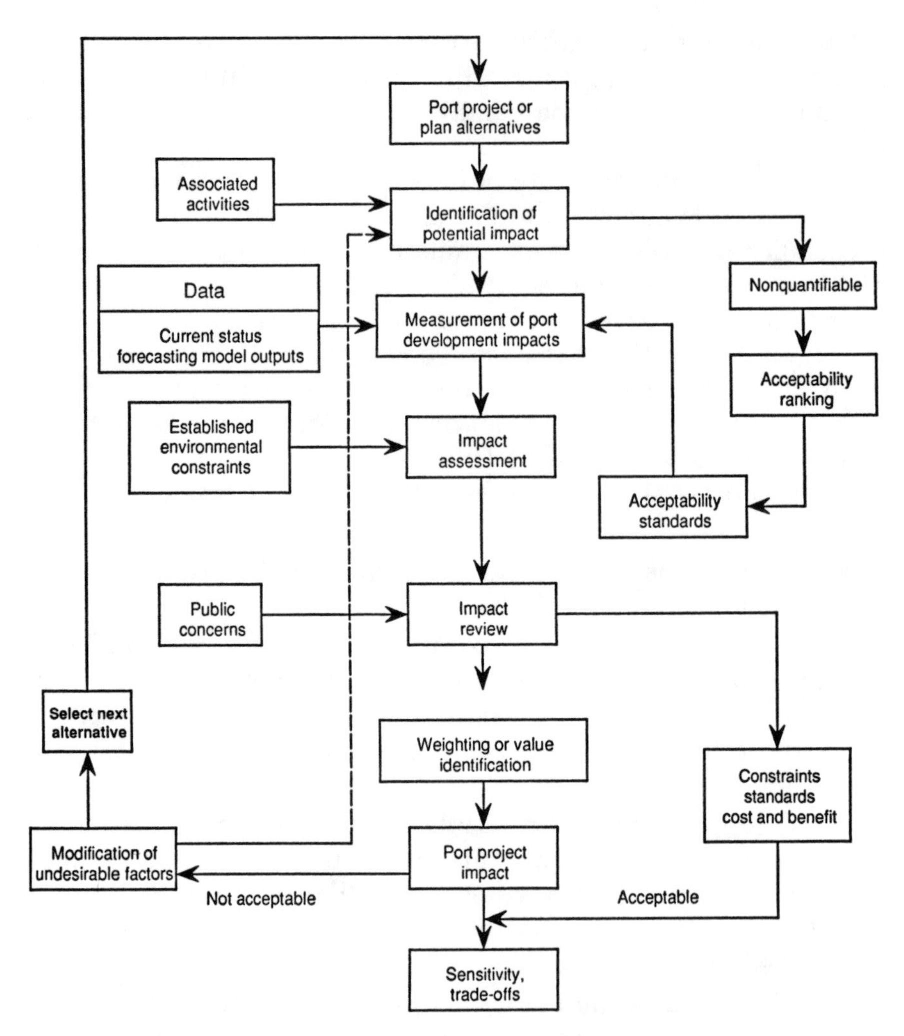

Figure 7–5 Port Environmental Impact Assessment Process. From E. G. Frankel, *Port Planning and Development* (New York: Wiley Interscience, 1987). p. 220.

tions are traded off objectively, subject to imposed constraints and limits such as standards. An assessment must be performed in a formal, organized, or structured manner to ensure that all independent and dependent impacts are considered and established early enough to eliminate unacceptable actions from consideration without affecting the project's timely, economic, and effective implementation.

7.8 MANAGED FISHING

Fishing is one of the oldest human activities in the oceans and actually precedes hunting of land animals, but it is surprising that although managing land animals was widely introduced over 3,000 years ago and hunting became significant as a method of animal food production nearly 800 years ago, people continue to hunt for fish in the oceans. Fish farming, even today, accounts for barely 3.8% of the world's ocean fish yield, although a much larger percentage of freshwater fish is produced in this manner.

Although it is true that fish "hunting" or fishing techniques have improved greatly over the years and fishers' labor productivity was, as a result, greatly increased, particularly since the early 1950s, it is increasingly evident that the current fishing or fish hunting methods have caused large-scale depletion of fish stocks and uncontrollable development of fishing resources.

Even though it should be possible to conserve or protect fish resources with traditional fishing (hunting), it is administratively difficult and has basically failed. Quotas and restrictions on fishing by species, age, season, or geographic area have been introduced, but these methods have largely failed for the following reasons:

1. They are difficult to control.
2. They are difficult to design.
3. They have little public support.
4. Fish migration often changes availability of fish population.
5. Ocean pollution often affects fish and fishing.

In fact, ocean pollution and unmanaged fishing together are causing a reduction in fish stock worldwide at a time when demand and consumption for fish is increasing at a rate of over 9% per year.

Managed fishing and fish farming not only increase fish resources, maintain fish resources in planned geographical areas, and improve the biological health and development of fish, they also reduce the costs of fish production significantly. Antarctic krill has long been recognized as the major food source of all kinds of marine animals. Krill are consumed by demersal fish, baleen whales, pelagic fish, squid, seals, and seabirds. The food chain is actually more complex than this; some of the intermediate species form part of the diet of higher-level fish and sea mammals.

In recent years, Antarctic krill, found in dense surface swarms, has been recognized as a potential new source of seafood for human consumption. Systems models are now used to manage this resource. Krill is very susceptible to damage by pollution; therefore, effective management of the swarms and harvesting will be important.

Krill plays a crucial role in the oceans' food chain and thereby an essential part in the ocean ecological system. Without krill, or as a result of a major depletion of krill, the house of cards on which the ocean life ecosystem is built would collapse. This makes it an extremely important issue now, not only because humans harvest krill for human consumption, but because oil, gas, and other ocean resource exploitations are planned in the Antarctic, which could cause serious damage to this highly sensitive ecosystem. For this reason, many feel that effective management systems with strict controls must be emplaced.

7.9 STRATEGIES FOR OCEAN ENVIRONMENTAL MANAGEMENT

Approaches to ocean environmental management have been diverse and often unfocused or diffused. They usually also lack planning and commitment. There are two major strategy choices by which ocean environmental management can be approached from a philosophical point of view:

1. *Source-related strategies:* development of alternative methods for the reduction of emissions and pollution, mainly by preventative measures, control of emission, and reduction of risk or potential of accidental or operational emissions.
2. *Environmental-related strategies:* quality criteria, objectives, and impact assessment designed to set emission requirements, usually including setting permissible standards, environmental condition benchmarks, and cleanup or corrective methods.

These strategies are defined as follows:

SOURCES-RELATED STRATEGIES	ENVIRONMENTAL-RELATED STRATEGIES
Emission standards	Environmental quality objectives

Percent reduction
Prevention principles:
- zero discharge
- maximum discharge
- best technology possible
- economically viable

Cross-media objectives
Condition benchmarks
Permissible cleanup:
- containment
- impact reduction methods

These strategies are different. Source-related strategies try to prevent pollution at the source by preventing emissions and reducing pollution volume and impact. On the other hand, environmental strategies are concerned with maintaining the quality of the environment under conditions when emissions cannot be prevented but when their volume and impacts can be controlled, contained, and corrected. The two strategies obviously overlap, and their differences are based more on emphasis than substance, as shown in Figure 7–6.

Catastrophic spills, such as from well blowouts, pipeline ruptures, tanker collisions or groundings, failure of sewage or other outflow controls, and flowing of polluted agricultural or waste areas, may result in a large and rapid release of large quantities of pollutants into ocean waters. To respond to such accidents, contingency plans that include effective access to strategically located response are required. If such an accident occurs, an effective spill response plan and effectively trained people must be in place to respond to the accident.

In many parts of the world, particularly in the United States, such environmental strategy management systems are in place. On the other hand, source strategy management systems that deal with both preventing of polluting accidents and eliminating operational spills are much less well organized. One reason probably is that such programs do not deal with problems in the limelight, such as a major accident, and therefore do not have much support.

Yet the contribution of accidental pollution is small compared with that caused by operational and preventable pollution. A large proportion of tanker and similar accidents can be effectively prevented by developing a proactive source or strategic environmental management approach. Here not just limiting standards for the ocean environment in physical and chemical terms are set, but objectives, benchmarks, and most importantly operational and procedural standards by which users of the oceans and those who discharge

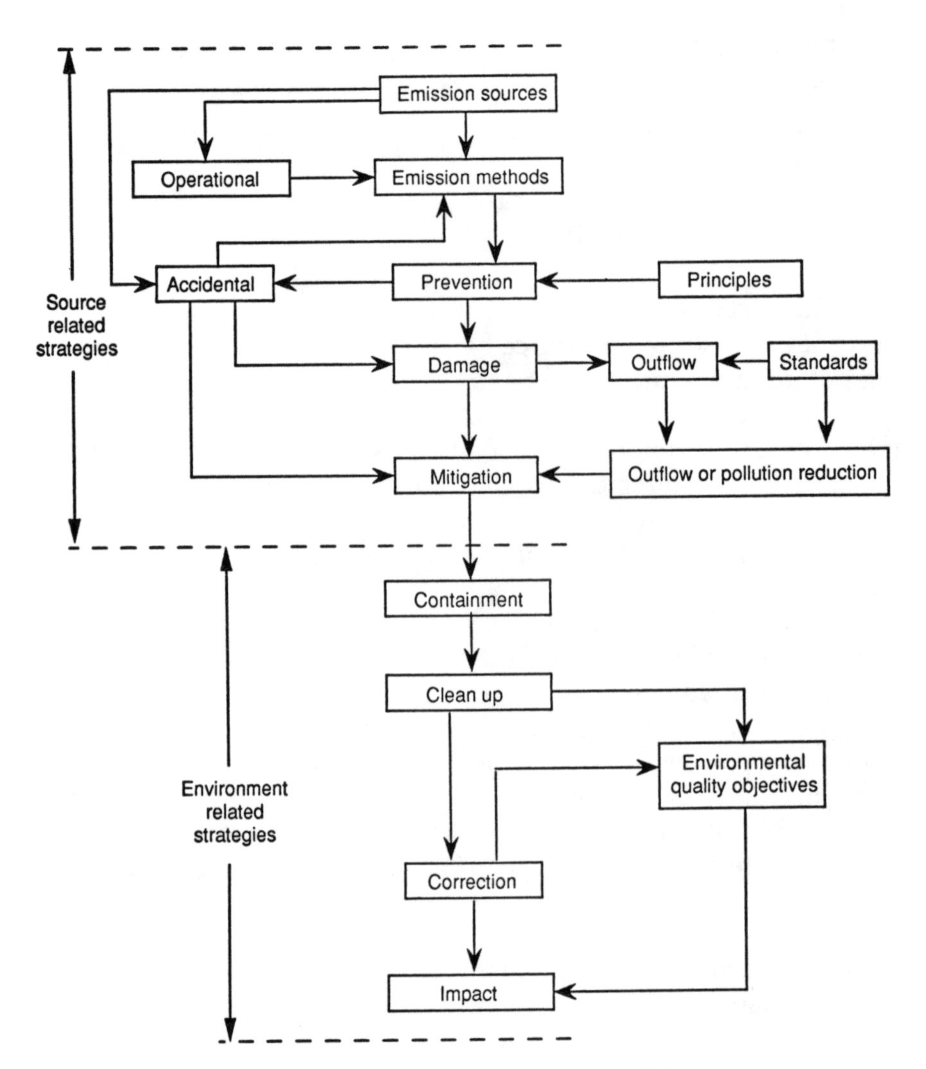

Figure 7–6 Strategies for Ocean Environmental Management.

anything into the oceans must abide. These standards must be imposed on those responsible for the immediate and also the original causes. In other words, standards on disposing of incineration waste at sea must be carried back toward controlling waste incineration that produces such waste, whether incinerated at sea or ashore.

Many claim that it may be difficult to identify the cause-and-effect chain as well as those responsible for the different causes that become sources of ocean environmental pollution. A beginning must be made, however, and experience shows that finding the direct causal perpetrators gradually leads to identifying the underlying cause and ultimately the whole chain. Such an approach not only permits identification but also fairer assignment of liability and a better understanding of the sequence of cause-and-effect chains in operational, physical, and chemical terms. It is quite often found that once the chain is recognized and the supposed economic incentives generating the causes are identified, their reduction or even elimination is economically and sometimes also operationally attractive.

Many companies and operators have, in fact, found that good source- or cause-oriented ocean environmental management and profitability actually feed upon each other and are mutually supportive. There is, however, the problem that many nations have not yet ratified MARPOL and other ocean environmental conventions and have not established national standards and enforcement mechanisms. In some cases, this is the result of limited funds. Yet it is becoming increasingly evident that the economic cost of a lack of ocean environmental protection far outweighs the cost of its effective management. Part of the reason is that when there is serious pollution of coastal waters or the oceans that damages coastal soils, use of beaches, and fishing, a nation's measured domestic income is not usually adjusted. Similarly, if such pollution occurs in coastal or open international waters, the world income is not adjusted. On the other hand, if a nation or the international community spends large sums of money for cleanup or prevention, then the measured income increases. Such costs are considered by economists purchases of final goods and services as eloquently described by R. Repetto in an article entitled "Wasting Assets."[3] He makes the point that there is an urgent need for national and global resource accounting. Methods to properly and fairly account for all the environmental impact costs and benefits must be taught, instead of just considering one side of the ledger.

7.9.1 Source and Cause of Environmental Management Strategy

The major ocean environmental management strategies today are based on the following basic approaches:

[3]R. Repetto, "Wasting Assets," in *Technology Review* (Cambridge, MA: Massachusetts Institute of Technology, January 1989).

1. setting ocean environmental standards,
2. organization pollution response plans and capabilities,
3. development or mandating outflow or pollution reduction technology (such as OPA-90 and double-hull tanker requirements),
4. enforcement mechanisms such as port state control regimes or agreements, and
5. making polluters pay.

Many believe that this environmental management strategy approach is expensive, difficult to enforce, and ineffective in the long run because it addresses problems reactively. In fact, it tries to reduce pollution or its impact, not to prevent it. Many recent studies in ocean environmental management as well as in other areas of environmental concern show that preventative or proactive measures are less expensive, more effective, and in many cases easier to introduce and enforce than reactional measures.

A recent study of the relative cost and effectiveness of installing double bottoms in oil tankers versus installing and enforcing vessel traffic control in coastal waters, where the bulk of tanker accident–caused oil pollution occurs, shows that it costs over $27,000 to reduce oil spills by 1 ton through using double bottoms; vessel traffic control investments would reduce oil spills by tankers in coastal zones for only $2,000 per ton of spill on average.[4] Furthermore, the potential of total spill reduction by installing double bottoms is only a fraction of that achievable by installing and mandating the use of vessel traffic control. The reason is that double-bottom installation only reduces the actual or potential outflow of oil resulting from a tanker or ship accident, while vessel traffic control prevents the accidents from occurring.

Unfortunately, vessel traffic systems (VTS) have only been provided in a limited number of places, such as Singapore and Hong Kong. These are the two busiest ports in the world, with up to 5,000 vessel movements per day. VTSs at this time act primarily as an information exchange by providing advisory alerts through tracking

[4]E. G. Frankel, "Technology and Economics of Tanker Accident Prevention and Spill Reduction," International Conference on Maritime Technology: Challenges in Safety and Environmental Protection Institute of Marine Engineers/Society of Naval (Architects and Marine Engineers of Singapore, Joint Conference, Singapore) November 1993.

vessel movements. Both Singapore and Hong Kong use computerized vessel tracking systems with radar input.

In addition to the very limited use made of VTS in coastal areas and navigational channels in the world, there is also a lack of uniformity in safety and environmental standards and their enforcement. National and international ocean environmental management still concentrates nearly exclusively on reactive management. It has become evident that adequate cleanup of a sizable oil spill requires an extremely large inventory of equipment and associated logistic capability.

Estimates for adequately equipped spill response capability worldwide are in the billions of dollars of investment and hundreds of millions of dollars a year in response capability maintenance. At this time, only a few major ports and petroleum terminal facilities outside North America and Europe have developed such capabilities. The United States and countries in the European Economic Community, claim to have imposed spill response capability, but there are questions of its effectiveness. One problem is that personnel expertise and readiness is as important, if not more important, than the timely availability and positioning ability of equipment.

For spill response capability to be effective, it will have to be organized on a regional or even continental basis. A source and cause ocean environmental management strategy superimposed on existing and planned reactive spill response and similar systems appears to be the best and certainly most effective approach in cost-benefit terms. It will require greater enforcement at the sources and greater preventative discipline than other strategies. But it will provide much lesser needs for spill response, cleanup, and similar capabilities that have been shown to be expensive, difficult to maintain, and even difficult to enforce.

A source-and-cause oriented ocean environmental management strategy concentrates on identifying sources that directly and indirectly cause ocean pollution. It also attempts to prevent or reduce these originating sources and, if that is not possible, to prevent or reduce the causes generated by these sources. It concentrates on eliminating the use of harmful pesticides or chemicals that may drain into rivers and drainage conduits and from there to the sea, and if that is not possible or cannot be completely prevented, it tries to deviate such pollutant flows or neutralize them before they reach the sea. Similarly, such a strategy identifies inadequate navigational aids, onboard training, ineffective ship management, lack of ship maneuvering controls, and navigational traffic management systems as the sources that cause the bulk of ship accidents in coastal waters which in turn cause most of the tanker-caused oil pollution.

Sources, causes, and effects chains are identified for each type of ocean pollution, and a strategy for managing the chain reaction at the initial source or as close to it as possible is identified for each. This in turn is translated into a management plan that consists of standards and reduction and prevention methods, and that uses reactive or cleanup only as a last resort. This is very much in line with the worldwide move towards greater concern for total quality management (TQM), which is based on the recognition that deficiencies are better solved by addressing the problems at the source than by correcting the defects after the accident or the fact. TQM and effective ocean environmental management have much in common. Correcting defects is most expensive after a product or service is completed and ready to be delivered; so is the correcting or cleaning up after ocean pollution. In addition, an after-the fact-correction can never bring the product to the level of quality that could be achieved if maximum quality had been observed from the beginning. The same is true in ocean environmental pollution. One can never clean up perfectly after a spill or bring the oceans back to their prepollution state, at least not in the short run.

Pursuit of quality has proven to not only be an attractive marketing objective but also to be an effective tool in containing costs and improving profitability. This also applies to ocean environmental management. Many companies that find that the principles that make TQM an essential corporate strategy now find that maintaining the highest quality in their operations as they affect the ocean environment holds as well. Several large oil and shipping companies have made ocean environmental management the focus of their total quality management and involve their staff, custodians, and community in their endeavors.

Increasingly, companies that maintain strict quality standards similarly maintain environment standards and environmental audits. Many have their own environmental auditors. Although in some cases this is the result of strict environmental enforcement, many companies do it as part of their own quality management program or to improve both their public image and their relations with government agencies.

Ocean environmental management is not new, and all governments and most companies and individuals accept it. They also accept that they have a responsibility to maintain the ocean environment, even if some take the responsibility lightly.

Ocean environmental responsibility is more international than most other environmental concerns, as the impact of ocean pollution usually affects more than one country or region. Just consider the countries bordering the Mediterranean or Baltic seas. Serious pollution of the Gulf of Finland, for example, caused by run-offs from plants in the former Soviet Union caused most of the fish population in the rest of the Baltic Sea to seriously decline.

In a way, the problems and certainly the source, cause, and effect problems are very similar to those faced in atmospheric environmental management. Although pollutants do not distribute as rapidly or widely in the oceans as in the atmosphere, their movements or transport are also uncontrollable, although in many cases more containable in the oceans. Air pollution standards have been introduced by most European and North American nations, as well as South Korea, Japan, and Singapore. In most, there standards are enforced. As mentioned earlier, efficient economic environmental credit transfer systems have also been allowed in the United States and other countries are seriously considering like schemes.

Much progress in controlling air pollution has been made, and in many parts of the world the total amount of pollutants discharged is actually declining. This is largely being accomplished by controlling the source or basic cause of pollution. It is suggested that a similar approach may work in ocean environmental management. It will not only require the setting of limits or standards for all direct and indirect sources, but also impose requirements for monitoring, inspection, and training. Although this is being done with ships and particularly tankers in some respect, both monitoring and enforcing standards are still highly deficient. They also are nonexistent with respect to many other potential sources of pollution.

A source of ocean environmental management approach that covers all aspects of ocean pollution is, in the final analysis, the only way to ensure effective ocean environmental management and maintenance of a healthy ocean environment.

7.9.2 Ocean Environmental Management Financing

Among the major stumbling blocks in ensuring effective ocean environmental management are financial requirements. The costs are not only very large and often not affordable, but the benefits are sometimes remote, are difficult to identify, and in many cases are assumed in part by others. As a result, self-financing ocean environmental management systems has been considered and in some cases been found feasible. Among the first self-financing systems were waste reception facility costs covered through users' fees. These costs include costs of their use and the maintenance of spill response capability. Revenues are also obtained from the sale of processed waste to end users (for example, for power generation). Similarly, preventative methods such as the use of VTS are now provided as a mandatory service that charges a user fee.

Future active vessel traffic management or movement control systems may include remote piloting or vessel maneuvering (Los Angeles/Long Beach, California, and Milfordhaven, England, are experimenting with such systems), again to be provided on a fee basis. These and other ocean environmental management systems are ultimately expected to become self-financing or even profitable enough to attract private investment.

The issues of ocean environmental management must be addressed in the near future, and to date few have dealt satisfactorily with the underlying issues of enforcement, finance, and choice among strategies for compliance and management. There is a scarcity of existing analysis on the costs of compliance or the opportunities for cost-sharing or fee assessment. Little is known about the potential impacts of environmental actions on the efficiency of ocean use. Other than topical outlines for some of the broad subject areas, there are no comprehensive studies on the consequences of ignoring environmental considerations or implementing environmentally sensitive measures.

A key issue is finding a cost-effective or profitable strategy to provide ocean environmental management. Recent experience shows that a source management approach may offer the most effective way of financing ocean environmental management.

7.9.3 Application of Source-Oriented Ocean Environmental Management

Source-oriented ocean environmental management aims at preventing the discharge of pollutants that usually end up in the ocean at their source. Most of the sources of ocean pollution are well known and could be regulated, given the will of governments at national and local levels to cooperate. In many cases, the issue is one of economic viability or attractiveness as well as corporate and community environmental responsibility. By showing that economic growth and well-being and environmental responsibility are interdependent and that bad government and corporate and community management and a lack of environmental responsibility go hand in hand, the advantages of environmental responsibility can be shown.

Today, people search for quality in work and life, and firms oriented toward quality are usually the most successful economically as well. Similarly, like quality, effective environmental management does not cost but saves money. For effective source-oriented environmental management, the most important first step is to convince people at all levels of the community, business, and government of this basic fact. Although it is usually easy to make the point of the long-term benefits of effective environmental management, it is much harder to show short-term savings, particularly at the source. Unfortunately, many in government, industry, and private life primarily consider short-term horizons in their decisions. It is therefore important to show the short-term benefits, such as improvement in public and quality image, societal and community responsibility, and improved relationships, even if direct, monetary short-term benefits are not immediately evident.

Just as recycling of solid waste has finally caught on as an effective short-term policy with social and sometimes even economic benefits, so environmental management at the source can be shown to pay both short-term and long-term benefits.

Source-oriented ocean environmental management relies primarily on pollution prevention by reducing or eliminating pollution causes at the source. Starting with land-based sources—such as industrial wastes, sewage, port-generated waste, and agricultural fertilizers, pesticides, and other chemicals draining into irrigation waters and thus rivers and bays—effective remote monitoring is now possible. Similarly, efficient and economic methods for sewage and waste treatment, including recycling, are now available. In some cases, they have proven to be economically attractive.

The use of gravity-holding or separating tanks that often incorporate filtration systems often permits the extraction, recuperation, and reuse of valuable chemicals for the same or an alternative use. Very much like extraction of oil from oily water ballast, chemical extraction from industrial and agricultural wastewaters is becoming a viable approach. In some cases, the use of simple holding ponds, using evaporation to produce concentrated brines that can then be recycled, has been found to be both effective and economically viable.

Increasing pressure must be imposed on suppliers to make their products or the residue and waste generated by their products recyclable. If this is not feasible, materials used should at least be safely disposable. One approach currently under consideration is to charge suppliers of polluting products for their disposal after use. This charge would be in the form of a sales tax that suppliers would, in all probability, pass on to their customers. Thus the funds collected would be used to pay for the cleanup. This would apply to industrial and agricultural chemicals as well as consumer and hard goods that cannot be economically recycled and that may pollute waters.

Recycling treated organic waste may include its use as fertilizer or food for fish in a controlled environment. Similarly, many chemical wastes can often be recycled for use in other processes. The idea is to prevent the discharge of pollutants into waters that affect the oceans, to reduce such discharges significantly, or to recycle pollutants for reuse or into materials that have little, if any, detrimental effects if discharged into the oceans.

Many processes and techniques to accomplish this have been developed, but few have been tested on a commercial scale and even fewer have been subjected to a formal operational and economic analysis to establish their performance. In fact, the amount of money spent on preventative and recycling technology, particularly as applied to liquid waste, is pitifully small, even though the payoff may be large in economic and environmental terms, as shown by the development of large-scale oil/waste separation methods. These developments will only occur if, as in the case of oil pollution at sea, strict regulations with effectively planned future enforcement are announced.

Effective monitoring equipment exists, and it would be advisable to monitor the largest known outflows of land-based ocean pollution so as to identify their sources. The bulk of this pollution is generated in developed countries, and most of it is discharged into the ocean through rivers, waterways, and large bays that serve as drainage basins.

Tracing pollution sources up a river or bay today can be performed by monitors mounted on moving boats. Once a polluter has been identified and the source of their pollution has been determined, it is often expedient to require installation of river- or bayside cells around the outflow if the detrimental ingredients of the outflow cannot be turned off or removed in a short time. This type of barrier cell can be made of wood, metal, or plastic reinforced sheet pile and can be designed as gravity separation cells or equipped with multistage filters. The purpose is to extract and retain as much of the pollutant particles, which can then be removed periodically in concentrated form, as possible. Obviously, if the pollutants are already dissolved at the outflow, osmotic filtering, chemical cleansing, neutralizing, or dilution may be required. In many cases, radiation may reduce biological pollution dangers.

Such cells or caissons can be built at outflows or, more effectively, may be prefabricated and then towed and sunk at the required outflow pipe location to receive and treat the outflow pollutants. With above-surface outflow, this requires such cells or caissons simply to be positioned under the outflow. Such measures should only be used as temporary solutions, and polluters should be forced to achieve a permanent solution during a specified period of time.

Outflow and drainage pollution must be subjected to similar pollution emission reduction standards as those used to reduce air emissions (automobile, electric power plants, industrial plants, and so forth). In addition, it is advocated to introduce economic source reduction incentives such as pollution credits.

Ports and similar facilities are already required to provide waste reception facilities for their users and their own operations under existing international agreements, such as MARPOL. Unfortunately, many lack effective treatment and disposal facilities, even where reception facilities are established. To manage pollution at this course effectively may require imposing of port environmental charges on users, both ship and cargo owners and operators, with the proviso that ports are responsible to provide and maintain pollution prevention facilities.

Pollution at sea is primarily caused by ship discharges, voluntary or accidental, and oil well platform accidents. Here, as pointed out before, source-oriented ocean environmental management emphasizes preventing polluting accidents and not on reducing outflow, spills, containment, and cleanup. Although most major sources of pollution are well known and their causes have been identified, ocean environmental regulation is still largely concerned with pollution response. Few hard rules and requirements are in place. Just as vessel traffic control or management systems designed to prevent ship accidents are mainly advisory and not mandatory, so pollutant outflows into rivers and bays are often only subject to recommended outflow reduction and not source or cause elimination efforts. This situation is often the result of concern with economic impact, assignment of liability, and so on. Most important, however, is that regulators, policy makers, and the public are concerned with and are willing to take often unpopular action when a high-visibility accident occurs. They usually ignore continuous, nonaccidental pollution even though its contribution to ocean pollution far outweighs that caused by large newsworthy accidents. As a result, a completely different approach must be taken to ocean environmental management.

7.9.3.1 Techniques of source-oriented ocean environmental management. Source-oriented ocean environmental management starts with identifying all major sources by location, process, type, and method of discharge; volume; physical and chemical composition; and dilution, if any. The continuity of the discharge and variations over time are next established, as are facilities available for reducing or treating of pollutant outflows.

Where the information is not available, comparatively inexpensive tests or surveys can be used to identify the sources. Source surveys are then conducted to identify those components listed above followed by developing plans for source reduction or elimination using alternatives such as described in the examples mentioned before. A time table, which includes a benefit/cost analysis, is then developed. The analysis is performed both in financial terms, to estimate the financial costs and benefits to the source-generating enterprise, and in economic terms, to establish measures of benefits and costs to society at large. It is often found that a source reduction or elimination may cause a financial cost that exceeds financial gains but simultaneously introduce economic benefits that far outweigh the economic and financial costs. Although invisible in the short run, these benefits, such as an increase in the value of the enterprise's waterfront real estate, may generate some real, in both financial and economic terms, long-term benefits.

The same applies to changes in potential liability and certainly improvements in the public image of the enterprise. Some jurisdictions allow an enterprise that cleans up its land and facilities to revalue them on their books and thereby establish an increase in their real assets. This, plus the possibility of gaining trailable environmental credits, is often a sufficient incentive. Obviously, to implement it requires the setting of standards and basic regulations. But again, experience shows that if standards and associated regulations are introduced sensibly and are not only achievable but consider operational and financial limitations or implementability, progress can be made quite rapidly.

The same applies to offshore ocean environmental management. Although mandatory vessel traffic control or management systems are often opposed for reasons of tradition or assumed financial costs, it can easily be shown that their introduction does not only prevent or reduce potential ship and boat accidents but that passage costs and passage times are reduced. Furthermore, arrival and departure times can be predicted more accurately.

Offshore platforms and ship accident prevention can also be greatly enhanced by effective training, greater onboard discipline, better communications, and improved cooperation. Similarly, placing floating or caisson-type holding or reception tanks for the discharge of platform waste, including sewage, oil polluted cuttings, and so forth, should be required. Such tanks can be inflatable and towable and could also be used for the disposal of accidental spills. As in the case of land-based polluting enterprises, offshore platforms should be required to place remote recording monitors in the water and be offered similar incentives as land-based ocean polluting enterprises are.

Recent studies[5,6] indicate that source-oriented ocean environmental management would not only save large amounts of money but would also greatly reduce ocean pollution. The approach offers major opportunities for business, not just business in the ocean cleanup and response area, but more importantly, businesses engaged in the productive uses of the oceans.

7.9.3.2 Costs and benefits of ocean environmental management. The cost of getting rid of pollution is much greater than the cost of preventing pollution in the first place. Similarly, as the cost of cleaning up the bulk of the pollution is cheaper per ton removed than the cost of cleaning up the last residues of pollution, so the cost of pre-

[5] "Environmental Policy: How to Apply Economic Instruments," *Organization for Economic Cooperation and Development,* (OECD) [Paris, France: 1991]

[6] "The State of the Environment," *Organization for Economic Cooperation and Development,* (OECD) [Paris, France, 1991]

venting large pollution discharges is less than the cost of preventing small emissions per unit of outflow.

Surveys are traditionally used to estimate the value of environmental impacts. People are usually asked how much they value an asset that may be degraded by ocean pollution. Their response depends largely on their use of that asset, such as a beach, coastal zone, fishing area, and so on. Similarly, costs of prevention and cleanup can often be estimated. The cost of the impact is the economic benefit that is compared with the cost of prevention. Surveys have many drawbacks, though, not the least of which are the large differences in answers and resulting large statistical deviations in the asset value or environmental impact cost estimates.

Some economists prefer to use a market approach. In other words, they estimate the value the market (such as potential investors or users) places on the environmental assets. Environmental damage quite often causes directly measurable costs by which the benefit cost ratio of preventing the damage can usually be estimated.

One difficulty in setting environmental impact costs is that estimates of the value of environmental assets differ among countries and peoples. Beaches have a high value in the Western world, less in East and Southern Asia, and much less in most poor developing countries, particularly in Africa, not popular with or used by tourists. Similarly, politicians and insurers often skew the value of ocean environmental assets.

Sometimes ocean environmental regulations may actually have a negative effect on the maintenance of the ocean environment. Ocean environmental benefits are compared with ocean environmental costs to show the advantages of maintaining the waters not only for social, community, and physical reasons but also economic and financial reasons.

Many governments introduce environmental regulations or requirements that increase costs and decrease benefits of ocean environmental management. This is true both for governments that habitually interfere in the marketplace and those that are ideologically opposed to it. In both cases, political considerations often result in the mismanagement of ocean resources by imposing unrealistic or ineffective policies and regulations, which can affect both the costs and benefits. In some cases, governments interfere by setting unrealistic rates for water, fishing rights, sewage disposal, or other services or rights. Often water supplies are highly subsidized, which results both in a waste of water and in increased pollution of rivers and seas. The same applies quite frequently in the pricing or taxing of fuel. Similarly, farm growers' subsidies, price supports, or a low-cost supply of fertilizers and agricultural chemicals will add to pollution and greatly distort the environmental cost benefit balance.

One of the most difficult issues faced in ocean environmental management is that many countries consider it a political issue, or at least an issue that can be used to achieve or advance political ends. As a result, it usually takes a very long time to get agreement and even longer to have an agreement ratified. Even then, the interpretation and enforcement may be greatly affected by political considerations. This is particularly true in agreements that affect both developing and developed nations where the first will often use the opportunity to extract advantages. Similarly, enforcement in many countries is not only lax but involves bribes and other payments that distort both the costs and benefits of ocean environmental management.

7.9.4 Company Involvement in Ocean Environmental Management

Effective environmental management and quality go hand in hand, and more and more companies find that to manage the environment on which their operations are based is not only the right thing to do, but is also a very attractive approach to their business. This approach develops an image of social responsibility and also makes increasingly economic and financial sense. Effective ocean environmental management is complex at the company level. Not only is it highly politicized, but the number of interested parties or stakeholders involved is usually quite large, and many of these in turn may be unknown and only emerge when threatened.

Companies that succeed in ocean environmental management usually have a policy that emphasizes the importance of it to the overall, including the profit, objectives of the company. They also make it a point to involve their employees and use them and the policy both to establish and then to tighten community relations. Most importantly, such companies will involve their customers in that effort and make sure not only of customer feedback but also of communication with customers and the market in general on ocean environmental matters. Furthermore, they will try to use their expertise, their knowledge, and their presence and involvement to further the advance of ocean environmental management.

7.9.5 Financing Ocean Environmental Management

Financing ocean environmental management, and in particular financing a removal of or change in pollutant sources, has become a very difficult problem. For this reason many jurisdictions have assumed a polluter pay approach. This works only if the polluter is capable of paying or has assets of adequate value, however. In the case of ships, for example, owners habitually incorporate each ship separately to limit their exposure or liability to the ship at fault. Many other polluters have adopted a similar approach.

The problem is that investments in pollution prevention usually attain only low and indirect levels of cost recovery; the benefits are largely economic and not financial. Furthermore, returns, if any, are usually in local currency or in intangible benefits. Other issues that deter potential investors are the lack of definition of public liabilities and inadequate enforcement. As a result, ocean environmental investment financing is difficult and must often rely on short-term sources, allocations of funds from environmental taxes, creation of earmarked funds, or income from pollution fees or fines, or some combination of these.

Sometimes loan financing through international banks or municipal bond issues is possible, but only if the project is sizable and well defined. Increasingly limited financial resources must be stretched to make any impact. In many cases, a maximum impact at minimum cost approach is now assumed. Financing the worst polluting projects only for a partial reduction in the pollution level may be required. This is because it usually costs much less to reduce actual or potential pollution by 50% than to reduce it by a further 25%, and so forth. Therefore, with limited financial resources, it may be more attractive to reduce the bulk of the worst pollution sources than to attempt to eliminate only a few as far as possible.

To make a proper choice of pollution sources to be financed, the use of analytical hierarchical analysis models has been found to be useful. Sources of financing may include loans (international, national, commercial, and private) as well as private and public equity contributions, national counterpart funds, external concessionary funds, local and municipal assets (on and off budget), user fees, and environmental credits.

7.9.6 Priority Financing of Ocean Environmental Management

Usually, many ocean environmental projects compete for limited resources. In the past, people have simply chosen among them and a few were implemented, with the choice often driven by politics. Considering the increased demand for funding for the environment and a decline in available resources, more effective environmental project investment strategies are required to ensure the most effective use of funds. As a result, projects are increasingly selected on the basis of their impact as a function of investment and at the same time how far projects should go in terms of effective use of resources is also considered. For example, in a typical oil spill cleanup project, 20% of funding is usually spent to remove 50% to 60% of the spill, 30% of funding is spent to remove 75% to 85% of the spill, and 70% of funding is spent to remove the last 15% to 25% of the spill.

Many feel that money would be more wisely spent if the emphasis was on preventing and removing the bulk of the pollutant sources of pollution instead of trying to eliminate all the sources or remove all the spills or other pollution caused. Effective methods are available today to develop an efficient strategy for the choice of projects and the extent of funding to be applied to each project that permits the most effective use of available funding.

Epilogue

As humans becomes more dependent on the oceans for resources and other uses, methods of ocean environmental management will have to be improved. The largely reactive approach now practiced will have to become large-scale preventative methods that minimize the potential for environmental damage. Management of the ocean environment must be planned effectively so that environmental damage can be prevented. If damage occurs, it must be readily contained. Later, a most effective rational approach that would assist nature clean up the damage or even better would reduce or eliminate the real or potential impacts of the damage must be identified.

Pollution cleanup is often a hazard to the environment itself. The well-publicized massive *Exxon Valdez* cleanup effort, touted everywhere as a responsive action that prevented major long-term environmental damage, was found in 1992 to have been less than an environmental cleanup success. In fact, it may have done more damage than good. The toxic fumes of detergents used not only killed numerous harbor seals but also affected many of the cleanup personnel. Many workers who participated in the cleanup experienced severe respiratory problems within three years. Marine animals released after cleaning are spreading diseases and have infected or even decimated large herds sometimes at long distances from the site of the spill.

There are many other examples of overzealous efforts to return the ocean environment to its natural state by use of often artificial physical or chemical methods. Nature quite often does a better job at healing itself gradually, just as the human body, if given time and the right environment, will usually heal itself better than large doses of drugs or radical physical treatments, such as surgery or physical therapy.

Humans have to learn not to immediately and radically correct damage to the ocean environment caused by them. They should prevent, limit, and contain to their best ability, but reversing environmental damage is often done much more effectively by nature itself. It often looks as if humans react like some animals and children do: on causing some damage, they will immediately try to repair it by whatever means available, even if the repair aggravates the damage.

Somehow people feel that they must actively correct what they have caused, more out of feelings of guilt than as a result of a rational decision process designed to correct the damage permanently.

Much more effective environmental management decision tools that can evaluate cause-and-effect relationships and, by the use of artificial intelligence or expert systems, weigh all the alternatives to permit choice of a most effective strategy are needed. People must learn to minimize the use of chemicals of all sorts, which are often the initial or prime source causing the damage but are again resorted to in cleanups.

Chemical and even physical methods of dispersal or cleanup often cause more damage than the spill or pollution itself and may even impede or delay the ability of natural processes to correct the damage.

The oceans are certainly very resilient and have many self-correcting, cleaning, and biological revival capabilities that people must allow to act and not counteract by trying to do a more efficient job than nature.

At present, contingency plans largely consist of bureaucratic documentation identifying response methods and responsible authorities or agencies. Yet in most cases, equipment for combating environmental damage either is not available or is not ready when needed. In fact, most responsible authorities employ more people in the administration of ocean environmental management than in operational prevention containment and cleanup activities.

The links between economic growth, industrial activity, income redistribution, and protection of the environment become more and more evident each day. Energy consumption used to be an important measure of economic condition, but now it is a negative measure of the protection of the environment and has lost some of the direct linkage with economic efficiency and growth. People must learn how to improve economic effectiveness without environmental impact and how to increase real and well-distributed income without economic hardships. There is much to learn before this is achieved.

Appendix A

Ocean Environmental Regulation in the United States

In considering U.S. ocean environmental regulation, it is important to be sensitive to the federal-state relationship involved. Have the federal requirements preempted state regulations? Do federal and state regulations coexist insofar as they are not contradictory? Is state authority given priority under federal guidelines? Environmental regulation seems to fall primarily in the latter two categories so that minimum requirements are established nationwide while more stringent requirements may be established locally without the problem of federal preemption. Thus in any given case, if federal regulations do not preempt state regulations, a particular state's regulations must be checked to determine whether compliance with the state regulations is adequate. Another common provision of federal law is one requiring appropriate state approval prior to the issuance of federal approvals.

The requirements should be analyzed to determine who is affected: a government official (and through that person, the individual), as in the case of filing an environmental impact statement (EIS). Are the present activities of the individual directly regulated as they are in the case of existing pollution dischargers, or will only future activities be affected? An analogous problem is to determine which agency sets the standards, which agency applies the standards, and which agency investigates and prosecutes violations. Although it has not always been possible to make this determination as straightforward as possible, it can be said by way of generalization that the Environmental Protection Agency (EPA) sets standards and engages in enforcement unless another agency has been designated to serve these functions. Two other agencies most frequently mentioned here are the Corps of Engineers when dredging or filling is involved and the Coast Guard when vessels and other transportation-related pollution sources are involved.

A.1 NATIONAL ENVIRONMENTAL POLICY ACT

Major federal legislation designed to protect the ocean environment from further degradation has been enacted largely since 1970. Although much of this legislation recognizes that it is the duty of the states to reduce and control pollution, the federal government "stick" is in provisions that require that if states do not meet federal standards in their enforcement, the federal government will take over the job.

The National Environmental Policy Act of 1969 (NEPA)[1] mandated concern for the environment in federal agency decision making. Section 102(C),[2] the backbone of this mandate, requires that recommendations for

> major federal actions significantly affecting the quality of the human environment [shall include] a detailed statement by the responsible official on—(i) the environmental impact of the proposed action, (ii) any adverse environmental effects which cannot be avoided should the proposal be implemented, (iii) alternatives to the proposed action, (iv) the relationship between local short-term uses of man's environment and the maintenance and enhancement of long-term productivity, and (v) any irreversible and irretrievable commitments of resources which would be involved in the proposed action should it be implemented.

[1] "National Environmental Policy Act of 1969" (NEPA) 42 U.S.C. § 4331 et. seq. (1970).

[2] Section 102(C), 42 U.S.C. §4332 (c) (1970).

> Prior to making any detailed statement, the responsible federal official shall consult with and obtain the comments of any federal agency which has jurisdiction by law or special expertise with respect to any environmental impact involved.

The act also established the Council on Environmental Quality (CEQ) in the Executive Office of the President. The CEQ advises the president on environmental affairs and legislation. The CEQ has also developed guidelines for agency compliance with NEPA. It does not directly regulate any activities outside the government.

Pursuant to CEQ guidelines, each agency has developed procedures for including environmental concerns in its decision-making process. If more than one agency is involved in a decision, only one need prepare an environmental impact statement.

Frequently, the person promoting a major federal action will hire a contractor specialized in preparing EISs to gather the data and prepare an EIS to go along with the application. The agency, however, is responsible for the content of any EIS prepared for action that agency takes.

The review of EISs by the courts is a study in itself. It may be generally stated that courts will only investigate whether an EIS has been adequately prepared with respect to environmental impacts considered and agencies consulted. In general, an EIS

1. should be understandable and nonconclusive,
2. should refer to the full range of knowledge, and
3. must discuss certain impacts that are typical of some types of action.

If an EIS is held to be inadequately prepared, further agency action may be enjoined until an adequate statement has been prepared. The courts may be vigilant in seeing that all views on environmental effect are considered by the agency (the EIS "procedure"), but may refuse to assess the merits of the contentions included in an EIS or the balance struck between negative effects on the environment and other benefits unless the balance struck is arbitrary, capricious, or an abuse of discretion.

The extent of the effects to be considered in an adequate EIS is also a study in itself. NEPA has been interpreted to be a "full disclosure" law, ensuring that decision makers and the public are alerted to possible environmental consequences of proposed actions. Generally, an EIS must consider the direct effect of the action with reference to the five factors in Section 102(C) of NEPA, including the following: whether the action will lead to violation of other laws to protect the environment whether or not such other laws are policed by the agency preparing the EIS; the EIS must consider alternatives to the proposed action that must be discussed; the EIS must consider the cumulative effect of this action with other known or proposed government actions affecting the same area; and the EIS must also consider secondary effects, such as increased development, congestion, school crowding, and the impact of constructing support facilities (such as, new highways) for the proposed project.

A.2 PORT ENVIRONMENTAL REGULATION

Construction in the navigable waters of the United States is lawful only if permitted by the secretary of the Army. More specifically, Section 10 of the Rivers and Harbors Act of 1899 prohibits construction of wharves, booms, breakwaters, jetties, and the like, either outside established harbor lines or where no harbor lines have been established, unless the chief of engineers recommends the plans and the secretary of the Army authorizes the work. Similarly, excavation or filling in the navigable waters or harbors of the United States is prohibited unless the work is recommended by the chief of engineers and authorized by the secretary of the Army.

Section 13 of the same statute, known as the Refuse Act, which prohibited dumping or discharging any material into navigable waters of the United States, has been superseded, except for discharges obstructing navigation, by provisions of the Federal Water Pollution Control Act (FWPCA) Amendments of 1972 (discussed below).

In deciding whether to issue a permit, the Corps of Engineers (Corps) must consider whether issuance of the permit constitutes a "major federal action," thereby compelling preparation of an EIS. The Corps is required by statute and regulations to prepare a preliminary assessment of possible environmental impacts. Based on this environmental assessment, a decision is to be made whether or not an EIS is required. If it is decided that an EIS is not required, a statement to this affect and the reasons for this decision are to be placed in the file. The statement is to be available to the public on request, and notice of the determination is published in accordance with a schedule. Should the project generate controversy, the Corps may reconsider a no-EIS decision.

It has been held that in issuing a permit for dredging, the Corps may take environmental effects into consideration and not just the effects on navigation presumably contemplated by the statute. Presumably, this authority to consider environmental factors would extend to permits for construction of objects that might obstruct navigability (such as, booms) but might not have readily identifiable environmental impact (as filling would). This does not mean that all dredging permits "significantly affect the environment" and therefore require the preparation of an EIS.

According to a paper published by the Maritime Administration's Western Region:[3]

> The earliest basis for the regulation of dredging is the Commerce Clause of the U.S. Constitution which gives Congress the power to regulate interstate commerce. The U.S. Army Corps of Engineers, under Section 10 of the Rivers and Harbors Act of 1899, was delegated authority over nearly all navigational concerns including dredging and filling. Also, that same law gave the Corps control over the disposal of refuse in navigable water of the U.S. under a section known as the Refuse Act.
>
> An important consideration in government regulation of activities in navigable waters is the definition of the phrase "navigable waters". This definition establishes the Government's jurisdiction. Traditionally, under the Rivers and Harbors Act, the Corps considers waters navigable if they are, have been in the past, or may be in the future used in the transportation of interstate or foreign commerce. The Corps' jurisdiction extends laterally over the entire surface of the body of water.

The navigational interests of Congress, originally directed towards the development of waterborne commerce, have expanded to include the consideration of water quality, conservation, state and local concerns, and national interests. A dredging permit may not be issued unless the project is found to be "in the public interest." Because of this broad permit authority, the Corps of Engineers repre-

[3]U.S. Department of Commerce, Maritime Administration, Western Region, "Untangling Dredging Regulations," June 1976 (GPO Number 691–529–1976).

sents what may be called "a common denominator" in the regulatory process.

However, the Rivers and Harbors Act is not the only federal law regulating activities in navigable waters. Recent water quality legislation has considerably increased controls on dredging and has seriously affected port operations. Regulations on the disposal of dredged material in Chesapeake Bay in 1974, for example, caused lengthy delays in completing an important channel-deepening project at the Port of Baltimore. Routine maintenance dredging at the port virtually stopped due to problems in finding an acceptable site to dispose of dredged material. These regulatory problems lead to the diversion of cargo from the Port of Baltimore in 1974 due to inadequate channel depths.

Two acts regulate the disposal of dredged material into bodies of water or the addition of fill material into bodies of water: the Federal Water Pollution Control Act Amendments of 1972 (FWPCA) and the Marine Protection, Research, and Sanctuaries Act, of October 1972.[4]

> The FWPCA completely reorganized the ways in which water quality goals are to be achieved in the U.S. Besides increasing the authority of the Corps over the regulation of water quality, the FWPCA gave the major federal responsibility for water quality to the Environmental Protection Agency (EPA). (See footnote 3, pg. 303.)

Under FWPCA, the government undertook the National Pollution Discharge Elimination System (NPDES). Discharge of pollutants (which are defined to include dredged spoils) into navigable waters was outlawed unless in accordance with a permit issued under the FWPCA. "The term 'navigable waters' means the waters of the United States including the territorial seas [out to 3 mi]." The ambiguity of this language may reflect congressional inability to agree on clear language. It may be intended to bring under the FWPCA permit system discharges into all waters to the maximum extent of the Commerce Clause, unfettered by the traditional concepts of navigability, noted above. The EPA has adopted this view for the permits it issues.

Section 404[5] grants to the Corps of Engineers sole authority to

[4]"Marine Protection, Research and Sanctuaries Act" Public Law No 92–532, 86 Stat. 1052, codified at 33 U.S.C. § 1401.

[5]33 U.S.C. § 1344 (Supplement II, 1972).

issue permits for the disposal of dredged and fill material in "navigable waters" subject to the FWPCA. A recent court decision[6] adopted the expansive definition of navigable waters suggested above and found that the secretary of the Army abused his discretion by adopting a narrower definition of navigable waters. The court therefore ordered that new regulations reflecting the maximum extent of federal power under the Commerce Clause be prepared. "New regulations, issued on July 23, 1975,[7] extend the Corps' jurisdiction under Section 404 in a three phase program to include wetlands, primary and secondary tributaries of navigable waters, and natural lakes greater than five acres in surface area." (See footnote 3, pg. 303.) Phase two of this program, however, was suspended on July 2, 1976, for 60 days by Secretary of the Army Martin R. Hoffman on orders from President Gerald R. Ford. The purpose of the suspension was presumably to allow time for Congress to complete action on legislation designed to limit the Corps' jurisdiction.[8]

Section 404 (see footnote 5, pg. 304) requires that:

1. The Corps may issue permits, after public hearings, for the disposal of dredged material in navigable waters at specific disposal sites.
2. Dumping sites shall be specified by the Corps using guidelines developed by the EPA [in conjunction with the Corps].
3. The EPA may veto the Corps' designation of disposal sites if [after consulting with the Corps] the EPA determines that the proposed discharges may have adverse effects on water supplies, shellfish beds, fishery areas, wildlife or recreation areas.

Note that the guidelines may additionally take into account the economic impact on navigation and anchorage of failure to select the site.

The EPA issues permits under the FWPCA for the discharge of pollutants other than dredged or fill material unless it has approved a state plan for issuing such permits. In addition, the EPA is responsible for enforcement if there is a discharge of dredged or fill material without a permit under Section 4.4. The EPA reported to Con-

[6] *National Resources Defense Council, Inc.* v *Callaway*, 392 Fed. Supp. 685 (D.D.C. 1975).

[7] 40 Fed. Reg. 31320 (July 23, 1975), amending 33c. C.F.C. § 909.120.

[8] BNA, Environmental Reporter, "Current Developments-435" (1976).

gress an average of more than 20 enforcement actions per year since 1975 for discharge of dredged or fill material without a permit.

The states have another method under the FWPCA for ensuring that activities in their waters will neither be conducted contrary to their permit programs nor will endanger their water quality. Any applicant for a federal permit relating to an activity that may result in any discharge into the navigable waters (which includes the sea out to 3 mi under the act) must obtain certification from the state that the discharge will comply with the FWPCA. No permit may be issues without such certification. Hence, the states may exercise a veto power over the award of permits (of any kind) to potential polluters. No federal agency is deemed an applicant for purposes of this section, however. Therefore, dredging done by the Corps presumably does not require state certification. Private dredging activity for dumping in navigable waters (including the territorial seas) would require state certification before the Corps could issue a permit for the disposal of the dredged material.

The division of authority between the Corps and the EPA under the Ocean Dumping Act is almost identical to that under the FWPCA, but the states are given almost no role. This act forbids the transportation from the United States of material for dumping in the ocean, except under the permit program provided for. After hearings, the secretary of the Army may issue a permit for the transportation of dredged material for ocean dumping; the EPA issues the permits for all other materials. The secretary must use criteria established by the EPA in assessing the effects of dumping. The secretary is also required to assess the "effect of permit denial on navigation, economic and industrial development, and foreign and domestic commerce" to determine the need for dumping. Before issuing a permit, the secretary must notify the EPA, which may veto the issuance of a permit if the EPA believes that its criteria have not been complied with or that the secretary's determination of the effect on the ocean environment is erroneous. If the secretary of the Army certifies to the EPA that there is no feasible alternative to ocean dumping at a particular site, however, the EPA shall grant a waiver unless it finds that the dumping will result in acceptably adverse impacts.

In addition, the Ocean Dumping Act provides that no state may enforce any regulation with respect to activity regulated by the act; any state, however, may propose criteria relating to dumping in waters subject to its jurisdiction that, if consistent with the act, may be applied by the EPA. The act also provides that no other permit purporting to authorize transportation for ocean dumping is valid.

There is potential conflict between the Ocean Dumping Act and the FWPCA because both purport to regulate activities in the territorial seas. If the FWPCA were paramount, the states would have a veto power over dumping in the territorial seas. If the Ocean Dumping Act were paramount, the states would be precluded from regulating activities regulated under the act, and a permit under Section 404 would be invalid. The Corps of Engineers and the EPA have followed the same path in resolving this conflict. The EPA has issued regulations under the FWPCA for discharges inside (inland from) the base line for measuring the territorial seas. Discharges in the territorial seas are subject to the Ocean Dumping Act and the state certification requirement under the FWPCA (so that no permit will be issued unless the discharge complies also with a state's water pollution program). Discharges beyond the territorial seas are regulated under the Ocean Dumping Act with no involvement of the states. The Corps of Engineers has administratively defined Section 404 to apply to discharges into the territorial seas only of fill material, not dredged material. Like the EPA, the Corps' regulations apply the state certification requirements to Ocean Dumping Act permits for discharges into the territorial seas.

> The EPA is also responsible for establishing federal water quality criteria for dredging. The EPA reviews projects according to these criteria and they are also used as standards by state water quality agencies. To carry out this responsibility, the EPA published on September 5, 1975 interim final regulations which established general disposal policies. Where spoils are found to be contaminated beyond certain levels, the EPA requires ocean or dry land disposal.
>
> It is difficult to assess the effect of the new interim regulations on dredging permit procedures because no numerical guidelines were set for water quality. The regulations contained only general evaluation policies and the appropriate tests to obtain required data. However, higher costs and permit approval delays to the applicant for the disposal of "contaminated" spoils will probably be the result.[9]
>
> Water quality legislation and the regulatory programs it has created are continuing to evolve and change. New regulations are being de-

[9]40 Federal Regulation 41291 (Sept 5, 1975).

veloped at all government levels and will affect the dredging and disposal permit process. (See footnote 3, pg. 303.)

The U.S. Fish and Wildlife Service of the Department of the Interior is the primary federal agency concerned with wildlife protection and conservation. In the regulation of dredging, the agency has special status because of the 1958 Fish and Wildlife Coordination Act. This Act requires the Corps of Engineers, before issuing a dredging permit, to consult with the U.S. Fish and Wildlife Service (USFWS) and the head of the state agency concerned with wildlife resources for purposes of considering the effects on wildlife. By a subsequent agreement with the Corps under this Act, any objections by USFWS to the issuance of a permit can only be overridden by the Secretary of the Army in Washington, DC. This in effect gives USFWS indirect "veto power" over a dredging project because of the difficulties and very long delays in submitting a proposed project to the secretarial level for approval.

Dredging projects are reviewed by USFWS on a case-by-case basis following policies and standards developed by the Department of the Interior. Generally, the USFWS does not object to dredging and disposal activities if the spoils do not exceed EPA criteria for contaminant levels, disposal will not affect wetlands, and the activities do not conflict with its resource protection objectives. (See footnote 3, pg. 303.)

For information about a proposed dredging project, the USFWS relies on environmental documents and staff knowledge about the project area. Because of limited staff size to cover large geographic areas, the USFWS relies on individual state fish and wildlife agencies for more detailed knowledge of project sites acquired by field investigations. (See footnote 3, pg. 303.)

An additional agency concerned with marine life resources and involved in the regulations of dredging is the National Marine Fisheries Service (NMFS) of the Department of Commerce. The NMFS is mandated to protect fisheries resources and plays a regulation role similar to that of the U.S. Fish and Wildlife Service. However, the comments made by NMFS to the Corps' Public Notices do not fall under the provisions of the Coordination Act and so they do not have potential "veto power". In protecting the marine, estuarine and anadromous resources of the nation, the NMFS does case-by-case reviews of proposed projects. (See footnote 3, pg. 303.)

There is a high degree of coordination and cooperation between the two federal agencies and state fish and wildlife agencies. They share almost identical interests and responsibilities, and in the case of

USFWS and stage agencies, the same regulatory "clout" under provisions of the Coordination Act. (See footnote 3, pg. 303.)

It is interesting to compare fish and wildlife protection with water quality regulation. In both cases, major federal laws (FWPCA and the Coordination Act) provide agencies (EPA and USFWS) with the authority to protect certain valuable resources. With regard to dredging activities, both agencies carry out their responsibilities through Corps of Engineers permit procedures. The Corps permitting process is used as a vehicle for implementing both national water quality and wildlife protection policies.

A.2.1 Performing Construction in Wetlands

Dredging or filling in wetlands is becoming increasingly difficult. A 1973 article reviewed cases and legislative hearings and suggested that the Corps' procedure for wetlands through considerations of environmental factors.[10]

The Corps' regulations discuss factors to consider if the proposed work will alter wetlands, stating generally that

> As environmentally vital areas, they [wetlands] constitute a productive and valuable resource, the unnecessary alteration or destruction of which should be discouraged as contrary to the public interest.

Certain functions that wetlands perform are considered to be important to the public interest; therefore, alteration of wetlands performing these functions should be forbidden unless it is shown that the benefits outweigh the damage to the wetlands and that the benefits cannot be realized without altering the wetlands. The applicant must provide sufficient data so that the feasibility of alternative sites can be evaluated. The cumulative effect of piecemeal changes must also be considered.

Because of the concern for wetlands, the Corps in 1974 and again in 1985 denied a dredging permit to two projects at Marco Island, Florida. The projects involved residential housing, and there was no demonstration that either no other sites or no construction alternatives existed that would fulfill the basic purpose, the provision of shelter.

In light of the policy of the Corps and Congress, the regulations

[10]Kramon, L. "Section 10 of the Rivers and Harbors Act: The Emergence of a New Protection for Tidal Marshes" 33 Maryland Law Review. 229 (1973).

conclude by stating that great weight will be given to state programs for protecting wetlands. The Corps' policy referenced is that permits will not be granted to projects that require other federal, state, or local authorization that has been denied. The congressional policy referenced to was contained in a law authorizing a study of the nation's estuaries so as to balance protection of estuaries as national resources against the need to develop them to further the nation's growth. Congress declared that its policy was "to recognize, preserve, and protect the responsibilities of the states in protecting, conserving, and restoring the estuaries in the United States."

According to a 1974 Senate study, 14 states have also acted to protect wetlands from land uses that will injure the wetlands. This is primarily a local issue varying with the state laws and is not discussed further at this point. Yet many states have introduced protective legislation for wetlands in recent years.

A.2.2 Deep-Water Port Construction

The construction and operation of deep-water ports for oil are regulated under the Deep Water Ports Act of 1974. This act provides that the department of transportation (DOT) will issue licenses for the construction and operation of such ports. An application to DOT will constitute the application for all other federal authorizations. This means that the Corps will get notice of the application from DOT; thereafter, the Corps will determine whether to issue an ocean-dumping permit if fill material is to be deposited. Hearings are to be "consolidated insofar as practicable with hearings held by other agencies."

DOT is to prepare a single EIS for all applications in any "application area." The environmental criteria to be used in evaluating an application are to be established by DOT and must include:

1. the effect on the marine environment;
2. the effect on oceanographic currents and wave patterns;
3. the effect on alternative uses of the oceans and navigable waters, such as scientific study, fishing, and exploitation of other living and nonliving resources;
4. the potential dangers to a deep-water port from waves, winds, weather, and geological conditions, and the steps that can be taken to protect against or minimize such dangers;
5. the effect of land-based developments related to deep-water port development;

6. the effect on human health and welfare; and
7. such other considerations as the secretary deems necessary or appropriate.

The EPA determines whether a proposed deep-water port will comply with the Clean Air Act, the FWPCA, and the Marine Protection, Research, and Sanctuaries Act. If the port will not comply with these acts, the EPA may block the issuance of a license if the EPA notifies DOT within statutory time limits. The governor of any state connected to such a port by pipeline or within 15 mi of the port may also block issuance of the license. If a deep-water port proposal conflicts with plans to construct a deep draft channel and harbor in a port of a state that will be connected by pipeline with the deep-water port, the license for the deep-water port shall not be issued until the relative effects of the two plans are assessed.

DOT has retained some of the authority under the act and delegated the rest. Among the powers retained is the power to issue licenses, to approve fees charged by states for use of deep-water ports and directly related land-based facilities, to intervene in civil suits, and to recover for damages to natural resources. Delegated to the Coast Guard was most of the remaining authority except authority delegated to the Materials Transportation Bureau director to establish regulations for the safe construction and operation of pipelines on the outer continental shelf.

The Coast Guard has established regulations generally covering the application for and approval of licenses, with the environmental review criteria included as an appendix; the design, construction, and equipment required for a deep-water port; and regulations concerning the operations of a deep-water port. The Coast Guard also requires notice before site evaluation for a deep-water port begins and a report on site evaluation activities actually undertaken, including any activities that had an adverse environmental impact, at the conclusion of the evaluation.

A.3 WATER POLLUTION REGULATION

A.3.1 Nonoily Water Pollution

Under the FWPCA, there are two complementary approaches to water pollution control: definition of acceptable water quality for a body of water and elimination of discharges of pollutants into the water. These two approaches are exemplified by the two statutory goals (although achievement of the goals is not required): "swimmable" water by 1983 (water quality) and no discharge by 1985 (effluent limitation).

These goals are pursued by a somewhat novel federal and state partnership. Rather than dividing the responsibility on a federal waters versus state waters basis, the FWPCA permits each state to enforce standards that meet federal guidelines over all waters within a state's boundaries (including the sea out 3 mi). The federal guidelines ensure some uniformity and protect the national interest with respect to interstate waters.

The states set water quality standards for each body of water. An example is a requirement of no more than 1,000 fecal coliform bacteria per 100 milliliters. Once these standards are approved by the EPA, they are to be reviewed and revised by the states through public hearings at least every 3 years. Meanwhile, the EPA is required to publish national water quality criteria to be used in establishing and reviewing state water quality standards.

To achieve water quality standards, the discharge of pollutants into a body of water must be controlled. Two types of discharges are identified: point sources and nonpoint sources. Point sources are any discrete sources of discharge identifiable by virtue of some conduit of discharge identifiable by virtue of some conduit to the waterway such as vessels, manufacturing plants, and sewage treatment plans. Nonpoint sources reflect pollution caused by runoff, such as from agricultural land (water containing pesticides, for example) or construction sites. The two types of sources are subject to different regulation.

Point sources are not permitted to discharge pollutants except in accordance with a permit issued by the EPA or the state under an EPA-approved plan. The EPA will approve a state plan that ensures that the permit will comply with the FWPCA. After the EPA approves the state plan, the state becomes the permit-granting authority, and the EPA only monitors state performance with two devices: the ability to overrule the state on a case-by-case basis and the ability to rescind approval of the state program after a hearing. The EPA may waive its right to object to a particular application unless the application involves discharge in the territorial sea.

A permit under the FWPCA (NPDES) authorizing the discharge of pollutants will specify effluent limits. These limits might be in terms of pollutants per time period (such as $\frac{1}{10}$ lb of mercury per day), in terms of concentration of pollutant (such as no more than 0.01 parts per million of copper), or in terms of maximum discharge per unit of production (such as no more than 5 lb of suspended solids per ton of paper produced). Discharges of toxic pollutants in toxic amounts are prohibited. In addition, any permit for discharge from a vessel is subject to regulations issued by the secretary of the department in which the Coast Guard is operating that establish "specifications for safe transportation, handling, carriage, storage, and stowage of pollutants."

What this means to the existing point source was the use of "best practicable" pollution control technology by July 1977; achievement of effluent limitations on toxic pollutants by the same time; and use of the "best available technology economically achievable" by July 1983. In addition, the EPA was required to establish effluent limitations for 27 specific industries (none of which is related to ports) and for such other industries as are selected by EPA. These limitations now apply to "new" point sources (those on which construction is begun after the regulations were issued) and the regulations must require "the greatest degree of effluent reduction . . . achievable through the application of the best available demonstrated control technology, processes, operating methods, or other alternatives, including, where practicable, a standard permitting no discharge of pollutants." Thus if an existing port is a point source, it is subject to the requirements in its permit but not to special EPA standards. At this point, no regulations have been issued by the EPA concerning discharge standards to be met by new ports.

It is not enough to know the effluent limitations for a particular activity, however. If water quality goals cannot be met through existing effluent limitations, the direct discharger will have to conform to limitations designed to meet the water quality goal. Similarly, even if the water quality goal could be met at a higher level of effluent discharge, the discharger must comply with a more stringent effluent limitation level. Furthermore, under prior law covering water quality, the federal government adopted a "nondegradation" policy; that is, waters of better than required water quality were to maintain their high quality. The 1972 amendments say nothing specific about this problem, and as a practical matter, such a provision may not add anything of substance to the rest of the regulatory scheme. Nevertheless, as a general matter, it may be safe to assume that difficulties will be encountered in introducing a new source of pollution into waters that exceed established water quality standards.

If the port is not a point source but discharges into a publicly owned treatment system, the port is not required to obtain a permit under the FWPCA. The treatment works must obtain a permit, however, that provides for notice to the issuer (state or EPA) of a substantial change in the character or volume of pollutants introduced into the treatment works. The permit issuer may restrict or prohibit new tie-ins to the works. If the treatment works are federally funded after March 1, 1973, industrial users must pay a portion of the cost of construction as well as a proportionate share of the cost of operation.

Under the FWPCA, state or regional agencies are required to establish regulatory programs to control various types of nonpoint source pollution. Included within the list of nonpoint sources are construction-related sources of pollution. Control of nonpoint sources is likely to be on an ad hoc basis.

A.3.2 Oily Water Pollution

Oil pollution prevention and liability have been the subject of legislation and international conventions. Without attempting a thorough history, it can be noted that oil pollution control legislation dates back to the Oil Pollution Act of 1924, as amended in 1966 and repealed in 1970 by the predecessor of the FWPCA Amendments of 1972. Legislation inspired by the International Convention for the Prevention of the Pollution of the Sea by Oil in 1954 led to legislation in 1961; amendments to the convention led to the Intervention on the High Seas Act and the Oil Pollution Act Amendments of 1973.

It is necessary at the outset to discuss the applicability to vessels and to ports of the various acts relating to oil pollution because they are discussed here as a group. The acts are discussed in more detail subsequently.

One section of the FWPCA deals with discharges of oil or hazardous substances in harmful quantities. It deals with discharges into the navigable waters of the United States (not "navigable waters" as with other provisions of the act); this term presumably includes the territorial seas and discharges into the contiguous zone. It deals with discharges from vessels and from onshore or offshore facilities. It does not deal with discharges into the ocean seaward from the contiguous zone.

The Ocean Dumping Act applies to discharges of oil "only to the extent such oil is taken on board a vessel or aircraft for the purpose of dumping." This act regulates transportation from the United States or in U.S. flag ships for dumping anywhere in the ocean.

The Oil Pollution Act regulates discharge of oil or an oily mixture by ships and establishes standards for the construction of tankers in the United States after the act's effective date.

The Intervention Act permits the United States to take action on the high seas to prevent damage to its shoreline resulting from a marine disaster.

In addition, liability for the discharge of oil associated with a deep-water port is provided for by the Deepwater Port Act.

In discussing the pertinent section of the FWPCA, it is necessary to establish what constitutes oil and hazardous substances within the meaning of that section. According to the act:

> "[O]il" means oil of any kind or in any form, including, but not limited to, petroleum, fuel oil, sludge, oil refuse, and oil mixed with wastes other than dredged spoil.
>
> Also according to the act: "[H]azardous substance" means any substance designated pursuant to subsection (b) (2) [section 1321 (b)(2)].

Subsection (b)(2) provides that the EPA shall designate as hazardous substances those substances that when discharged into the water "in any quantity . . . present an imminent and substantial danger to the public health and welfare."

The president has delegated to the EPA both his authority to determine what constitutes a harmful amount of oil or a hazardous substance and his authority to issue regulations prescribing what discharges are not harmful.

What, then, are hazardous substances, and what discharges of hazardous substances are harmful? Beginning with hazardous substances, neither question has been answered. At the end of 1975, the EPA gave notice of proposed rule making with respect to a list of 370 hazardous substances. At the same time, the EPA proposed regulations concerning harmful quantities for each of the substances.

The penalties for discharges of hazardous substances are assessed only if the substance is determined to be not removable from the water. If it is not removable, the penalty may be either a single amount of $500 to $5,000 as determined by the EPA or an amount determined under a formula that multiplies the amount discharged by a dollar figure of $100 to $1,000. In the latter case, the maximum penalty is $5 million for discharge from a vessel and $500,000 for discharge from an onshore or offshore facility. In the case of any discharge of a hazardous substance, the person responsible for the discharge is entitled to the defenses applicable to liability for the cleanup costs for an oil discharge (discussed subsequently) in resisting the penalty assessment. For the 370 hazardous substances identified, the EPA has proposed determinations of removability and penalty rates for substances judged not removable. Presumably, the discharge of a hazardous substance judged removable is subject to the other penalty provisions of the FWPCA.

A harmful discharge of oil has been administratively defined to include discharges that (a) violate applicable water quality standards or (b) cause a film or sheen upon or a discoloration of the water's surface or adjoining shorelines or cause a sludge or emulsion to the deposit beneath the water's surface or upon adjoining shorelines.

A variety of penalties and liabilities apply to an oil spill. The person in charge of a vessel or facility that discharges oil or a hazardous substance must immediately notify the "appropriate" U.S. government agency or be subject, on conviction for failure to notify, to a fine of up to $10,000, imprisonment of up to 1 year, or both. The "appropriate" agency is the Coast Guard in Washington, D.C. The owner or operator of the vessel or facility responsible for a discharge is subject to a civil penalty, assessed by the Coast Guard after a hearing, of up to $5,000 for each offense. The commandant is entitled to consider several factors, including the gravity of the violation in determining the appropriate amount of the penalty.

Regulations "establishing procedures, methods and equipment and other requirements for equipment to prevent discharges of oil and hazardous substances from . . . [non–transportation-related] onshore facilities and offshore facilities, and to contain such discharges"[11] are established by the EPA. Similar regulations for vessels and transportation-related facilities as well as regulations for inspecting vessels carrying such cargoes and the cargoes themselves "in order to reduce the likelihood of discharges of oil"[12] are established by the Coast Guard. Violation of these regulations can result, after a hearing, in the assessment of a penalty of up to $5,000 by the EPA or Coast Guard, as appropriate.

The philosophy of the act and regulations seems to be that the

[11]33 U.S.C. § 1321 (j)(1)(c) Supplement IV, 1974.

[12]Executive Order No 11, 735 § 1(4), 3 C.F.R. 370 (1974).

discharger should attempt to remove the oil from the water. If removal efforts are improper or if the identify of the discharger is unknown, the government may take over the cleanup effort including, if necessary, the destruction of a discharging vessel. The government effort is coordinated under the National Contingency Plan. The discharger is liable for the removal costs; the owner or operator of an onshore or offshore facility is liable up to $8 million; the owner or operator of a vessel is liable up to the lesser of $100 per gross ton or $14 million. The discharger is not liable if he or she proves that the discharge was caused solely by an act of God, an act of war, the negligence of the U.S. government, an act of a third party, or some combination of such causes. If the discharge is caused by a third party, that person is liable. Similarly, if a discharge caused by one of the above causes is removed by a person, that person can be reimbursed by the government.

Because a vessel may be the cause of a discharge and be subjected to liability for removal costs, the owner or operator of a vessel must establish financial responsibility up to the lesser of $100 per gross ton or $14 million. If two or more vessels are owned, financial responsibility must be established only to the maximum liability applicable to the largest of the vessels owned. The Federal Maritime Commission carries out this program. In addition, the secretary of the treasury may withhold the clearance necessary before departure for a foreign port from a vessel that has not established its financial responsibility or, if requested to do so by the commandant of the Coast Guard, from a vessel against which a civil penalty for a discharge has been assessed. The Coast Guard may deny any vessel entry to navigable waters of the United States or detain in port any vessel bound for a point in the United States if the vessel does not furnish evidence of financial responsibility on request. The Coast Guard is also entitled to board and inspect any vessels in enforcing the act or to arrest without warrant anyone violating the act's provisions within the Coast Guard's view.

Despite all that has been said about liability for oil discharges under this federal law, it may be only the tip of the iceberg. The act clearly provides:

> Nothing in this section shall be construed as preempting any state or political subdivision thereof from imposing any requirement or liability with respect to the discharge of oil or hazardous substance into any waters within such state.

The Supreme Court has ruled that this waiver of preemption is valid and to so hold is not in conflict with federal admiralty jurisdiction. Thus Florida did not lack the power to impose liability without fault for damage to its property or private property, to claim liability for state-incurred cleanup costs, and to prescribe "containment gear" for vessels and onshore facilities. The validity of the regulations actually enacted was not litigated, however. The Court suggested that aspects that conflicted with Federal law, rather than supplementing or extending it, might later be struck down. For example, the Federal Limited Liability Act would limit vessel liability to the "value of such vessels and freight pending."

The Oil Pollution Act Amendments of 1973 did not take effect until their enactment (which took place October 4, 1973) and the ratification by the Senate of the 1969 and 1971 amendments to the International Convention for the Prevention of the Pollution of the Sea by Oil in 1954 which was ratified in 1989. After the various amendments take effect, every tanker built in the United States will have to comply with the construction provisions of Annex C to the Convention. In addition, the amendments purport to require that, after they are effective, every tanker delivered after January 1, 1977, must also comply with the Annex C provisions. Whether the amendments can, if they become effective in the future, require compliance with its provisions based on actions taken prior to its effective date lies beyond the scope of this book. In addition the requirements of OPA-90 apply.

The act and the 1973 amendments apply only to discharges from ships. Other provisions, when they become effective, will prohibit charges unless the ship is en route, unless fewer than 60 liters are discharged each mile, and unless other limitations that are different for tankers than for nontankers apply.

The amendments continue the present requirement that a tanker keep a record book that remains the property of the government whose flag the tanker flies in which are recorded all activities of a specified nature relating to the cargo.

The Intervention of the High Seas Act was adopted after the Senate accepted the 1969 amendments to the convention previously discussed. These amendments were designed to clarify the international acceptability of a coastal state's intervention in the case of a marine disaster in international waters and were precipitated by the 1967 grounding of the *Torrey Canyon*. According to the act, whenever a situation creates "a grave and imminent danger to the coastline . . .

from pollution . . . of the sea by oil," the United States may coordinate and direct all removal efforts or undertake necessary salvage operations or remove and destroy the ship causing the danger without liability for damage except "damage caused by measures which exceed those reasonably necessary to prevent, mitigate, or eliminate that danger." Anyone willfully violating the act or willfully refusing to comply with orders given pursuant to the act may be fined up to $10,000, imprisoned for up to 1 year, or both.

Under the Deepwater Ports Act, liability for oil discharge is treated almost the same as it is under the FWPCA. Discharges must be reported to the Coast Guard, and penalties are provided for failure to report. The maximum liabilities for removal costs and damages are somewhat greater than those under the Oil Pollution Act Amendments: for vessels, the lesser of $150 per gross ton or $20 million; for licensees, $50 million. Liability is imposed without fault except for the defenses of an act of war or the negligence of the government in establishing or maintaining aids to navigation, and there is no liability to a person for damages caused by the discharge if that person's negligence was the sole cause of the discharge. Financial responsibility to meet these liabilities must be demonstrated. A fund of $100 million was created, derived from a loading or unloading fee of 2¢ per barrel, which can be used for all cleanup costs in excess of the amounts provided for above.

As under the FWPCA, according to the Deepwater Ports Act, states are not precluded from "imposing additional requirements or liability for any discharge of oil from a deep-water port," although a person may not recover compensation under more than one state or federal law. Presumably in recognition that the various laws relating to liability for oil discharges (including liability for activities on the outer continental shelf) are not uniform, the attorney general was directed to study the feasibility of a uniform law.

Under provisions of the Ports and Waterways Safety Act of 1972, the Coast Guard may establish regulations for the protection of the marine environment relating to the design, construction, and operation of vessels that carry onboard liquid cargo in bulk that is inflammable, oil, or a hazardous substance under the FWPCA. These regulations are to be effective not later than June 20, 1974, for vessels in the domestic trade and not later than January 1, 1976, with respect to foreign and U.S. flag vessels in the U.S. foreign trade, unless similar regulations are issued before that time and are consistent with an international treaty, convention, or agreement that has goals similar to the act's goals. Congress was reluctant to take unilateral action in establishing standards and therefore left the door open establishing regulations consistent with multilateral standards. Since then, and particularly after the *Exxon Valdez* disaster in 1989, the Congress has taken a more proactive approach, which finally led to OPA-90.

This rather extended introduction into efforts to eliminate discharges of oil into the water is only intended to suggest that regulation in areas other than port development may help reduce the adverse environmental effects associated with port development.

As an indication of the continuing international efforts to abate oil discharges from ships, the following paragraphs are quoted from a 1975 study by the Office of Technology Assessment.[13]

> To serve as the institutional mechanism for establishing worldwide vessel standards, the Intergovernmental Maritime Consultative Organization (IMCO) was founded in 1959 under the auspices of the United Nations. Since its inception, IMCO has been primarily a maritime nation agency dealing with technical maritime problems. The costs of IMCO administration are divided among the maritime nations according to the tonnage of vessels flying each nation's flag. Non-maritime nations have a standing invitation to attend IMCO meetings, but few have done so and their voting power has not been substantial.
>
> The following international conventions developed by or under the jurisdiction of IMCO relate to vessel safety and pollution prevention:
>
> 1. Convention for Safety of Life at Sea, 1960. (General life saving requirements for vessels.)
> 2. International Convention on Load Lines, 1966. (Establishes load limits.)
> 3. International Regulations for Preventing Collisions at Sea, 1971. (Voluntary rules of the road.)
> 4. International Convention for the Prevention of Pollution of the Sea by Oil, 1954. (Operation discharge standards and prohibited discharge zones; amended 1962, 1969 and 1971; amendments not yet in force.)
> 5. International Convention Relating to Intervention on the High Seas in Cases of Oil Pollution, 1971. (Right of coastal nation to protect itself from a disabled vessel carrying oil.)

[13]Office of Technology Assessment, Congress of the United States "Oil Transportation by Tankers: An Analysis of Marine Pollution and Safety Measures," 76–80 (1975).

6. International Convention on Civil Liability for Oil Pollution Damage, 1969. (Sets strict liability with limits for ship owners in cases of oil pollution—expected to be in force by mid 1975.)
7. Convention on the Establishment of an International Fund for Compensation for Oil Pollution Damage, 1971. (Creates an international fund to cover oil pollution damages beyond the liability of the ship owner up to about $36 million—not yet in force.)
8. International Convention for Prevention of Pollution from Ships, 1973. (New discharge and construction standard treaty for all polluting substances designed to substitute for the 1954 Convention—not yet in force.)

International efforts to strictly control vessel-source pollution were actually initiated at the behest of the United States. A conference on the subject convened in 1926 in Washington, DC, but a U.S. proposal for a total prohibition of oil discharges from ships was defeated two to one. It was not until 1954 that a convention was finally concluded—but without a discharge ban. Intentional discharges were merely limited and enforcement was to be carried out by the flag-nation, using penalties it determined appropriate. Nations other than the flag-nation could inspect the vessel's oil record book (mandated by the Convention) only when it called at their ports and, if discrepancies were discovered, they would have to request the flag-nation to take enforcement action.

The discharge standards and prohibited zones were made more stringent in 1962. The 1969 amendments (not yet in force) did away with zones altogether and limited the rate of discharge of oil even further. But the discharge standards adopted would still permit a 300,000 deadweight ton tanker to discharge a maximum of 20 tons during the course of any one ballast voyage at a rate not to exceed 60 liters per mile.

The 1971 amendments to the 1954 convention are more significant. For the first time construction standards were developed to prevent or minimize oil outflow in the event of an accident. These requirements restrict cargo tank size as a means of limiting maximum oil outflow resulting from a tanker collision or grounding. Unfortunately, these amendments have not entered into force.

Although the recently agreed-upon IMCO Convention for Prevention of Pollution from Ships will, when ratified, substitute for the 1954 Convention, the 1954 Convention is still existing law for signatory nations on the subject it covers. However, the history of its enforcement is extremely poor, and it is generally viewed as being largely ineffectual in stemming the growing incidence of vessel-source oil pollution in the ocean. [The U.S. Coast Guard's EIS on the IMCO 1973 Pollution Convention described U.S. experience with flag state enforcement of the 1954 Convention. Of seven cases discharged during 1969–1972 and referred to the flag state, only two were observed to receive any action.]

In 1969, the IMCO assembly decided to convene in 1973 an International Conference on Marine Pollution for improving international constraints on the contamination of the sea by ships. Two years later, the Assembly further decided by Resolution A. 237 (VII) that "the Conference should have as its main objectives the achievements by 1975 if possible, but certainly by the end of the decade, of the complete elimination of the willful and intentional pollution of the sea by oil and noxious substance other than oil, and the minimization of accidental spills.

The IMCO Convention on Marine Pollution from Ships developed in London in November 1973 is the most comprehensive treaty yet on the question. Included are measures to control more pollutants than ever before and greater stress is put on prevention rather than cleanup and other post-accident measures. Briefly, the new treaty includes the following salient features:

1. regulates ship discharges of oil, various liquid substances, harmful package goods;
2. controls for the first time tankers carrying refined products;
3. requires segregated ballast for all tankers over 70,000 DWT contracted for after December 31, 1975 (but does not require double bottoms);
4. prohibits all oil discharges within 50 miles of land (as did the 1969 amendments);
5. mandates all tankers to operate with the load-on-top system if capable;
6. reduces maximum permissible discharge for new tankers from 1/15,000 to 1/30,000 of cargo capacity (note: no *total* discharge prohibition);
7. regulates the carriage of 353 noxious liquid substances with requirements ranging from reception facilities to dilution prior to discharge;
8. controls harmful package goods in terms of packaging, labeling, stowage and quantity limitations;*
9. prohibits disposal of sewage within four miles of land unless the ship has an approved treatment plant in operation, and from 4 to 12 miles unless the sewage is macerated and disinfected; and *
10. prohibits disposal of all plastic garbage and sets specific mini-

mum distance from land for disposing of other kinds of garbage.*

In the area of enforcement, the international legal status quo was modified to some degree. The flag-nation must punish all violations by the ship. But, a coastal nation has the right (as well as the duty) to punish a violation by a foreign-flag vessel occurring in its waters or to refer the violation to the flag-nation for prosecution. A provision giving nations the right to prosecute vessels in their ports for discharge violations wherever they occurred was defeated. Nations must also deny permission to leave their ports to ships which do not substantially comply with the treaty's construction requirements until such ships can sail without presenting an unreasonable threat to the marine environment. Nations which ratify the treaty must apply its terms to all vessels, including those flying flags of nations which do not sign the treaty, in order to prevent vessels of non-signatory nations from gaining competitive advantages. To settle any disputes, compulsory arbitration is a treaty requirement.

On the question of standard-setting authority, a provision was defeated which would have made the treaty provisions exclusive on the subjects it addressed. Consequently, there are no treaty restrictions on the right of coastal nations to set more stringent requirements within their jurisdictional waters.

As yet, the treaty has not been submitted to the Senate for ratification and complete international approval is not expected until later in this decade. This convention must be ratified by at least 15 nations which, between them, represent at least 50 percent of the total tonnage in the world fleet. (In that previous conventions required ratification by 32 nations, this represents a significant easing of the ratification process.) So far, only Australia has ratified the 1973 Pollution Convention. It is expected that this convention will come before the U.S. Congress for ratification in 1975.

The 1973 Convention by no means covers the entire area of pollution prevention from ships. In fact, the official end-of-Conference press releases notes that it "may not cover completely the problem of accidental pollution". IMCO is proceeding with additional work on matters not covered in the Convention: crew training, improvements of traffic separation schemes, development of effective methods of cleaning up, and other safety and pollution prevention measures.

*These features are stated as optional annexes to the Convention, i. e., a state could adopt the Convention with or without any of these features.

A.3.3 Marine Sanitation Devices

Another example of regulation of potential polluters that may lessen the effect on the environment is the regulation of marine sanitation devices. One section of the FWPCA sets up the federal regulatory scheme for these devices.

It has been pointed out previously that a vessel may be a point source. Strictly speaking, however, it must be noted that "vessel sewage" within the meaning of the above section is not a pollutant within the meaning of the FWPCA. Thus a vessel does not come under the permit program of the NPDES, and the only regulation of sewage discharge is under the specific provision related to marine sanitation devices. If a discharge of human waste meets the requirements of this section and the regulations, it is permitted.

Essentially, the law provides that if a vessel has installed toilet facilities, then the discharge (if any) from these facilities must meet certain standards. There are distinctions between existing and new vessels that are not pertinent here. The performance standards for marine sanitation devices are set by the EPA. These standards provide for no discharge in some landlocked waters. For all other waters, the device may retain, dispose of, or discharge sewage. If there is a discharge, the effluent must have less than 1,000 fecal coliform bacteria per 100 milliliters with no visible floating solids. The standards became more stringent after January 30, 1980, with an exception for some devices that were installed before then. A summary of U.S. regulary requirements affecting the oceans is presented in Table A–1.

The FWPCA permits a state to establish no-discharge zones applicable to other state waters if necessary to protect or enhance water quality. Such a no-discharge zone may not go into effect until the EPA determines that adequate facilities are available for the removal and treatment of vessel sewage. In determining that the pump-out facilities are adequate, the EPA requires assurance that the vessel sewage will be treated in accordance with existing rules and regulations of the EPA and that facilities will be able to service all vessels reasonably expected to require such services. A state may also apply for an EPA regulation (promulgated after a hearing) establishing a no-discharge zone. The EPA regulations suggest that no-discharge regulations will be promulgated primarily to protect fisheries, water supplies, or water recreation areas. Under the doctrine of preemp-

TABLE A–1 Summary of Regulatory Requirements

CAUSE OF POLLUTION	ACTIVITY REGULATED	AGENCY	STATUTORY AUTHORITY	REQUIREMENTS
Waterways construction	Piers and so forth in navigable waters	Corps	33 U.S.C. § 403	Permit required before construction
		Corps	84 Stat. 1823	Environmental assessment required
Disposal of dredged materials, deposit of fill	In navigable waters	Corps	33 U.S.C. § 1344	Permit subject to EPA veto and practical veto of USFWS
		Corps	84 Stat. 1823	Environmental assessment
		EPA	33 U.S.C. § 1344	1. Guidelines for Corps permits 2. Veto over Corps disposal sites 3. Regulation of disposal of contaminated spoil
		USFWS	16 U.S.C. § 661–64	Consults with Corps on permits regarding effect on wildlife
	In navigable waters, out to sea 3 mi	State	33 U.S.C. § 1341	No federal permit until it certifies to compliance with FWPCA
	In wetlands	Corps (?)	33 U.S.C. § 1344	Some doubt as to scope of Corps' jursidiction. See Section 6.2 of text. See also Subsection 6.2.1.
	In ocean (beyond 3 mi from shore)	Corps	33 U.S.C. § 1411	Permit
		EPA	33 U.S.C. § 1413	Issues guidelines for Corps' use in assessing effects
		Coast Guard	33 U.S.C. § 1417(c)	Surveillance to prevent unlawful transportation
		State	33 U.S.C. § 1416	No power beyond 3 mi; may suggest criteria to EPA for use inside 3 mi. Compare 33U.S.C. § 1341.

TABLE A–1 Continued

CAUSE OF POLLUTION	ACTIVITY REGULATED	AGENCY	STATUTORY AUTHORITY	REQUIREMENTS
Marine sanitation devices		EPA	33 U.S.C. § 1322	Performance standards
		Coast Guard	33 U.S.C. § 1322	Design standards
		State	33 U.S.C. § 1322	May suggest no-discharge zones
	Vessel sewage not "pollutant"		33 U.S.C. § 1322	
Oil pollution; hazardous substance pollution	Spill liability	Coast Guard	33 U.S.C. § 1321	1. Receives report of spill 2. Assesses civil penalty for spill from vessel or transportation facility 3. Inspects vessels
		EPA		1. Assesses civil penalty for spill from onshore, nontransportation facilities 2. Determines what is harmful amount
		FMC		Certifies financial responsibility of vessel owner
		Treasury		May refuse clearance to vessel without evidence of financial responsibility
		State	33 U.S.C. § 1325	State not precluded from establishing higher liability or other requirements
	Cleanup	CEQ	33 U.S.C. § 1321 and E.O. 11735	Establishes National Contingency Plan, to C.F.R. § 1510
		Coast Guard		Various duties under National Contingency Plan
		EPA		Various duties under National Contingency Plan

TABLE A–1 Continued

CAUSE OF POLLUTION	ACTIVITY REGULATED	AGENCY	STATUTORY AUTHORITY	REQUIREMENTS
	Other legislation		33 U.S.C. §§ 1471–81	Intervention on the High Seas Act
			33 U.S.C. §§ 1001–16	Oil Pollution Act Amendments
			33 U.S.C. § 1517	Deepwater Ports Act (Oil Spill Liability)
Other water pollution	Effluent limitations	EPA or state	33 U.S.C. § 1342	National Pollution Discharge Elimination System, permit program
	Construction and other nonpoint sources	State	33 U.S.C. § 1288	
	Ports and waterways environmental regulation	Coast Guard	33 U.S.C. § 1221	1. Safety equipment, traffic service equipment, and control of access to areas
				2. Investigation of incidents affecting, *inter alia*, environmental quality of port
Deepwater ports	Environmental impact	DOT	33 U.S.C. § 1503	1. Licensing
	Regulation	DOT and Coast Guard		2. EIS
				1. Approval criteria
			40 C.F.R. § 148–150	2. Design criteria
	Veto	EPA		3. Operational regulations
			33 U.S.C. § 1503	Certifies plan will comply with Clean Air Act, FWPCA, and MPRSA
	Veto	State		
			33 U.S.C. § 1502	May block nearby deepwater port

tion, it is likely that a state is prevented from establishing no-discharge zones except in accordance with one of the two methods above.

The Coast Guard establishes regulations "governing the design, construction, installation, and operation of any marine sanitation device."[14] The Coast Guard is also involved in certifying that a test device meets the performance standards. If a manufacturer chooses to install a device on a vessel after the effective date of Coast Guard regulations, the device must be substantially similar in all material respects to a certified test device. No state may adopt or enforce regulations concerning the "design, manufacture, or installation or use of any marine sanitation device."

This is not a particularly comprehensive regulatory scheme. There is no requirement that a vessel be outfitted with a marine sanitation device, presumably to prevent a requirement for such a device in a boat in which it would be wholly inappropriate. Any device newly installed must conform to regulations that may include the ability to retain vessel sewage. But there is not really a federal requirement that pump-out facilities be provided. Of course, it would be in a state's interest to require pump-out facilities so as to qualify for a no-discharge zone, but there is no national requirement that pump-out facilities be provided. If pump-out facilities are provided, adequate treatment, which may well be superior to shipboard treatment, must be provided. This is the point at which the rest of the FWPCA could impinge on a port. If, for some reason, the port seeks to discharge the vessel sewage into the water, it will need a permit under the NPDES, even though the vessel did not. If the port desires to pass the sewage on to a municipal treatment plant, the port will have to make sure that there is treatment capacity for the additional load.

A.4 PORTS AND WATERWAY SAFETY

Under Title I of the Ports and Waterways Safety Act of 1972, certain aspects of port operations may be affected by Coast Guard regulations promulgated in the interests of avoiding vessel damage, damage to structures, or environmental damage. The Coast Guard may

[14]Section 312 of the FWPCA as amended and 33 U.S.C. § 1322 delegated to the commandant of the Coast Guard.

1. establish vessel traffic services;
2. require vessels to carry equipment necessary to use vessel traffic services;
3. control vessel traffic in hazardous areas or under hazardous conditions;
4. prescribe minimum safety equipment for structures; and
5. limit or control access to areas to protect vessels, structures, waters, or shore areas.

The act is not designed to modify any treaty. State regulations are preempted except for regulations prescribing higher safety equipment standards for structures, but the Coast Guard regulations may incorporate regulations issued by the port or other state or local authorities.

In issuing regulations under the act, the Coast Guard is to take into account environmental factors, among others, and the comments of environmental groups among others. If there is an incident involving damage to vessels or structures or affecting the safety or environmental quality of navigable waters of the United States, the Coast Guard is authorized to investigate.

The Coast Guard then has been given rather broad authority to prescribe equipment for ports and vessels in the interest of navigational safety and the environment; rules and regulations for the same purposes may be established; and investigations of incidents affecting those purposes may be conducted. How broadly this act will be construed as a mandate to establish equipment requirements solely for the purpose of preventing environmental damage is not clear. It seems highly probable, however, that any but the most trivial regulations established solely for the purpose of protecting the environment will be attacked as being contrary to the Coast Guard's historic role of protecting the safety and navigability of the waters of the United States. Such an attack seems certain to fail. But any onerous requirements would probably fail in a court challenge if the Coast Guard had failed to consider, as is required, the "economic impact and effects" of such regulations.

A.5 FEDERAL AIR POLLUTION LAW

Development of a port might have an impact on the quality of the air in its vicinity, but federal air pollution law has little that would directly affect port siting or operations. This could change at any time as a matter of either legislative or administrative action, although in the near term, any effective constraints will be imposed by state governments. Still, some introduction to federal law is necessary to understand the type of state regulation it has sought to require. Although this description is an oversimplification, the Clean Air Act of 1970 sought to set national standards of air quality to be met within a certain time frame, but to be implemented by the states in the case of individual polluters and polluting situations.

A brief, selective view of its provisions is in order. The provisions relating to moving sources are ignored as they are largely concerned with automobile emissions.

Each state has primary responsibility for air quality within its borders. This responsibility is to be discharged by submitting an implementation plan to specify the manner of achieving the national primary and secondary ambient air quality standards within each state. The EPA lists pollutants that have an "adverse effect on public health or welfare" and thereafter determines the national primary ("requisite to protect the public health") and secondary ("requisite to protect the public welfare from any known or anticipated adverse effects associated with the presence of such air pollutant in the ambient air") ambient air quality standards for each pollutant on the list. Each state then adopts a plan, subject to EPA approval, that will attain the primary standards within 3 years of the plan's approval and the secondary standards within a reasonable time. If the plan meets eight statutory criteria, the plan is to be approved by the EPA. In addition, the EPA adopts lists of categories of stationary sources of pollution and prescribes for new sources in the listed categories standards of performance based on, according to the act, the "best system of emission reduction which . . . has been adequately demonstrated." Each state may implement these standards. Each state may also adopt a plan of emission standards with respect to pollutants other than those listed by the EPA if emitted by an existing source that if it were an EPA-listed new source, would be under the "new source" regulations. The EPA also sets emission standards for hazardous pollutants that are, roughly, those contributing to an increase in mortality or incapacitating illness. States may enforce any other measure for pollution control, although any such emission standards must be more stringent than the standard in a state's implementation plan or the federal standard for new stationary sources or hazardous pollutants.

To recap, the EPA lists pollutants and then sets the concentration of pollutants allowed in the air (ambient standards). It is up to each state (or the EPA, if a state is recalcitrant) to establish a plan to achieve EPA-set levels of ambient air quality and to enforce the plan. The state may establish emissions standards as a facet of the plan. The EPA normally sets emissions standards only for

1. new stationary sources, which must be of a category of source previously identified by the EPA (such as cement plants); and
2. hazardous pollutants emitted by any source.

It should also be noted that the new development may be restricted not only by the "new stationary source" regulations (if of a listed category) but also by the "nondegradation" policy of the act. The act states that one of its purposes is to "protect and enhance the quality of the nation's air resources so as to promote the public health and welfare and the productive capacity of its population." The nondegradation policy means that air of higher quality than the national standards may not be degraded to the limit imposed by the national standards. After a court suit affirmed this as a policy of the 1970 act, the EPA adopted regulations that limit a state's ability to allow degradation. If ambient air quality standards are already being exceeded, a state implementation plan (SIP) might deny a construction permit for a stationary source that would meet emissions standards (although this would mean that some pollutants would still be emitted) because allowing construction (allowing even limited emission of pollutants) might make it more difficult for the state to meet the required ambient air quality. This may be true whether or not the source is an EPA-designated "new source."

The current national ambient air quality standards (NAAQS) are in terms of six pollutants: sulfur dioxide (SO_2), particulates (100 to 0.1 microns in diameter), carbon monoxide (CO), oxides of nitrogen (NO_x), hydrocarbons (HC), and photochemical oxidant (O_x). Emission standards for hazardous pollutants have been promulgated for asbestos, beryllium, and mercury.

Various new stationary sources have been designated by the EPA. None of them covers port activities explicitly. A few of these sources, however, involve activities that might take place in a port. For example, new storage vessels for petroleum liquids of greater than 40,000 gallons capacity must utilize vapor recovery systems or equivalents. The regulation of new coal preparation plants might impinge on operations within a port from which coal is shipped. The definition of "coal preparation plant" is "any facility . . . which prepares coal by one or more of the following processes: breaking, crushing, screening, wet or dry cleaning, and thermal drying." If a facility is a coal preparation plant, the following processes are included among the regulated activities: "coal processing and conveying equipment (including breakers and crushers), coal storage systems, and coal transfer and loading systems." Gases discharged into the atmosphere from these operations may not equal or exceed 20% capacity. It should be pointed out that unless a facility meets the definition of "coal preparation plant" and is a new source, these standards should not apply. Nevertheless, the standards and measures to comply with them may become important evidence of technological feasibility if the emissions from these operations are regulated outside the context of coal preparation plants.

Regulation of other plants presumably affects the entire manufacturing process and not just the loading for shipment of the product away from the plant. Under the rationale indicated in the preceding paragraph, however, the means of complying with emission regulations used in a production facility may be considered feasible in considering the regulation of emissions in the shipment process alone.

The following are a few examples of the new production facilities currently under regulations extending to either loading or storage facilities: portland cement plants; asphalt concrete plants; triple superphosphate plants; and granular triple superphosphate storage facilities. In most cases, the emission of particulates is restricted by limiting the opacity of the emissions.

At present, there is very little of interest in the federal air pollution regulations of importance for port operations generally, except for the coercive impact on the states in their establishment of SIPs. It bears reemphasizing, however, that this could change at any time, most likely as the result of administrative action. The effect of the EPA's designation of an activity is that future installations would require the use of the best-available pollution control technology. Once federal law requires the use of such equipment in new sources, states might require the use of such equipment in existing sources.

Because the regulation-writing process could begin at any time, it may be desirable for port authorities and other interested persons to keep abreast (through the *Federal Register* or special reports put out by the Bureau of National Affairs, the Commerce Clearing

House, or the Environmental Law Institute) of developing regulatory policy. It is also important for these people to keep abreast of pollution control techniques as they become feasible.

A.6 STATE AIR POLLUTION REGULATION

When Congress enacted the Clean Air Act in 1970, it was actually amending an existing statute. There remains in the statute the congressional finding "that the prevention and control of air pollution at its source is the primary responsibility of states and local governments." That this is no longer entirely true should have been suggested by the quick sketch of the Clean Air Act. The present situation gives states complete freedom to do whatever they like about air pollution as long as they do the federally mandated minimum. Still, it is clear that federal power has not preempted air pollution control by setting minimum standards for state air pollution control. Thus it seems clear that any state or local air pollution control law may affect interstate commerce as long as it neither discriminates against interstate or foreign commerce nor disrupts any uniformity required in the regulation of interstate commerce.

Even with the effect of the federal requirements as a unifying factor in the development of state air pollution control laws, state laws differ considerably. This would make it difficult to study the laws of many states in depth. Therefore, only a quick overview of some of the similarities and differences in state laws for states on the Atlantic Ocean will be offered here. This is not intended to be an accurate picture of differences in the law; in some cases, provisions may have been overlooked. But after considering some relevant provisions of these states' laws, there may be a better appreciation of the kinds of specific restraints that need to be considered in any particular state. One final caveat is necessary. There is no consideration here of any kind of local restraint on port development.

Environment Reporter, the source of the regulations compared here, publishes state laws similar to NEPA enacted in Connecticut, Maryland, and Massachusetts. Another source indicates that New York, North Carolina, and Virginia, among the surveyed states, also have statutes of this type. These statutes would presumably require that any action by a state in approving the development of a port would require preparation of an environmental impact statement.

Of the states surveyed, only Maine is included in the statute-specific requirements such as the ambient air quality standards. The other states' laws tended only to define the authority of a state agency to issue regulations concerning air pollution.

Ships are explicitly included in the definition of sources of pollution in at least three states. All states regulate the opacity of visible emissions, measured either by the percentage of light obscured or by comparison with the Bureau of Mines' Ringelmann Chart. Four states explicitly include ships as sources to which the visible emission regulations apply; presumably other states could regulate the visible emissions of ships without specific mention. But Connecticut exempts vessels for transportation on water from the emissions standards otherwise applicable to moving sources. A fairly representative regulation forbids more than 20% opacity for more than 3 minutes per hour. Virginia exempts ships during dock trials, the lighting of cold machinery and getting under way, simulation of dock or sea trials, soot blowing, and breakdown (provided a report is made).

State emission standards for particulates are not applicable to ships in New Jersey. The SO_2 standards in South Carolina are not applicable to "ocean-going vessels actually engaged in . . . national or international trade or defense." The terms of other states' emission standards may exempt ships for a variety of reasons. Limitations on the use of high-sulfur fuel do not apply to ships in four states.

States also customarily regulate the emissions of fuel-burning sources. In some cases, the definitions suggest fixed facilities, not mobile sources (like ships) while stationary. It is not clear, therefore, whether the standards for the emission of particulates or other pollutants apply to ships while in port. Generally, these standards are only in terms of particulates. For example, Connecticut exempts mobile sources from meeting NO_x standards; New York exempts marine vessels from standards applicable to diesel-powered vehicles. Emissions of SO_2 are generally regulated by limiting the sulfur content of fuel sold. For particulates, the emissions allowed are calculated in terms of pounds of particulates per million Btu of heat input, with declining levels allowed as the heat input increases. Maine's chart may be fairly typical. At 10 million Btu per hour, 0.6 lb per million Btu may be emitted. Graphed on log-log paper, this amount declines in a straight line through 0.5 lb at 20 million Btu per hour to 0.3 lb at about 105 million Btu per hour. The standards apply to units producing 3 million Btu per hour or more.

The states usually seek to control pollution sources through registration or permit systems. It is customary to require new sources of pollution to obtain permits before construction or modification. It is also customary to require new and sometimes existing sources to obtain permits to operate. States differ in the length of the lists of exemptions. In Maryland, the state agency is simply authorized to issue permits if it chooses to do so. These permits to construct or operate sources of pollution are generally inapplicable to ships: either expressly, by implication because permits apply only to stationary sources or by inferences based on omission from the list of sources to which the regulations apply.

Turning to requirements that would affect the development of the port and its operation, it is much more difficult to determine whether permit requirements might be applied to the construction or operation of a port. The application of state permit requirements will depend on how comprehensive the requirement is and the extent to which ports can be found to be sources of air pollution under the existing law. No state law specifically mentions port operations. Therefore, the need for a permit would depend on the absence of an exception from an all-inclusive permit requirement or on some other inclusion under a general category such as "all types of commercial and industrial plants and works."

For example, in Delaware, construction and operation permits are not required for sources emitting 25 tons per year or less of any air contaminant unless the equipment used is involved in specified industries. This would probably exclude most port activities from general permit requirements. On the other hand, Georgia has one of the shortest lists of exemptions, although the list includes sources of minor significance as determined by the director. In Connecticut, sources emitting less than 8 tons per year of any combination of air pollutants are exempt. In Maryland, it would appear that construction of a port would require a permit to construct (because it does not fall within one of the exemptions) but not a permit to operate (because it does not fall within the list of installations requiring a permit). It should therefore be clear that no generalization concerning state permit requirements for construction or operation of a port may safely be made.

Another method of state control over pollution sources is the establishment of emission standards. This has already been suggested with respect to the visible emissions standards that might apply to ships. Port operations might naturally be a source of dust. Comparison of the states' regulations on dust emission reveals an assortment of potentially applicable provisions.

At least seven states define "fugitive dust" (or something similar) as particles emitted into the atmosphere, not through a flue. Of these seven, at least five states have regulations requiring reasonable precautions to control such emissions and include examples of control measures. Operations that are generally subject to these regulations include building demolition, transportation of materials, road work, and agricultural operations. Pennsylvania exempts "the stockpiling of materials," but Delaware indicates that such operations shall be conducted without causing air pollution.

A somewhat similar category of regulated operations in five states is the category of materials handling. In addition, three states regulate pneumatic material handling equipment, with New Jersey adding bucket and belt systems and requiring permits to construct and operate such equipment.

Other states, if they regulate particulate emissions from port operations as a whole at all, would probably proceed under the process weight formula applicable to unspecified industries. These formulas indicate the amount of emissions allowable for a given amount of production. It is beyond the ken of the author how these formulas could be applied to port operations. The process weight formula for grain elevators (Pennsylvania) is the only formula found that would apply to an operation that might be conducted in a port.

In addition, a state may require construction or operation permits for only certain kinds of equipment. As noted, New Jersey requires a permit for certain material-handling equipment. Operating permits may be required for grain elevators in Delaware and are required in South Carolina. South Carolina also requires a permit to operate a steam-powered harbor dredge.

Federal regulations exist for construction of new storage vessels for petroleum products with a capacity of 40,000 gallons or more. At least six states have additional regulations on the handling and storage of volatile hydrocarbons. Connecticut's requirements range over tanks with capacities of 250 to 40,000 gallons, equipment for loading facilities (transfer of 10,000 or more gallons per day in lots of 200 gallons or more), and facilities for separating these compounds from water. Virginia is similar, extending also to insuring that pumps have seals. Rhode Island, New Jersey, and Florida also have requirements to reduce emissions. Maryland requires an operation permit.

Finally, it should be pointed out that in at least six states, the local governments may also become involved in regulating air pollution. This presumably would only increase the nonuniformity of requirements.

Appendix B

Ocean Environmental Conventions and Agreements

B.1 INTERNATIONAL AGREEMENTS

1. *International Convention for the Prevention of Pollution of the Sea by Oil (OILPOL)*, entered into force in 1958, was the first international agreement on marine pollution. Amendments were made in 1962 and 1969 and entered into force in 1967 and 1978, respectively. The convention applies only to persistent petroleum oils, that is, crude, fuel, heavy, diesel, and lubricating oils.
2. *International Convention for the Prevention of Pollution from Ships, 1973, as amended in 1978 (MARPOL 73/78)*. This convention entered into force in October 1963 and is the first to regulate all forms of marine pollution from ships, except dumping.

Abstracted from: Hans Peters, "Marine Pollution in the Mediterranean," World Bank Report, 1990; and IMO reports.

3. *International Convention Relating to Intervention on the High Seas in Cases of Oil Pollution Casualties (1969).* This convention, which entered into force in 1975, gives a coastal state the right to intervene on the high seas only after a casualty has occurred and there is grave and imminent danger of pollution to its coastline, territorial waters, or related interests. According to the convention, a coastal state may take such action, as is necessary, to avoid a pollution danger after having first consulted the flag state of the vessel concerned. This convention legitimizes contingency plans that coastal states develop to deal with marine pollution disasters.

4. *Protocol Relating to Intervention on the High Seas in Cases of Marine Pollution by Substances Other Than Oil (1973).* This protocol to the 1969 convention entered into force in March 1983 and extends the provisions of that convention to the threat of pollution by substances other than oil.

5. *Convention for the Prevention of Marine Pollution by Dumping of Wastes and Other Matter (London Dumping Convention, 1972)* . This convention entered into force in September 1975 and deals with dumping on a global basis. Contracting states are required to apply a licensing system to any waste dumped at sea from vessels or aircraft. Before clearance is given, authorities should give careful consideration to environmental effects. Normal discharges from vessels are excluded, but all other conventional wastes are included, although special exemption is available for abnormal circumstances, such as those due to stress of weather or when the safety of human life or of a ship or aircraft is threatened. The convention prohibits dumping, except in trace quantities, of certain substances deemed to be toxic, persistent and bioaccumulative, such as crude oil, fuel, and lubricating oils, radioactive waste, and industrial wastes. Licenses to dump waste at sea must contain information about the characteristics and quantity of the wastes to be dumped and may also specify the site and method of dumping.

6. *Convention for the Safety of Life at Sea (SOLAS) of 1974, as amended in 1981, and the 1978 Protocol.* This convention entered into force in May 1980 and establishes minimum standards for the construction, equipment, and operation of

ships, such as provisions regulating fire protection, lifesaving equipment, and safety of navigation. States are responsible for ensuring that ships under their flags comply with the requirements of the convention, and various certificates are prescribed as proof that this has been done. Contracting parties can inspect ships of other contracting states if there is reason to believe that a ship does not comply with the requirements of the convention. The 1978 protocol, which entered into force in May 1981, strengthens the provisions for ship inspection by including unscheduled inspections and mandatory annual surveys. The 1981 amendments, which entered into force in September 1984, involve major changes and technical aspects covered by the original convention that are designed to strengthen its effectiveness. A second set of amendments, adopted in 1983, came into force in July 1986.

7. *International Convention on Standards of Training, Certification, and Watchkeeping for Seafarers (STCW) of 1978.* This convention entered into force in April 1984 and is the first attempt to establish global minimum professional standards for seafarers. The provisions are especially important because it is generally recognized that the vast majority of accidental pollution is due to human error. The convention specifies minimum standards that contracting parties are obliged to meet or to exceed. Reasonable standards had to be set to make the convention acceptable to most members of the international community.

8. *International Regulations for Preventing Collisions at Sea (COLREG) of 1972, as amended in 1981.* These regulations entered into force in 1977. They provide for the mandatory observance of traffic separation schemes adopted by the International Maritime Organization (IMO), the observance of which had previously not been binding. The regulations specify rules to be observed by the proceedings through waters where such schemes are in operation. The 1981 amendment to these rules came into effect in June 1983.

9. *International Convention of Civil Liability for Oil Pollution Damage of 1969 (CLC) and the 1984 Protocol.* The convention entered into force in 1975 and was adopted by the International Legal Conference on Marine Tonnage convened in

Brussels; the 1984 protocol was agreed at the diplomatic conference held by the IMO in 1984. The convention applies only to persistent oils. The shipowner is strictly liable, subject to certain limited exceptions, for pollution damage caused by oil that has escaped from a tanker carrying oil in bulk. In return for strict liability, and in the absence of fault or privity on the owner's part, the owner may limit liability to a sum set by reference to the size of the vessel concerned. Ships carrying more than 2,000 tons of oil in bulk must be insured against their maximum liability, and a claimant is able to sue the insurer, rather than the owner, directly.

10. *International Convention on the Establishment of an International Fund for Oil Pollution Damage of 1971 (Fund Convention, FC) and the 1984 Protocol.* The convention, which entered into force in 1978 with the establishment of the International Oil Pollution Compensation (IOPC) Fund, provides compensation for pollution damage additional to the sums available under the CLC so that, where CLC liability ends, fund provision begins. Compensation payable to victims was raised by the Assembly of the IOPC Fund during the ninth session, in October 1986, to a maximum of U.S. $60 million per incident. Liability may also arise under the fund in certain cases where the CLC does not apply, such as pollution damage resulting from natural phenomena of an exceptional kind.

The scope of the fund is governed by CLC provisions in that the convention relates only to persistent oil carried in bulk, to damage occurring in the territory (including the territorial seas) of a contracting state, and to preventive measures. The convention indemnifies shipowners for part of the cleanup costs incurred under the CLC. Indemnification may be denied if it can be proved that the polluting ship, with the owner's knowledge, did not comply with relevant international conventions on safety and oil pollution.

In addition to the two international conventions dealing with liability and compensation for oil pollution damage, there also exist two voluntary industry agreements providing for compensation; namely, the Tanker Owners' Voluntary Agreement Concerning Liability for Oil Pollution of

1969 (TOVALOP) and the Contract Regarding an Interim Supplement to the Tanker Liability for Oil Pollution of 1971 (CRISTAL), which deal with liability of shipowners and cargo owners, respectively. It is intended that these agreements will eventually disappear once states become parties to the CLC and FC. The 1984 diplomatic conference also established an international regime of liability and compensation for pollution damage caused by harmful and noxious substances other than oil (HNS). Consensus could not be reached, however, which leaves an important deficiency in applicable international law.

11. *United Nations Convention on Law of the Sea (UNLOSC).* This umbrella convention, adopted at Montego Bay in 1982, deals, *inter alia,* with all areas of marine pollution. Part XII of this convention does not only provide general rules that are supposed to be supplemented by technical conventions (such as, IMO rules on vessel source pollution and regional and subregional rules); it also provides for a far more efficient enforcement system than any other currently in force. The rules are based on flag state jurisdiction that are of limited value, especially in view of the flags of convenience vessels. UNLOSC recognizes flag state jurisdiction but supplements this concept by port state jurisdiction that enables states to prosecute vessels using their ports and terminals for offenses committed anywhere at sea. The importance of this new, progressive rule can best be applied if one analyses the level of prosecutions, currently undertaken by governments, for pollution offenses committed at sea.

Even in countries such as the United Kingdom, only a few prosecutions are undertaken every year. Part of the problem, of course, is physical; it is not always possible to identify a polluter. Even if a polluter can be identified, however, port states frequently lack jurisdictional powers to prosecute. Unfortunately, the Law of the Sea Convention is not yet in force and is not likely to become effective in the near future. The reason is opposition from the United States and some other countries (including the United Kingdom) to some of the provisions relating to deep seabed mining. There exists, however, a broad consensus on environmental provisions that could possibly apply as customary law, as was done with provisions of the convention relating to the 200-mile exclusive fishing zone.

B.2 REGIONAL AGREEMENTS

In addition to globally applicable international agreements, international law also encourages cooperation in the field of marine pollution prevention and control. This is based on the assumption that the necessary political will is easier to generate in a regional setting where states share similar, if not identical, interests and where geographic and other factors may render environment more vulnerable to pollution than that of the world's seas at large. The MARPOL Convention designated the Mediterranean as a "special area". Moreover, the Mediterranean was the first sea in which the U.N. Environment Program (UNEP) became involved through its Regional Seas Program. The other type of regional control of marine pollution applicable, *inter alia,* in the Mediterranean, is through legal instruments of the European Communities (EEC) [now the European Union, EU]. The EEC's competence in environmental affairs was sometimes questioned in the past because it was not expressly referred to in the Treaty of Rome. This is no longer the case, however, following recent revision of the treaty.

Convention for the Protection of the Mediterranean against Pollution (Barcelona Convention). The convention was signed by all Mediterranean coastal states (except Albania) in 1976, was joined by the EEC in 1977, and entered into force in February 1978. The area covered is the Mediterranean from the Strait of Gibraltar to the Dardanelles, except for the internal waters of the states concerned. The status of "special area," given to the Mediterranean Sea under MARPOL, implied that *no oil discharges are allowed anywhere.* The convention is a comprehensive umbrella document that UNEP subsequently broadly copied in other regional seas. Unlike the Helsinki Convention of 1974 for the Baltic (another "special area" under MARPOL), where coastal states acted outside UNEP umbrella, there is no mechanism to protocols that were adopted to supplement the Barcelona Convention. They include the following:

Protocol Concerning Cooperating in Combating Pollution of the Mediterranean Sea by Oil and Other Harmful Substances in Cases of Emergency. This protocol was agreed in 1976 and came into force in 1978. The contracting parties agreed to cooperate in dealing with emergencies in the region to reduce or eliminate any damage caused by an incident. They must also notify UNEP and any other state likely to be affected. Under the protocol, UNEP has established, in cooperation with the IMO, a Regional Oil Combating Centre (ROCC) in Malta to receive reports and to coordinate action.

"Dumping" Protocol to Barcelona Convention. Following the main provisions of the global 1972 London Dumping Convention (paragraph 9) and the 1972 Oslo Convention (applicable to northwestern Europe), this protocol prohibits dumping of "black list" substances and provides that "gray list" substances may be disposed of at sea only under special license from relevant authorities. All other dumping must have a general permit.

Protocol to the Convention for the Protection of the Mediterranean Sea against Pollution of 1976, and Concerning Mediterranean Specially Protected Areas of 1982. For the purpose of this protocol, specially protected areas are limited to the territorial waters of the contracting parties. These areas can be established to safeguard sites of biological and ecological value; breeding grounds and population levels of marine species and habitats; and sites of particular importance because of their scientific, aesthetic, historical, archaeological, cultural, or educational character.

B.3 EEC DIRECTIVES

The EEC instruments are not limited to the Mediterranean or to special areas as such. They are, however, the result of regional cooperation of a very special character and are the only example of what is generally called supranational legislative action.

B.4 SUBREGIONAL AGREEMENTS AND BILATERAL TREATIES

Only a few subregional initiatives can be reported. They are limited to the Adriatic Sea (Greece, Italy, and the former Yugoslavia), and to the Lighurian Sea (Italy, France, and Monaco). In the latter case, cooperation is more at the communal level along the Riviera coast. For the Adriatic Sea, the three abutting countries have drawn up agreements (Italy and Yugoslavia in 1974, and Italy and Greece in 1979) for sharing facilities in case of accidental pollution and to harmonize pollution control arrangements. The lack of political and other differences among abutting states, in these cases, encouraged cooperative agreements.

What are the prerequisites for translating global and regional legal instruments into national legislation, and how is the experience recorded? Contracting parties assume legal duties under relevant international treaties at the time of ratification. It is apparent that proper implementation cannot be assumed until international rules are incorporated into national legislation. The truth is, however, that many Mediterranean states have not yet translated into national legislation relevant provisions of global conventions and of legal instruments that are applicable to the region.

B.5 INSTITUTIONAL ARRANGEMENTS FOR REGIONAL MARINE POLLUTION CONTROL

Possibly the most serious constraints to effective marine pollution control at the national level in regional states are inadequate institutional and procedural arrangements. Complicating matters further is that a host of parties in the public sector are directly or indirectly involved. Quite frequently, coordination is poor and objectives are ill-defined. National laws establishing the role of the institutions involved are generally ambiguous, which results in debilitating conflicts. But most importantly and in many cases, national laws do not provide a plausible framework for organizing marine pollution control and abatement. Furthermore, the applicable global and regional conventions (see Chapter 6) have not been translated into national legislation. This observation also applies to cases where governments have ratified such international legal provisions but have then failed to take the necessary steps to amend national legislation. Unfortunately, this is a regionwide shortcoming among Mediterranean states.

Where regulations exist, they are largely ineffective because enforcement is very frequently poor. Polluters usually get away with no risk of being held responsible for what they have inflicted on the local marine environment. *These facts are at the very core of regional pol-*

lution problems. Governments commonly cite limited financial resources and lack of experienced personnel as the main reasons for this deplorable state of affairs. Although such arguments certainly carry some weight, there is, however, the undeniable first and foremost requirement to coordinate and harmonize the arrangements and responsibilities for marine pollution control at the national, provincial, and communal levels. Much can be achieved if such prerequisites are met.

Generally speaking, it is quite difficult to understand why individual regional governments are so slow in taking the required legislative and institutional measures, despite their openly expressed commitment to pollution abatement. In some states, proactive measures by the maritime community (Greece) have served to overcome public sector inertia. In other countries, a progressively growing popular "environmentalist" movement (Turkey) appears to be instrumental in inducing a government to take affirmative action. But the ubiquitous issue of organization and management continues to loom large in the Mediterranean region.

Appendix C

London Dumping Convention

ANNEX I

1. Organohalogen compounds.

2. Mercury and mercury compounds.

3. Cadmium and cadmium compounds.

4. Persistent plastics and other persistent synthetic materials, for example, netting and ropes, which may float or may remain in suspension in the sea in such a manner as to interfere materially with fishing, navigation or other legitimate uses of the sea.

***5.** Crude oil and its wastes, refined petroleum products, petroleum distillate residues, and any mixtures containing any of these, taken on board for the purpose of dumping.

6. High-level radio-active wastes or other high-level radio-active matter, defined on public health, biological or other grounds, by the competent international body in this field, at present the International Atomic Energy Agency, as unsuitable for dumping at sea.

7. Materials in whatever form (e. g. solids, liquids, gases or in a living state) produced for biological and chemical warfare.

8. The preceding paragraphs of this Annex do not apply to substances which are rapidly rendered harmless by physical, chemical or biological processes in the sea provided they do not:
   (i) make edible marine organisms unpalatable, or
   (ii) endanger human health or that of domestic animals.

   The consultative procedure provided for under Article XIV should be followed by a Party if there is doubt about the harmlessness of the substance.

9. This Annex does not apply to wastes or other materials (e. g. sewage sludges and dredged spoils) containing the matters referred to in paragraphs 1–5 above as trace containments. Such wastes shall be subject to the provisions of Annexes II and III as appropriate.

   NOTE: * Paragraph 5 was amended by the Fifth Consultative Meeting of Contracting Parties in 1980. The original text of paragraph 5 reads as follows: "5 Crude oil, fuel oil, heavy diesel oil, and lubricating oils, hydraulic fluids, and any mixtures containing any of these, taken on board for the purpose of dumping." The amendment entered into force on 11 March 1981.

ANNEX II

The following substances and materials requiring special care are listed for the purposes of Article VI(1) (a).

A. Wastes containing significant amounts of the matters listed below:

   arsenic
lead
copper
zinc } and their compounds

   organosilicon compounds
cyanides

fluorides
pesticides and their by-products not covered in Annex I.

B. In the issue of permits for the dumping of large quantities of acids and alkalis, consideration shall be given to the possible presence in such wastes of the substances listed in paragraph A and to the following additional substances:

beryllium, chromium, nickel, vanadium } and their compounds

C. Containers, scrap metal and other bulky wastes liable to sink to the sea bottom which may present a serious obstacle to fishing or navigation.

D. Radio-active wastes or other radio-active matter not included in Annex I. In the issue of permits for the dumping of this matter, the Contracting Parties should take full account of the recommendations of the competent international body in this field, at present the International Atomic Energy Agency.

ANNEX III

Provisions to be considered in establishing criteria governing the issue of permits for the dumping of matter at sea, taking into account Article IV (2) include:

A. CHARACTERISTICS AND COMPOSITION OF THE MATTER

1. Total amount and average composition of matter dumped (e. g. per year).
2. Form, e. g. solid, sludge, liquid, or gaseous.
3. Properties: physical (e. g. solubility and density), chemical and biochemical (e. g. oxygen demand, nutrients), and biological (e. g. presence of viruses, bacteria, yeasts, parasites).
4. Toxicity.
5. Persistence: physical, chemical, and biological.
6. Accumulation and biotransformation in biological materials or sediments.

7. Susceptibility to physical, chemical and biochemical changes and interaction in the aquatic environment with other dissolved organic and inorganic materials.
8. Probability of production of taints or other changes reducing marketability of resources (fish, shellfish, etc.).

B. CHARACTERISTICS OF DUMPING SITE AND METHOD OF DEPOSIT

1. Location (e. g. co-ordinates of the dumping area, depth and distance from the coast), location in relation to other areas (e. g. amenity areas, spawning, nursery and fishing areas and exploitable resources).
2. Rate of disposal per specific period (e. g. quantity per day, per week, per month).
3. Methods of packaging and containment, if any.
4. Initial dilution achieved by proposed method of release.
5. Dispersal characteristics (e. g. effects of currents, tides and wind on horizontal transport and vertical mixing).
6. Water characteristics (e. g. temperature, pH, salinity, stratification, oxygen indices of pollution-dissolved oxygen (DO), chemical oxygen demand (COD), biochemical oxygen demand (BOD)—nitrogen present in organic and mineral form including ammonia, suspended matter, other nutrients and productivity).
7. Bottom characteristics (e. g. topography, geochemical and geological characteristics and biological productivity).
8. Existence and effects of other dumpings which have been made in the dumping area (e. g. heavy metal background reading and organic carbon content).
9. In issuing a permit for dumping, Contracting Parties should consider whether an adequate scientific basis exists for assessing the consequences of such dumping, as outlined in this Annex, taking into account seasonal variations.

C. GENERAL CONSIDERATIONS AND CONDITIONS

1. Possible effects on amenities (e. g. presence of floating or stranded material, turbidity, objectionable odor, discoloration and foamings).
2. Possible effects on marine life, fish and shellfish culture, fisk stocks and fisheries, seaweed harvesting and culture.
3. Possible effects on other uses of the sea (e. g. impairment

of water quality for industrial use, underwater corrosion of structures, interference with ship operations from floating materials, interference with fishing or navigation through deposit of waste or solid objects on the sea floor and protection of areas of special importance for scientific or conservation purposes).

4. The practical availability of alternative land-based methods of treatment, disposal or elimination, or of treatment to render the matter less harmful for dumping at sea.

RESOLUTION LDC.23(10) GUIDELINES FOR THE APPLICATION OF THE ANNEXES TO THE DISPOSAL OF DREDGED MATERIALS

THE TENTH CONSULTATIVE MEETING,

RECALLING Article I of the Convention on the Prevention of Marine Pollution by Dumping of Wastes and Other Matter, 1972, which provides that Contracting Parties shall individually and collectively promote the effective control of all sources of pollution in the marine environment,

RECOGNIZING that the major part of the sediments dredged from the waterways of the world are either not polluted or may possess mitigative properties that diminish the development of adverse environmental impacts after disposal at sea,

RECOGNIZING FURTHER that the major cause of the contamination of sediments requiring to be dredged is the emission of hazardous substances into internal and coastal waters and that problems will continue until such emissions are controlled at source,

RECOGNIZING ALSO the need for maintaining open shipping lanes and harbors for maritime transport and that undue burden should be avoided with regard to the interpretation and application of the provisions of the Convention on the Prevention of Marine Pollution by Dumping of Wastes and Other Matter, 1972 (London Dumping Convention, 1972),

RECALLING that the Eighth Consultative Meeting by resolution LDC.17(8) adopted Guidelines for the Application of Annex III to the London Dumping Convention with a view to providing guidance for the uniform interpretation of the factors to be considered in establishing criteria governing the issue of permits for disposal at sea,

RECOGNIZING that for the disposal of dredged material at sea not all of the factors listed in Annex III and their corresponding interpretations are applicable,

RECALLING FURTHER that the Fourth Consultative Meeting adopted Interim Guidelines for the Implementation of paragraphs 8 and 9 of Annex I to the Convention with a view to providing guidance for the interpretation of certain conditions under which permits may be issued for disposal at sea of hazardous substances for which sea disposal is otherwise prohibited,

NOTING the discussion which took place within the Scientific Group on Dumping on the need to prepare specific guidelines for the application of the Annexes to the Convention with regard to the disposal at sea of dredged material,

HAVING CONSIDERED the draft Guidelines for the Application of the Annexes to the Disposal of Dredged Material at Sea prepared by the Scientific Group on Dumping,

1. ADOPTS the Guidelines for the Application of the Annexes to the Disposal of Dredged Material at Sea as set out here:

2. RESOLVES that Contracting Parties to the Convention when assessing the suitability of dredged material for disposal at sea shall take full account of the Guidelines for the Application of the Annexes to the Disposal of Dredged Material at Sea;

3. AGREES to review the Guidelines for the Application of the Annexes to the Disposal of Dredged Material at Sea within five years time in light of experience gained by Contracting Parties with these guidelines, in particular with regard to the application of the terms "trace contaminants", "rapidly rendered harmless" and "special care" as defined for disposal of dredged material at sea;

4. REQUESTS Contracting Parties to submit to the Organization for distribution to all Contracting Parties information on their experience gained with the above guidelines, including case studies;

5. CALLS UPON Contracting Parties to take all practicable

steps to reduce pollution of marine sediments, including control of emissions of hazardous substances into internal and coastal waters.

GUIDELINES FOR THE APPLICATION OF THE ANNEXES TO THE DISPOSAL OF DREDGED MATERIALS

1. INTRODUCTION

1.1 In accordance with article IV(1)(a) of the Convention, Contracting Parties shall prohibit the dumping of dredged material containing substances listed in Annex I unless the dredged material can be exempted under paragraph 8 (rapidly rendered harmless) or paragraph 9 (trace contaminants) of Annex I.

1.2 Furthermore, in accordance with article IV(1)(b) of the Convention, Contracting Parties shall issue special permits for the dumping of dredged material containing substances described in Annex II and, in accordance with Annex II, shall ensure that special care is taken in the disposal at sea of such dredged material.

1.3 In the case of dredged material not subject to the provisions of articles IV(1)(a) and IV(1)(b), Contracting Parties are required under article IV(1)(c) to issue a general permit prior to dumping.

1.4 Permits for the dumping of dredged material shall be issued in accordance with article IV(2) which requires careful consideration of all the factors set forth in Annex III. In this regard, the Eighth Consultative Meeting in adopting Guidelines for the Implementation and Uniform Interpretation of Annex III (resolution LDC.17(8)) resolved that Contracting Parties shall take full account of these Guidelines in considering the factors set forth in that Annex prior to the issue of any permit for the dumping of waste and other matter at sea.

1.5 With regard to the implementation of paragraphs 8 and 9 of Annex I to the Convention, the Fourth Consultative Meeting adopted Interim Guidelines (LDC IV/12, annex 5) which provide advice concerning the conditions under which permits may be issued for dumping wastes containing Annex I substances, and concerning the evaluation of the terms "trace contaminants" and "rapidly rendered harmless".

1.6 Notwithstanding the general guidance referred to in paragraphs 1.4 and 1.5 above, subsequent deliberations by Contracting Parties have determined that the special characteristics of dredged material warrant separate guidelines to be used when assessing the suitability of dredged material for disposal at sea. Such guidelines would be used by regulatory authorities in the interpretation of paragraphs 8 and 9 of Annex I, and in the application of the considerations under Annex III. These Guidelines for the Application of the Annexes to the Disposal of Dredged Material have been prepared for this purpose and, more specifically, are intended to serve the following functions:

.1 to replace the Interim Guidelines for the Implementation of paragraphs 8 and 9 of Annex I as they apply to dredged material; and,

.2 to replace *section A* of the Guidelines for the Implementation and Uniform Interpretation of Annex III (resolution LDC.17*b)).

2. CONDITIONS UNDER WHICH PERMITS FOR DUMPING OF DREDGED MATERIAL MAY BE ISSUED

2.1 A Contracting Party may after consideration of the factors contained in Annex III issue a general permit for the dumping of dredged material if:

.1 although Annex I substances are present, they are either determined to be present as a "trace contaminant" or to be "rapidly rendered harmless" by physical, chemical or biological processes in the sea provided they do not:
- make edible organisms unpalatable, or
- endanger human health or that of domestic animals; and

.2 the dredged material contains less than significant

amounts[1] of substances listed in part A of Annex II and meets the requirements of part C of Annex II.

2.2 If the conditions under 2.1.2 above are not met a Contracting Party may issue a special permit provided the conditions under 2.1.1 have been met. Such a special permit should either prescribe certain special care measures and/or give limiting conditions prescribed by national authorities to diminish the pollution source.

2.3 The assessment procedures and tests described in the following sections are considered to apply equally to the interpretation of "harmlessness" (paragraph 8 of Annex I) and "trace contaminants" (paragraph 9 of Annex I) when applied in association with sections B and C of the Annex III guidelines.

3. ASSESSMENT OF THE CHARACTERISTICS AND COMPOSITION OF DREDGED MATERIAL

This section replaces the Guidelines for the Implementation and Uniform Interpretation of Annex III, part A, and provides an interpretation for the assessment of dredged material. It should be considered in conjunction with parts B and C of the Guidelines on Annex III.

---

1 Total amount and average composition of matter dumped (e. g. per year)

2 Form, e. g. solid, sludge, liquid, or gaseous

For all dredged material to be disposed of at sea the following information should be obtained:

- gross wet tonnage per site (per unit time)
- method of dredging

[1]The following interpretations of "significant amounts" were agreed by the Eighth Consultative Meeting:

Pesticides and their by-products not covered by Annex I and lead and lead compounds:	*0.05% or more by weight in the waste or other matter*
All other substances listed in Annex II, paragraph A.	*0.1% or more by weight in the waste or other matter*

- visual determination of sediment characteristics (clay/silt/sand/gravel/boulder)

In the absence of appreciable pollution sources dredged material may be exempted from the testing referred to in these Guidelines in the following section if it meets one of the criteria listed below; in such cases the provisions of Annex III sections B and C should be taken into account:

.1 Dredged material is composed predominantly of sand, gravel, or rock and the material is found in areas of high current or wave energy such as streams with large bed loads or coastal areas with shifting bars and channels;

.2 Dredged material is for beach nourishment or restoration and is composed predominantly of sand, gravel, or shell with particle sizes compatible with material on the receiving beaches; and

.3 In the absence of appreciable pollution sources, dredged material not exceeding 10,000 tonnes per year from small, isolated and single dredging operations, e. g. at marinas or small fishing harbors, may be exempted. Larger quantities may be exempted if the material proposed for disposal at sea is situated away from known existing and historical sources of pollution so as to provide reasonable assurance that such material has not been contaminated.

---

3 Properties: physical (e. g. solubility and density), chemical and biochemical (e. g. oxygen demand, nutrients) and biological (e. g. presence of viruses, bacteria, yeasts, parasites)

For dredged material that does not meet the above exemptions, further information will be needed to fully assess the impact. Sufficient information may be available from existing sources, for example from field observations on the impact of similar material at similar sites or from previous test data on similar material tested not more than five years previously.

In the absence of this information, chemical characterization will be necessary as a first step to estimate gross loadings of contaminants. This should not mean that each dredged material should be subjected to exhaustive chemical analysis to establish the concentrations of a standard wide-ranging list of chemical elements or compounds; knowledge of local discharges or other sources of pollution, supported by a selective analysis, may often be used to assess the likelihood of contamination. Where such an assessment cannot be made the levels of Annex I and II substances must be established as a minimum.

Where this information, coupled with knowledge of the receiving area, indicates that the material to be dumped is substantially similar in chemical and physical properties to the sediments at the proposed disposal site, testing described in the following section might not be necessary.

Where chemical analysis is appropriate, further information may also be useful in interpreting the results of chemical testing, such as:

- density;
- per cent solids (moisture content);
- grain size analysis (% sand, silt, clay); and
- total organic carbon (TOC).

In addition, there are several other parameters which may facilitate the interpretation of the behavior, fate and effects of dredged material (e. g. sediment transport, pollutant transformation, sediment mitigative properties).

Sampling of sediments from the proposed dredging site should represent the vertical and horizontal distribution and variability of the material to be dredged. Samples should be spaced so as to identify and differentiate between non-contaminated and contaminated locations.

---

4 Toxicity

5 Persistence: physical, chemical and biological

6 Accumulation and biotransformation in biological materials or sediments

---

The purpose of testing under this section is to establish whether the disposal at sea of dredged material containing Annex I and II substances might cause undesirable effects, especially the possibility of chronic or acute toxic effects on marine organisms or human health, whether or not arising from their bioaccumulation in marine organisms and especially in food species.

The following biological test procedure might not be necessary if the previous characterization of the material and of the receiving area allows an assessment of the environmental impact. If, however, the previous analysis of the material shows the presence of Annex I or Annex II substances in considerable quantities or of substances whose biological effects are not understood, and if there is concern for antagonistic or synergistic effects of more than one substance, or if there is any doubt as to the exact composition of properties of the material, it may be necessary to carry out suitable biological test procedures. These procedures should be carried out on the solid phase with bottom dwelling macrofauna and may include the following:

- acute toxicity tests;
- chronic toxicity tests capable of evaluating long-term sub-lethal effects, such as bioassays covering an entire life cycle; and
- tests to determine the potential for bioaccumulation of the substance of concern.

Substances in dredged material, when entering the marine environment, may undergo physical and chemical alteration that directly affects the release, retention, transformation and/or toxicity of these substances. This shall be taken into particular account when carrying out the various tests mentioned and when interpreting the results of these tests for actual or future dumping site conditions.

7 Susceptibility to physical, chemical and biochemical changes and interaction in the aquatic environment with other dissolved organic and inorganic materials

Contaminants in dredged material, after dumping, may be altered by physical, chemical and biochemical processes to more or to less harmful substances. The susceptibility of dredged material to such changes should be considered in the light of the eventual fate and effects of the dredged material. In this context field verification of predicted effects is of considerable importance.

8 Probability of production of taints or other changes reducing marketability of resources (fish, shellfish, etc.)

Proper dump site selection rather than a testing application is recommended. Site selection to minimize impact on commercial or recreational fishery areas is a major consideration in resource protection and is covered in greater detail in section C2 of Annex III.

4. DISPOSAL MANAGEMENT TECHNIQUES

4.1 Ultimately, the problems of contaminated dredged material disposal can be controlled effectively only by control of point source discharges to waters from which dredged material is taken. Until this objective is met, the problems of contaminated dredged material may be addressed by using disposal management techniques.

4.2 The term "disposal management techniques" refers to actions and processes through which the impact of Annex I or Annex II substances contained in dredged material may be reduced to, or controlled at, a level which does not constitute a hazard to human health, harm to living resources, damage to amenities or interference with legitimate uses of the sea. In this context they may, in certain circumstances, constitute additional methods by which dredged material containing Annex I substances may be "rapidly rendered harmless" and which may constitute "special care" in the disposal of dredged material containing Annex II substances.

4.3 Relevant techniques include the utilization of natural physical, chemical and biological processes as they affect dredged material in the sea; for organic material these may include physical, chemical or biochemical degradation and/or transformation that result in the material becoming non-persistent, non-toxic and/or non-biologically available. Beyond the considerations of Annex III sections B and C, disposal management techniques may include burial on or in the sea floor followed by clean sediment capping, utilization of geochemical interactions and transformations of substances in dredged material when combined with sea water or bottom sediment, selection of special sites such as in abiotic zones, or methods of containing dredged material in a stable manner (including on artificial islands).

4.4 Utilization of such techniques must be carried out in full conformity with other Annex III considerations such as comparative assessment of alternative disposal options and these guidelines should always be associated with post-disposal monitoring to assess the effectiveness of the technique and the need for any follow-up management action.

Appendix D

Ocean Mining Technology

Vast amounts of research have been devoted to the development of ocean mining technology. Basically, ocean mining technology falls into mechanical, hydraulic, and pneumatic or dual modes. It is furthermore divided by depth of application such as continental shelf, continental slope, and deep ocean as well as by type of technology for particular minerals that are usually distinguished by density, hardness, nodule or particle size, adhesion, separability, surface tension, and other physical or chemical characteristics. Some of the major mining techniques in current or potential use are listed in Table D-1, and the present status of mining technology for some of the major ocean mining resources is shown in Table D-2.

Although several techniques for continental shelf applications are available today for depths of up to 1,000 ft and prototypes or experimental machines for depths of 3,000–5,000 ft have been tested, none of them has been proven an economically efficient method for ocean mining. This situation could drastically change with an increase in world prices or availability of minerals. An important consideration is that all these technologies have been developed as iso-

TABLE D–1 Mining Techniques: Current and Potential Uses

TECHNIQUE	COASTAL SHELF	DEEP CONTINENTAL SHELF	DEEP OCEAN
Trailing suction	Sand	—	—
Hopper dredge	Gravel	—	—
Anchored suction dredge	Heavy minerals	Phosphorite	— —
Cutterhead pipeline	Sand	—	—
dredge	Gravel	—	—
Bucket ladder dredge	Heavy minerals	Phosphorite	Various
Drag dredge	—	Phosphorite	Various
Continuous bucket line	—	Various	Various
Underground mining	Various	Various	Various
Solution mining	Various	Various	Various
Pneumatic mining	—	Various	Various
Hydraulic	—	Various	Various
Subsea mechanical gathering vehicles	—	Various	Various
Submarine with suction or mechanical dredge	—	Various	Various

TABLE D–2 Status of Ocean Mining Technology

ORES	OPERATING DEPTH (ft)	EQUIPMENT TYPE	EXPECTED MINING RATES (yd³/h)	STATUS
Manganese nodules	3,000–20,000	Pneumatic	200	Experimental
		Mechanical	200	Prototype (3,000 ft)
		Hydraulic	300	Prototype (2,000 ft)
Phosphates	0–150	Hydraulic cutterhead	500–1,000	Prototype
		Mechanical	300–500	Prototype
	150–300	Hydraulic cutterhead	300–500	Experimental
		Mechanical	200–400	Experimental
Heavy minerals	0–150	Hydraulic cutterhead	500–1,000	Prototype
		Mechanical	500–1,000	Operational
Burite	0–150	Mechanical	200–500	Operational

lated mining techniques and not as parts of an overall ocean mining, enrichment, storage, transport, and extraction system. As a result, total cost to market of ocean-mined minerals, independent of source, is by and large noncompetitive and will stay so for a long time to come unless the problem is considered from a total system point of view.

Essentially all present technology or ocean mining technology under development now depends on surface platform support. This approach becomes increasingly unattractive at attempts to operate in greater depths. Even at continental shelf depths of 500–1,000 ft, it is an expensive method, largely because the concentration of minerals per unit area is comparatively small and therefore a mobile platform is needed to permit mining over a large area. This is different from offshore petroleum and gas production where wells tap into large reservoirs below the bottom of the ocean.

It is therefore necessary to develop submerged ocean-bottom mining platforms that can crawl on the bottom, gather minerals, and dispatch them to the ocean surface. Recent advances in submerged petroleum production platforms and autonomous underwater vehicles provide an excellent baseline for these developments. Such vehicles would usually be unoccupied and attached to an efficient mineral transfer system to a surface or subsurface storage vessel that in turn has facilities for transfer to a surface or submarine transport vehicle for transport ashore. Effective ocean mining therefore requires an integrated mining, lifting, storage, transfer, and transport system.

The components of such a system are defined in Table D-3. The selection of a prospective system depends on:

1. density of deposits and expected rate of production;
2. type and composition of deposits and method of production (mechanical, hydraulic, or pneumatic);
3. spread of mining area;
4. depth of water;
5. environmental conditions in mining area; and
6. distance of mining area to mainland landing ports.

The selection of an appropriate production transport system is therefore complex. Although it is expected that initially ocean mining will rely heavily on existing offshore platforms and ship technol-

TABLE D–3 Ocean Mining Transport Systems

TYPE	CONCEPT	PRODUCTION	GATHERING	STORAGE AND TRANSFER	TRANSPORT
1	Mobile production incorporating storage	Displacement ships Catamarans Stable platforms Self-propelled barges Barges	Not available	Same as production	Ore carriers Slurry tankers Hopper barges Tank barges Slurry pipelines
2	Offshore gathering platforms	Mining ships Barges or submerged production platforms	Stable platforms, anchored storage vessel, artificial island, submerged storage vessel	Same as gathering	Ore carriers Slurry tankers Hopper barges Tank barges Slurry pipelines
3	Artificial island ports	Same as above; stable platform, tower structure	Artificial islands	Same as gathering	Same as above
4	Direct production platform to ship transport and transfer	Displacement ships Mining ships Stable platforms Self-propelled barges	Not available	Not available	Same as above, excluding pipelines
5	Production (mining) ships that serve themselves as transports	Same as above	Not available	Not available	Not available
6	Direct slurry gathering and transport	Same as above	Submerged pipline network and Single Point Moorings (SPMs)	Temporary storage on production vessels or submerged storage tanks	Slurry pipeline or slurry tankers

ogy, it is expected that once ocean mining becomes a large-scale operation, specialized vessels of all types will be developed.

Initially, systems are expected to consist of floating production (mining) vessels, which also serve as temporary storage as well as transfer terminals, and conventional displacement-type transport vessels. Later systems may involve multiple stable platform or submerged platform production facilities connected by a rigid or mobile gathering system to floating, fixed, or submerged storage facilities. The materials would then be transferred to a terminal (before or after enrichment or refining) for loading onto ship transport.

No special transport problems, except those problems normally involved with dry bulk transfer between floating, or between floating and fixed, vessels in exposed, open locations, are expected. Special problems may exist in locations such as the Arctic and Antarctic where exclusive submerged production (mining), submerged gathering, storage, and transfer as well as submarine transport may be required. Such technology, although not yet in use, exists today and would take only a decade or so to perfect for reliable use.

Appendix E

Abbreviations

AMOS	Australian Meteorological and Oceanographic Society
AMTEC-J	Advanced Marine Technology Conference
ASO	Australian Space Office
CCRS	Canada Center for Remote Sensins
COFI	Committee on Fisheries (FAO)
ECLA	Economic Committee for Latin America
EEC	European Economic Community
EEZ	Exclusive Economic Zone
ESA	European Space Agency
EU	European Union (formerly the European Economic Community)
FAO	Food and Agriculture Organization of the United Nations
GNP	Gross National Product
HDMSA	Hydrographical Department of Maritime Safety Agency- Japan
IAEA	International Atomic Energy Agency

IAMAP	International Association of Meteorology and Atmospheric Physica
IAPSO	International Association for the Physical Science of the Ocean
ILO	International Labor Organization
IMO	International Maritime Organization
IOC	International Oceanographic Commission
ISA	International Seabed Authority
ISO	International Standards Organization
JAMSTEC	Japan Marine Science and Technology Center
JEFERAD	Joint Venture for Exploration, Research and Development
JFA	Japan Fisheries Agency
JISYA	Japan International Space Year Association
JMA	Japan Meteorological Agency
MSJ	The Meteorological Society of Japan
NASA	National Aeronautic and Space Administration
NOAA	National Oceanic and Atmospheric Administration
NOAA	National Oceanographic and Atmospheric Administration
OECD	Organization for Economic Cooperation and Development
OETB	Ocean Economic and Technological Branch
OS	The Oceanography Society
OSJ	The Oceanographic Society of Japan
OTEC	Ocean Thermal Energy Convention
SASPFO	The Society of Airborne & Satellite Physical and Fishery Oceanography
SCOR	Scientific Committee on Oceanic Research
STA	Science & Technology Agency—Japan
UNCLOS	U. N. Conference on the Law of the Sea
UNCTAD	U. N. Conference on Trade and Development
UNDP	U. N. Development Program
UNED	U. N. Environmental Program
UNESCO	U. N. Educational, Scientific, and Cultural Organization
UNIDO	U. N. Industrial Development Organization
WGP	World Gross Product
WHO	World Health Organization
WMO	World Meteorological Organization

References

Aganbegyan, A. G. "Restructuring Environmental Management in the USSR: Problems and Perspectives." Prepared for the Soviet-American Conference on Economic Instruments for Environmental Protection: From Theory to Practice, Sochi, Russia, June 1990.

Aggerholm, D. A. "Sediment Regulation in Puget Sound." *Proceedings of the XII World Dredging Congress*. Orlando, Florida, 1989.

Albaiges, J., ed. *Marine Pollution*. New York: Hemisphere Publishing, Taylor Francis, Publisher, 1989.

Allen, D. "Bench/Pilot/Scale Studies to Support the Evaluation of Remedial Alternatives for the PCB-Contaminated Sediments in New Bedford Harbor, Massachusetts." Presentation at the Technology Transfer Symposium for the Remediation of Contaminated Sediments in the Great Lakes, International Joint Commission, Windsor, Ontario, Canada, 1988.

Amaral, Mark. "The Changing Role of Today's Harbormaster." Rhode Island Sea Grant, April 1990.

Anderson, F. R., and others. *Environmental Improvement through Economic Incentives*. Baltimore: Johns Hopkins University Press, 1977.

APCC. "Options for Cape Cod's Future." *APCC's Growth Report.* Orleans, MA: Association for the Preservation of Cape Cod, January 1985.

Assessing Potential Ocean Pollutants. Washington, DC: National Academy of Sciences, 1975.

Barnes, R. S. K., and K. H. Mann. "Fundamentals of Aquatic Ecosystems," *Oceanus.*

Baughman, G. L., and L. A. Burns. "Transport and Transformation of Chemicals: A Perspective." In *The Handbook of Environmental Chemistry,* vol. 2A, edited by O. Hutzinger, 1–18, Berlin: Springer-Verlag, 1980.

Baumol, W. J., and W. E. Oates, *The Theory of Environmental Policy,* 2d ed. New York: Cambridge University Press, 1988.

Beristain, M. "WCBS News 88 Earth Guide: 88 Action Tips for Cleaner Water from the Tri-State Area Sea Grant Programs." New York Sea Grant Extension Program, 1990.

Bidwell, J., ed. "Oil Spill Clean-Up: An Economic and Regulatory Model." MIT Sea Grant Marine Industry Collegium, Opportunity Brief 25 (MITSG 81–6), 1981.

Blokker, P. C. *Proceedings of the 4th International Conference,* Antwerp, 1964.

Brannon, J. M., R. E. Hoeppel, T. C. Sturgis, I. Smith, Jr., and D. Gunnison, "Effectiveness of Capping in Isolating Dutch Kills Sediment from Biota and the Overlying Water." Dredging Operations Technical Support Program Miscellaneous Paper D-86-2, U. S. Army Corps of Engineers, Waterways Experiment Station, 1986.

Brautigam, S., and R. L. Robin, *The Way to the Sea: Methods for Massachusetts Communities to Provide Public Access to the Coast."* Boston: Massachusetts Coastal Zone Management, 1985.

Brooks, D. B. *Ocean Mining—Political Opportunities and Economic Consequences.* Washington, DC: U. S. Bureau of Mines, 1979.

Buzzards Bay Project, *Buzzards Bay Comprehensive Conservation and Management Plan."* Marion, MA: Buzzards Bay Project, 1990.

Carlozzi, C., K. King, and W. F. Newbold, Jr. *Ecosystems and Resources of the Massachusetts Coast.* Boston: Massachusetts Coastal Zone Management Program, 1975.

Champ, M. A., and P. K. Park, eds., "Marine Waste Management: Science and Policy." In *Oceanic Processes in Marine Pollution,* vol. 3. Malabar, FL: Krieger Publishing, 1988.

Chapman, G. A. "Establishing Sediment Channels for Chemicals-Regulatory Perspective." In *Fate and Effects of Sediment-Bound Chemicals in Aquatic Systems,* edited by K. L. Dickson, A. W. Maki, and W. A. Brungs, 355–77. Elmsford, NY: Pergamon Press, 1987.

Chase Econometric Associates, Inc. "The Economic Impact of Pollution

Control: A Summary of Recent Studies." Prepared for the Council on Environmental Quality, Department of Commerce, and Environmental Protection Agency, March 1972.

Christiansen, G., F. Gallop, and R. Haveman. "Environmental and Health/Safety Regulations, Productivity Growth and Economic Performance: An Assessment." Prepared for the Joint Economic Committee, January 1980.

Clark, J. *Coastal Ecosystems,* Washington, DC: Conservation Foundation, 1974.

Coase, R. H. "The Problem of Social Cost." *Journal of Law Economics* 3, (1960): 1–44.

Commission on the European Communities. "Draft Proposal for a Council Regulation Establishing a Community Scheme for the Evaluation and Improvement of Environmental Performance in Certain Activities (Eco-Audit)." Document No. XI/83/91—Rev. 4, Brussels, July 1991.

Congressional Budget Office. "Environmental Regulation and Economic Efficiency." March 1985.

Congressional Budget Office. "Environmental Regulation and Economic Efficiency." June 1986.

Convention of the International Regulations for Preventing Collisions at Sea, 1972. London: International Maritime Organization, 1990.

Copeland, C. "Bubble Concept of Pollution Control." Congressional Research Service Issue Brief No. ISB82007, April 1982.

Cormack, D. *Response to Oil and Chemical Marine Pollution.* London: Applied Science Publishers, 1983.

Corrillon, P. C., M. L. Spaulding, and K. Hansen. *Oil Spill Treatment Modeling for Georges' Bank.* Oil Spill Conference, Kingston, RI, 1979.

Council on Wage and Price Stability. "Environmental Protection Agency National Ambient Air Quality Standards for Carbon Monoxide." Report of the Regulatory Analysis Review Group, November 1980.

Couper, A., ed., *The Times Atlas of the Oceans. London:* London Times Books, 1983.

Crandall, R. *Controlling Industrial Pollution.* Washington, DC: Brookings Institution, 1983.

Cusine, D. J., and J. P. Grant, eds., *The Impact of Marine Pollution.* London: Croom Helm, 1980.

Dales, J. *Pollution, Property and Prices.* Toronto: University of Toronto Press, 1968.

Daly, H. E. "The Economic Growth Debate: What Some Economists Have

Learned But Many Have Not." *Journal of Environmental Economics and Management* 14 (1987):323–36.

Darby, M. P. "Productivity Slowdown: A Case of Statistical Myopia." *American Economic Review* 74, no. 2 (June 1984).

David, John D., and others. *Environmental Considerations for Port and Harbor Developments*. Washington, DC: World Bank, 1989.

Davis, J. D., S. MacKnight, International Maritime Organization staff, and others. "Environmental Considerations for Port and Harbor Developments." World Bank Technical Paper No. 126, Washington, DC, 1990.

Dawson, A. *Environmental Handbook for Massachusetts Conservation Commissioners*. Medford, MA: Massachusetts Association of Conservation Commissioners, Lincoln Filene Center, Tufts University, 1985.

EarthWorks Group. *50 Simple Things You Can Do To Save the Earth*. Berkeley, CA: EarthWorks Press, 1989.

Environmental Program for the Mediterranean. "Marine Sector Assessment." Working Paper 4, World Bank and the European Investment Bank, undated.

Faulkner, J. "Biomedical Use of Natural Marine Chemicals." *Oceanus: Fundamentals of Aquatic Ecosystems*.

Fay, J. A. "Spread of Oil Slicks on a Calm Sea." In *Oil in the Sea*, edited by D. P. Hoult. New York: Plenum Press, 1969.

Frankel, E. G. "Study of Collision and Grounding Risk in Confined Waters." MIT Report 91-002, 1991.

Fujii, J., H. Yamanouchi, and A. Matui. "Survey on Vessel Traffic Management Systems and a Brief Introduction to Marine Traffic Studies." Fifth International Symposium of Vessel Traffic Services, 1984.

Gambrell, A. P., Khalid, R. A. and W. H. Patrick, Jr. "Disposal Alternatives for Contaminated Dredged Materials as a Management Tool to Minimize Adverse Environmental Effects." Dredged Material Research Program, Technical Report DS-78–8, U. S. Army Corps of Engineers, Waterway Experiment Station, 1978.

Georgescu-Roegen, N. *The Entropy Law and the Economic Process*. Cambridge, MA: Harvard University Press, 1971.

Gerlach, S. A. *Marine Pollution—Diagnosis and Therapy*. Berlin: Springer-Verlag, York, 1981.

Gold, E. *Handbook on Marine Pollution*. Arendal, Norway: Assuranceforeningen-Gard, 1985.

Gourlay, K. A. *Poisoners of the Seas*. London: Zed Books Ltd., 1988.

Govett, G. J. S., and M. J. Govett. *World Mineral Supplies*. Amsterdam: Elsevier, 1976.

Grimes, M. "Air Quality Management Practices in Selected Countries." Congressional Research Service, Library of Congress, CP1341, 1981.

Hahn, R. W. "Economic Prescriptions for Environmental Problems: How the Patient Followed the Doctor's Orders. *Journal of Economic Perspectives* 3, no. 2, (Spring 1989): 95–114.

Hahn, R., and R. Noll. "Implementing Tradeable Permits." In *Reforming Social Regulation,* edited by L. Gramer and F. Thompson. 1982.

Haveman, R., and G. Christiansen. "Environmental Regulations and Productivity Growth." In *Environmental Regulation and the U. S. Economy,* edited by H. Peskin, P. Portney, and A. Kneese. Baltimore: Johns Hopkins University Press, 1981.

Hearn, K., and D. H. Cushing. *Massachusetts Water Resources Authority: Five-Year Progress Report.* Boston: Massachusetts Water Resources Authority, 1989.

Humphries, S. M. "Chatham's Changing Coast." *Keeping Current.* MIT Sea Grant College Program, 1988.

International Association of Ports and Harbors. "Dangerous Goods and the Port Environment." Prepared by the COPSSEC Port Safety and Environment Subcommittee, Tokyo, 1991.

International Association of Ports and Harbors. "IAPH Guidelines for Environmental Planning and Management in Ports and Coastal Area Developments." Prepared by the COPSSEC Port Planning Subcommittee, Tokyo, 1991.

International Association of Ports and Harbors. "IAPH Guidelines on Port Safety and Environmental Protection. Prepared by the COPSSEC Port Planning Subcommittee, Tokyo, 1991.

International Association of Ports and Harbors. "Water Pollution, A Concern for Port Authorities." Prepared by the COPSSEC Port Safety and Environment Subcommittee, Tokyo, 1991.

International Chamber of Shipping. "Tanker Safety Guide (Chemicals)." 1974. (London)

International Chamber of Shipping. "Tanker Safety Guide (Liquefied Gas)." 1978. (London)

International Chamber of Shipping/Oil Companies International Marine Forum/International Association of Ports and Harbors (ICS/OCIMF/LAPH). "International Safety Guide for Oil Tankers and Terminals (ISGOTT)." 1984. (London)

International Maritime Organization. "International Convention for the Prevention of Pollution from Ships with Its 1978 Protocol (MARPOL 73/78)." As amended, 1973. (London)

International Maritime Organization. "Guidelines on the Provision of

Adequate Reception Facilities in Ports—Part I (Oil); Part II (Noxious Liquids and Substances in Bulk); Part III (Sewage); Part IV (Garbage)." 1978. London.

International Maritime Organization. "Control of Ships and Discharges." 1986.

International Maritime Organization. "Manual on Oil Pollution: Section I—Prevention (1983 revised edition); Section II—Contingency Planning (1988 revised edition); Section IV—Practical Information on Means of Dealing with Oil Spillage (currently under revision).

International Organization for Standardization. "Guidelines for Auditing Quality Systems—Part 1: Auditing." International Standard ISO 10011-1, Geneva, 1990.

James, I. C., III, J. C. Kammerer, and C. R. Murray, "How Much Water in a 12-Ounce Can?", USGS Annual Report, Fiscal Year 1976.

Jeftic, L. "UNEP Guidelines for the Protection of the Marine Environment against Pollution from Land-Based Sources: Their Implementation in the Mediterranean." In *Proceedings of the Canadian Conference on Marine Environmental Quality*, edited by P. Wells and J. Gratwick. Halifax, Nova Scotia, Canada, February 28–March 3, 1988.

Johnson, S. P. *The Pollution Control Policy of the European Communities.* London: Graham and Trotman Limited, 1979.

Jones, Richard D. "In Search of Certainty: Industry's Efforts to Define Environmental Due Diligence." *ASTM Standardization News* 99 (April 1991): 34–37.

Kamlet, K. S. *Dredged Material Ocean Dumping: Perspectives on Legal and Environmental Impacts in Wastes in the Ocean*, vol. 2. New York: John Wiley and Sons, 1983.

Koba, H. Y., and T. Shiba, "Test Dredging of Bottom Sediments in Osaka Bay." Presentation at the 7th U. S.-Japanese Experts Meeting on the Management of Bottom Sediments Containing Toxic Substances. Proceedings published by the U. S. Army Corps of Engineers, Water Resource Support Center.

Kopp, R., and V. F. Smith, "Productivity Measurement and Environmental Regulation: An Engineering-Econometric Analysis." In *Productivity Measurement in Regulated Industries*, edited by T. Cowing and R. Stevenson. New York: Academic Press, 1981.

Lazor, R. "Comparative Studies of Disposal of Dredged Materials from Black Rock Harbor, Connecticut." Presentation at the 7th International Ocean Disposal Symposium, Wolfville, Nova Scotia, Canada, 1987.

Leschine, T. M. "Setting the Agenda for Estuarine Water Quality Management: Lessons from Puget Sound." In *Ocean and Shoreline*

Management, edited by B. Cicin-Sain, I. P. Jollife, and R. W. Knecht, Vol. 13, Issue 3&4, p. 295–313.

Lim, T. S. "Management of Navigational Channels." Ph.D. thesis, MIT Department of Ocean Engineering, 1991. Cambridge, Mass.

Ludwig, R. G., and S. H. S. Almeida, eds. *Marine Disposal of Waste Water.* International Association on Water Pollution Research and Control, 1986.

MacKnight, S., and others. "The Environmentally Sound Disposal of Dredged Materials." World Bank Technical Paper, Washington, DC, October 1989.

Magaziner, I., and T. Hout. *Japanese Industrial Policy.* London: Policy Studies Institute, 1980.

Mann-Borgese, *The Future of the Oceans—A Report to the Club of Rome.* Montreal: Harvest House, 1986.

Manrin, R. D. "Policy Control Options for Comparative Air Pollution Study in Urban Areas." Environment Working Paper No. 28, April 1990.

Manual on Oil Pollution, sect. IV—"Combating Oil Spills." London: International Maritime Organization, 1988.

Markandya, A., and D. Pearce. "Environmental Consideration and the Choice of the Discount Rate in Developing Countries." Environment Working Paper No. 3, May 1988.

Meyers, Robert J., and associates, Research Planning Institute Inc. "Oil Spill Response Guide." Park Ridge, NJ: Noyes Data Corporation, 1992.

Milliken, A. S., and V. Lee. "Pollution Impacts from Recreational Boating." Rhode Island Sea Grant, 1990.

Motiuk, I. Leo, and others. *Environmental Audits: Evaluating and Responding to Environmental Concerns*, New York: Practicing Law Institute, 1991.

National Academy of Sciences, *"Oil in the Sea: Inputs, Fates and Effects."* Washington, DC: National Academy of Sciences, 1985.

Office of Technology Assessment. *Wastes in Marine Environments.* New York: Hemisphere Publishing, 1988.

Office of Technology Assessment. "Coping with an Oiled Sea." Congress of the United States, 1990.

O'Hara, K., S. Iudicello, and R. Bierce. *A Citizen's Guide to Plastics in the Ocean: More Than a Litter Problem.* Washington, DC: Center for Environmental Education, 1988.

"Oil Spill Studies: Strategies and Techniques." American Petroleum Institute, Publication No. 4286, 1977.

Olson, Per H. "Environmental Protection, Port and Shipping Safety with Emphasis on Noxious Liquid Substances." Port Management and Operations, Port of Gothenburg Consultancy AB, 24 pp., June 1987.

Olson, Per H. "Reception Facilities in Ports for Residues and Mixtures Containing Noxious Liquid Substances." *Ports and Harbors* (1987): 19–28.

OPRC Convention. *International Convention on Oil Pollution Preparedness, Response, and Cooperation 1990*. London: International Maritime Organization, 1991.

Organization for Economic Cooperation and Development. *Economic Implications of Pollution Control: A General Assessment*. Paris: Organization for Economic Cooperation and Development, 1974.

Organization for Economic Cooperation and Development. "Trade and Environmental Issues." Committee Document No. 5 for the 31st Session of the Environment Committee, April 1982.

Oshima, K. "High-Level Radioactive Waste Management." Keystone IV Conference, Keystone, Colorado, 1979.

Pequegnat, W. E. "Analysis of the Impacts of Dredged Material Disposal in the Deep Ocean." Second International Ocean Dumping Symposium, Woods Hole Oceanographic Institution, 1980.

Pequegnat, W. E. "Oceanographic Surveys Required for Sumpsite Selection, Official Designation and Monitoring of Dredged Material Dumpsites in the USA." Third International Symposium on Dredging Technology, Bordeaux, France, 1981.

Pezzey, J. "Economic Analysis to Sustainable Growth and Sustainable Development." Environment Working Paper No. 15, March 1989.

Pillay, T. V. R. Opening Address, Proceedings of the World Aquaculture Conference, Venice, 1981.

Portney, P. R., ed. *Natural Resources and the Environment*. Washington, DC: Urban Institute, 1984.

Post, A. *Deep-Sea Mining and the Law of the Sea*. The Hague: Nijhoff, 1983.

Psaraftis, H., G. Tharakan, and A. Ceder. "Optimal Response to Oil Spills: The Strategic Decision Case." *Operations Research* 34, no. 2 (March–April 1986).

Quon, T. K. D., G. E. Bushell, and J. A. Laube. "Risk Analysis of Vessel Traffic Systems." *Maritime Policy and Management* 19, no. 4, (1991):319–36.

Raufer, R., and S. Feldman. "Emissions Trading and What It May Mean for Acid Deposition Control." *Public Utilities Fortnightly*, August 16, 1984.

Rawson, K. "Wither Maritime Safety." *Shipbuilding International*. Royal Institute of Naval Architects, (London).

Repetto, R. "Wasting Assets." In *Technology Review*. Cambridge, MA: Massachusetts Institute of Technology, January 1989.

Ross, D. *Opportunities and Uses of the Ocean*. New York: Springer-Verlag, 1980.

Sebastian, I., and A. Alicbusan. "Sustainable Development: Issues in

Adjustment Lending Policies." Environment Department Divisional Paper No. 1989-6, October 1989.

Shusterich, K. *Resource Management and the Oceans—The Political Economy of Sea Bed Mining*. Boulder, CO: Westview Press, 1982.

Systems Study of Oil Spill Cleanup Procedures, Washington, DC: American Petroleum Institute, 1970.

Thurow, L. C. "Feasible and Preferable Long-Term Growth Paths." Prepared for the Council on Environmental Quality, Washington, DC, 1979.

Tiner, R. W., Jr. *Field Guide to Nontidal Wetland Identification*. Annapolis: Maryland Department of Natural Resources, 1987.

Ullman, A. "The Implementation of Air Pollution Control in German Industry." *Policy Studies Journal*, October 15, 1982: pp. 81–129.

United Nations Environmental Programs, Industry and Environment Office. "Environmental Auditing." Report of a United Nations Environment Programme/Industry and Environment (UNEP/IEO) Workshop, Technical Report Series No. 2, Paris, 1990.

Volpe National Transportation Systems Center. "Port Needs Study—Vessel Traffic Services Benefits." U. S. Department of Transportation paper, 1991.

Wall, G. "National Coping Styles: Policies to Combat Environmental Problems." In *International Journal of Environmental Studies*, vol. 9. New York: Gordon and Breach Science Publishers, 1976.

Waters, J. M., Jr. *Rescue at Sea*. Annapolis, MD: U. S. Naval Institute, 1990.

World Bank. "Environmental Guidelines." Office of Environmental and Scientific Affairs, Washington, DC, 461 pp., 1984.

World Bank. "Environment, Health and Safety Guidelines for the Use of Hazardous Materials in Small- and Medium-Scale Industries." Office of Environmental and Scientific Affairs, Washington, DC, 43 pp., 1985.

World Bank. "Manual of Industrial Hazard Assessment Techniques." Office of Environmental and Scientific Affairs, Washington, DC, 99 pp. and appendices, 1985.

World Bank. "Overview of Port-Related Industries." Prepared by E. G. Frankel, G. Panagakos, and G. Mahnken, Transportation Department, Washington, DC, 379 pp, 1986.

World Bank. "An Analysis of Port Engineering Standards." Prepared by J. E. Clifford and J. Lethbridge, Transportation Department, Washington, DC, 128 pp., 1987.

Zedler, J. B., and R. Langis. "A Manual for Assessing Restored and Natural Coastal Wetlands with Examples from Southern California." California Sea Grant, 1990.

Index

A

Abassal ocean, 154
Abyssal plain, 11
Accounting:
  ocean environmental, 197, 205
Acidic wastes, 99
Aerobic bacteria, 163
Agar, 36
Air pollution, 92
Algae, 6, 37
Algae:
  poisonous, 96
Aquaculture, 13, 17, 19
Aral Sea, 2
Arctic Ocean, 10
Auditing:
  ocean environmental, 200
Authigenic minerals, 33

B

Baltic Sea, 2, 7, 8
Bedrock subsurface, 32
Biogenic hydrocarbons, 13
Biological oxygen demand (BOD), 163, 164, 349
Biological plants, 163
Biological damages, 3
Biotic factors, 11
Black Sea, 2

Booms oil:
floating, 136
inflating, 142
net, 141
Bottom fish, 27
Bulk carrier operation, 85

C

Calcareous oozes, 11
Calcium carbonate, 11
Capping contaminated mud, 152
Carbon monoxide (CO), 331
Carbon dioxide, 5
Caribbean, 40
Carnivorous chaetonats, 12
Carrageenan algae, 36
Caspian Sea, 2
Cause and effect analysis, 273
Certificates of Financial Responsibility (USCG), 185
CFCs, 5
Chicago Board of Trade, 233
Chlorinated hydrocarbon pesticides (DDT, DDD, etc.), 47
Civil Liability Fund, 161
Clean Water Act, 186, 333
Coastal development, 5
Coastal ecology, 6
Coastal shelves, 7
Coastal zones, 8
Copolymer systems, 262
Council on Environmental Quality, 301
Council for Environmental Quality (CEQ), 172
Crabs, 27

D

Debt swaps, 210
Deep Water Ports Act (DPA), 180
Department of Transportation (DOT), 310
Diarrethic shellfish poisoning, 68
Dionuclides, 2
Dispersant chemical, 145
Dolphins, 27
Double hull standards, 184
Double hull tankers, 167
Dredging disposal, 5, 86–87

E

East Greenland Current, 10
Ecology ocean, 8
Environmental Impact Statement (EIS), 172, 301
Environmental hazards, 2
Environmental Protection Administration (EPA), 173, 174, 176, 302, 315, 324
Environmental response planning, 193
European Economic Community (EEC), 161, 343
Eutrophisation, 4
Exxon Valdez, 296, 320

F

Faecal coliforms, 163
Fault tree analysis, 270

Federal Water Pollution Control Act (FWPCA), 173, 174, 176, 302, 315, 324
Federal Maritime Commission (FMC), 178
Ferric oxide, 9
Ferromanganese nodules, 33
Fish farming, 159
Fishery:
  production, 16, 29
  resources, 18
Flocullents, 164
Food and Agricultural organization (FAO), 19, 20

G

Gas production, 15
Geotechnical engineering, 156
Global positioning system (GPS), 5, 132, 224
Global environmental facility (GEF), 260
Gross National Product (GNP), 270
Gulf of Labrador, 11
Gulf of Mexico, 10

H

Heavy metals, 46
Helium, 9
Hemiphalagic deposits, 11
Herbivorous crustaceans, 12
Hydrocarbons (HC), 331

I

Industrial waste, 76–78, 91
Infectious agents, 98
Inorganic materials, 98
International Maritime Consultative Organization (IMCO), 320
International Maritime Organization (IMO), 125, 160, 167, 215, 239

L

Law of the Sea Convention, 12, 158
Lime shells, 32
London Dumping Convention, 165, 188, 346

M

Macro algae, 6
Manganese dioxide, 9
Mangroves, 117
Marine Environmental Protection Committee, 160
Marine Pollution Law (MARPOL), 125, 127, 147, 160, 165, 166, 169–70, 240, 342, 337
Maritime Safety Committee (MSC), 160
Mediterranean Sea, 2, 7
Metabolic dysfunction, 4
Metallogenesis, 41

Minerals:
ocean, 31
Mining ocean, 113
Mollusks, 20
Monitoring, 242
Municipal waste, 72

N

National Ambient Air Quality Standards (NAAQS), 331
National Environmental Policy Act of 1969 (NEPA), 171, 300
National Marine Fisheries Service (NMFS), 308
National response system, 183
Nektons, 12
Nitrogen, 9
North Sea, 7
Nuclear fuel, 4
Nuclear pollution, 159
Nuclear weapons tests, 4
Nutrients, 46

O

Offshore:
gas production, 15
oil production, 15
platforms, 15
Oil pollution, 2, 49
Oil Pollution Act of 1924, 173
Oil Pollution Act of 1990 (OPA-90), 125, 127, 166, 181, 185, 210
Oil slick spreading, 63
Oil Spill Liability Trust Fund, 182
Organic chemicals, 45
Organization of Economic Cooperation and Development (OECD), 69, 74, 255
Oslo Convention, 189
Outfall, 148
Oxides of nitrogen (NO_x), 331

P

Pacific Ocean, 11
Passive outflow reduction, 218, 220
Pathogenic bacteria, 68, 107
Pathogens, 4, 46
Pelagic clay, 9, 11
Photoplankton, 12
Photosynthesis, 13
Physical ocean pollution prevention, 119
Phytoplankton, 2, 11, 12
Placer minerals, 33
Port pollution, 44, 75, 120
Port State Control (PSC), 164, 187
Pressures, 4

R

Radicals free, 107
Radioactive materials, 2
Radioactive wastes, 4
Radioactivity, 48
Radionucleotides, 95
Reactive spill response, 221
Recreational pollution, 104
Run-off, 64

S

Safety of Life at Sea (SOLAS), 128, 338
Sea level rise, 5
Seaborne trade, 38
Sewage, 97
Sharks, 27
Shellfish, 19
Ship traffic control system, 129 (*See also* Vessel traffic management)
Shipping safety, 61
Shrimp, 27
Siliceous, 11
Skimmers:
  belt, 143, 443
  mechanical, 143
  vortex, 144
Sludge, 45
Solid waste, 5, 45
Solid waste disposal, 190
South China Sea, 2
Spill containment, 136
Spill recovery, 136
Sulphur dioxide (SO_2), 331
Surfactants, 99
Suspended solids, 163
Synthetic organic compounds, 4

T

Tanker accidents, 52
Tanker design, 126
Toxic waste pollution, 152
Toxins (TBT), 128
Trace metals, 4
Transportation ocean, 38

U

United Nations Conference on Trade and Development (UNCTAD), 255
United Nations Convention on the Law of the Sea (UNCLOS), 341
United Nations Development Program (UNDP), 101, 255
United Nations Economic Program (UNEP), 161, 255, 342
United States Army Corps of Engineers (USACE), 171, 256
United States Coast Guard (USCG), 124, 256

V

Venice, 6
Very large crude carriers (VLCC), 227
Vessel Response Plan (VRP), 147, 262
Vessel traffic management, 131, 224

W

Waste water pollution, 66
Whales, 27
World Bank, 255